Inte
Textbook of

Mixed Gas
Diving

By Heinz K.J. Lettnin

BEST PUBLISHING COMPANY

International Textbook Of

Mixed Gas Diving

Theory
Technique
Application

By Heinz K.J. Lettnin

BEST PUBLISHING COMPANY

ISBN No. 0-941332-50-0
LIBRARY OF CONGRESS: 95-080957

Best Publishing Company
2355 North Steves Boulevard
P.O. Box 30100
Flagstaff, AZ 86003-0100 USA

Table of Contents

PREFACE

Worldwide exploitation of marine resources, especially the utilization of oil and gas resources, was impossible before recent enormous progress in diving and dive technology. The use of mixed gases and modern dive techniques has opened completely new dimensions for underwater exploration. Diving operations of several weeks' duration, at depths down to 300 msw and more, are standard today.

This book on mixed gas/saturation diving, based mainly on UK, French, and U.S. sources, gives a comprehensive overview of modern diving technology. Some air diving procedures are also included.

The book is directed to professional diving and offshore personnel as well as people interested in the technical aspects of mixed-gas diving. Diving procedures for depths of more than 165 feet (50 msw), methods for extending bottom times, and diving in contaminated waters are among the topics examined. In addition, the theoretical basics of mixed gas/saturation diving and gas management are discussed, with practice-oriented calculations and examples.

Decompression and treatment procedures comprise a large part of the book. Only technical methods, not medical issues, are included. Medical questions are referred to existing comprehensive references. Finally, safety and safety regulations, techniques for working offshore, and working conditions are discussed.

For further information about special topics, more than 130 references are provided. Throughout the text, references are noted with the reference number in brackets, i.e. [21]. This book is based on training activities of diving and topside personnel at the GKSS Research Center Geesthacht (GUSI).

CHAPTER 1

Introduction

Interdisciplinary research about and economic utilization of the "wet" continent are just beginning on a large scale. This is remarkable because more than 70% of the earth's surface is covered with water.

While our continents, which comprise only 29% of the total surface of the earth, have been explored and are comparatively well known, systematic exploration of the world's oceans, as well as understanding of the interactions between oceans and the atmosphere and the utilization of marine resources, have just began.

Water has always been a basic in human society. Early settlements were located at shores of rivers or oceans, which supplied vital water and a variety of food. Humans learned to move in the water and to use boats and ships for transportation.

The beginning of swimming was also the beginning of diving as man learned to move underwater by holding his breath. Professional diving is several thousand years old, if professional diving means diving for sponges, pearls, and corals, and, later, for sunken ships.

Even the use of diving bells is not a modern invention, but goes back more than 2,000 years to the third century B.C. A contemporary chronicler reports that Alexander the Great was lowered into the waters of the Bosporus by means of a glass diving bell (see Fig. 1.1). We do not know the details of the dive but it must have been short enough to avoid oxygen supply problems. Essential improvements to bell diving did not take place until the end of seventeenth century, when the well-known British astronomer Edmund Halley introduced a means of continuously replacing the air inside the bell. Air-filled barrels were sunk to the ocean floor and used to replenish the atmosphere in the bell.

The modern diving industry, as it is currently understood, was developed at the end of the last century when the necessary technical equipment was available. During the twenties, divers started experimenting with artificial breathing mixtures, replacing the narcotic nitrogen with helium. The most recent development in commercial diving was the introduction of saturation diving in the sixties. By means of this new technology man has greatly extended his thresholds under water. Diving operations under saturation conditions can take weeks or months at depths of several hundred meters. During an experimental chamber dive in 1993, French divers extended the record depth to 701 msw (2300 fsw). Saturation diving requires a complex diving system and sophisticated diving techniques. Fig. 1.2 shows the GUSI plant (GKSS Underwater Simulator) and gives an idea of the chamber system of a modern diving installation. Today's diving and diving technology are considered to be part of the discipline called ocean engineering, which includes several interdisciplinary marine activities.

Fig. 1.1 Contemporary picture of Alexander the Great in a diving bell

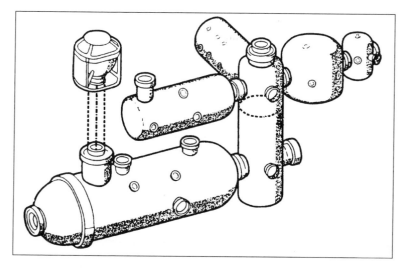

Fig. 1.2 Chamber system of a diving installation (GUSI)

The extension of diving operations, combined with new and demanding underwater tasks, requires more highly trained personnel in the diving industry. The professional diver must not only be expert in underwater technologies, but must also be sufficiently qualified to complete many different tasks safely and efficiently under raised pressure conditions in a hostile environment. Only the use of very complex technical systems and equipment allows divers longer durations under water. To guarantee a safe dive, professional divers must be able to meet substantial physical and psychological demands.

<u>NOTES</u>

CHAPTER 2

Units of Measurement

2.1 BASIC UNITS

In the interest of international standardization of technical and physical measures, the countries of the European Community have passed a law to introduce SI units, where SI stands for System International, also known as the metric system. In 1973, the law on German measures and weights came into force, according to reference [2]; this law stipulates units of measurement in DIN-regulation 1301, as evident in reference [3].

For diving, the following basic units (SI units) are essential:

QUANTITY:	BASIC UNIT:
length	meter (m)
mass	kilogram (kg)
time	second (s)
temperature	Kelvin (K)

Based on these units, derived units for force weight, pressure, energy, etc. are calculated.

Working with SI units often leads to numbers that are impractical to manipulate. Therefore, the use of multiples is more comfortable. An overview of standard multiples is given on the next page.

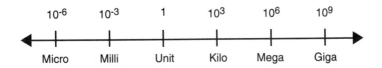

2.2 DERIVED UNITS

Force   The unit of force F is Newton (N) — 1 N = 1 kgm/s^2.

According to the British physicist Newton, the force (F) is mass (m) times acceleration (a)

$$F = m \times a \qquad (2.1)$$

One Newton is the force acting on a mass of 1 kg with an acceleration of 1 m/s^2. The gravity (g) of earth in our latitudes is 9.81 m/s^2 or roughly 10 m/s^2. Other planets and the sun show different gravities or accelerations due to their different masses. Examples are the sun, with an acceleration a = 274 m/s^2, the moon with a = 1.6 m/s^2, and the planet Venus with a = 8.5 m/s^2.

While a mass of 1 kg has a weight on the earth of 9.81 N (Newton's law) or approximately 10 N, the same mass on the sun weighs 274 N, on the moon only 1.6 N, and on Venus 8.5 N. Mass does not change under the influence of different gravitational fields; only its weight changes.

Pressure   The unit of pressure p is Pascal (Pa) — 1 Pa = 1 N/m^2.

The definition of pressure is equal to the force (F) per unit of area (A).

$$p = F/A. \qquad (2.2)$$

One Pascal is the pressure (p), acting as force (F) of 1 (N) on an area (A) of 1 m^2. Because in diving considerably higher pressures occur, the derived unit bar is used.

$$1 \text{ bar} = 10^5 \text{ Pa} = 10 \text{ N/cm}^2 \qquad (2.3)$$

In international diving, pressure units are in use which differ from the SI standard. See Pressure Table (Fig. 2.1) on the next page.

bar	kPa	Pa	ATM	msw	fsw	psig	psia
1	100	$1 \cdot 10^5$	0	0	0	0	14.7
2	200	$2 \cdot 10^5$	1	10	33	14.7	29.4
3	300	$3 \cdot 10^5$	2	20	66	29.4	44.1
4	400	$4 \cdot 10^5$	3	30	99	44.1	58.8
5	500	$5 \cdot 10^5$	4	40	132	58.8	79.5
6	600	$6 \cdot 10^5$	5	50	165	79.5	94.2

Fig. 2.1 Pressure Table

To compare the different pressure units in the pressure table, the unit 1 bar is equated to 1 atm equated to, 10 msw for simplification. The exact conversion of 1 atm equated to, 10 msw corresponds to 0.981 bars. In general, all pressures are understood as absolute pressures. This is particularly important in cases of over- and underpressures.

For a given water depth the pressure is

$$p = msw/10 + 1 \quad \text{in bars.} \tag{2.4}$$

A given pressure corresponds to a water depth of

$$msw = (p - 1) \times 10 \quad \text{in meters.} \tag{2.5}$$

Density The density (ρ) of matter is defined as the ratio of mass (m) to its volume (V). The dimension is 1 t/m^3, 1 kg/dm^3 or 1 g/cm^3.

$$\rho = m/V \tag{2.6}$$

The density of matter is related to the density of water at 4°C, which has by definition the density (ρ) of 1000 kg/m^3, 1 kg/l or 1 g/cm^3. So the density of matter indicates by how many times it is heavier or lighter than water. The density of gold is 19.3 g/cm^3, (ρ) of alcohol is 0.8 g/cm^3, and the density of air is only 1.29 x 10^{-3} g/cm^3 or 1.29 g/l. That means that gold is 19.3 times heavier than water, alcohol has a mass 0.8 times that of water, and the density of air is roughly only 1/1000 that of water.

Energy   The unit of energy (E) or work is Joule (J) — 1 J = 1 Nm or 1 Ws.

Energy (E) or work is defined as force (F) times distance l or power (P) times time (t).

$$E = F \times l = P \times t \qquad (2.7)$$

Power   The unit of power P is Watt W — 1 W = 1 Nm/s = 1 J/s. Power P is defined as energy E or work per unit of time t.

$$P = E/t \qquad (2.8)$$

Temperature   Temperature is a basic unit, but because it is often converted to absolute temperatures it is dealt with as a derived unit. The unit of temperature (T) is Kelvin (K) (absolute temperature), but temperature (t) in degrees Celsius (°C = Centigrade) is also used. While the absolute temperature scale starts from absolute zero, zero for the Centigrade scale starts from the freezing point of water. So 0 °C = 273 K

The conversion of Centigrade (t) into absolute temperature (T) is

$$T = t + 273 \quad \text{in K.} \qquad (2.9)$$

To convert absolute temperature T into Centigrade t

$$t = T - 273 \quad \text{in Centigrade (°C).} \qquad (2.10)$$

2.3   CONVERSION OF U.S. UNITS

While in the interest of European Community harmonization, the UK has changed its measurement system to international SI units (metric system), the U.S. uses the British system with units of pounds, feet, and seconds (pfs system). The unit of length in the pfs system is 1 foot which is equal to 0.305 m — 10 msw equals 33 fsw (see also Fig. 2.1).

For conversion of fsw into absolute pressure (p), see Fig. 2.1.

$$p = (\text{fsw} + 33) / 33 = \text{fsw} / 33 + 1 \quad \text{in bars or ata.} \qquad (2.11)$$

For conversion of fsw into absolute pressure (psia), see Fig. 2.1.

$$p = \text{fsw} \times 0.445 + 14.7 \qquad \text{in psia.} \qquad (2.12)$$

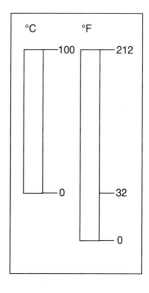

Conversion of temperatures The freezing point of water is defined as zero on the Centigrade scale, which corresponds to 32°F on the Fahrenheit scale. The boiling point of water at 100°C corresponds to 212°F.

Conversion of degrees Fahrenheit into Centigrade:

$$t = \frac{t\ (°F) - 32}{1.8} \quad \text{in °C.} \qquad (2.13)$$

Conversion of Centigrade into degrees Fahrenheit:

$$t = t\ (°C) \times 1.8 + 32 \quad \text{in °F.} \qquad (2.14)$$

Absolute zero in the U.S. measurement system is 460 Rankine (R), so that 460 R = 273 K.

Conversion of degrees Fahrenheit into absolute temperature T:

$$T = t\ (°F) + 460 \qquad \text{in R.} \qquad (2.15)$$

NOTES

CHAPTER 3

Properties of Water

Water is the medium of special interest to the diver; he must understand its acoustical, optical, and thermodynamic properties. Seventy-one percent of the earth's surface is covered with water, at depths from a few meters to 11,000 meters (36,000 ft). Roughly 8% of the world's oceans are 200 m deep, 15% have depths between 200 and 3,000 m, and most ocean waters, 76%, are between 3,000 and 6,000 m deep. Only a very small part, approximately 1%, is deeper than 6,000 m.

Seawater consists of 96.5% pure water; the remaining 3.5% contains mainly sodium and magnesium chloride, better known as salt. Moreover, traces of almost all elements can be found in seawater, according to reference [4]. The salt content can vary considerably in different oceans. While the western Baltic Sea contains only 0.8% salt, the North Sea and all oceans have a salt content of approximately 3.5%. The most saline body of water is the Dead Sea with a dissolved salt content between 20 and 26%.

3.1 THERMODYNAMIC PROPERTIES OF WATER

A molecule of water consists of one oxygen atom and two hydrogen atoms. Pure water has a freezing point of 0°C (32°F) and it boils at 100°C (212°F) under normal conditions. An unusual physical property of water is that its highest density is reached at +4°C. Further cooling corresponds to a decrease in density. The reason for this phenomenon is the restructuring of molecules from the liquid state to the solid state at the freezing point. Molecules in the solid state fill a larger volume.

Therefore the density of ice is reduced approximately 9%, compared with liquid water. This explains why ice floats on water. But as the salt content increases, the freezing point decreases (see Fig. 3.1). The density of pure water is by definition $\rho = 1$ g/cm^3. Seawater, with an average salt content of 3.5%, has a slightly higher density of 1.025 g/cm^3.

Water is incompressible under normal conditions, but at higher pressures of several hundred bars a volume reduction of up to 1% occurs. When the pressure is in the range of approximately 1000 bars, the volume reduction is roughly 4%. Another remarkable property of water is its high specific heat capacity, which slows down temperature oscillations and allows only small temperature changes in the world's oceans. The surface temperatures of oceans vary between 28°C at the equator and approximately -2°C at polar zones, according to reference [5]. But these figures do not include temperature peaks at the surface of 35°C and more in limited areas, as for example, in the Persian Gulf.

Typical temperature profiles of different climatic zones show a fixed temperature of about +4°C at depths of about 1000 msw. The average temperature of all the world's oceans is near +3.8°C. Seasonal temperature changes and mixing processes near the surface are limited to upper water layers of roughly 200 m only.

The thermodynamic properties of water determine the heat loss of a body in the water. A diver's heat loss occurs basically by heat conduction due to the temperature difference between his body and the surrounding water. Here the heat conductivity of water plays an essential role. Water has the highest heat conductivity of all liquids; it is 25 times higher than that of air.

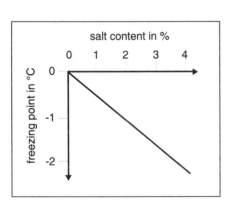

Without any heat protection a human being has very little chance of surviving in cold waters. The chance increases enormously in warmer waters. Reference [6] states that survival times in cold waters can be increased by using proper heat protection (Fig. 3.2). Relatively high heat loss takes place via the head and neck due to the high rate of blood circulation and the lack of fat layers in these areas.

Fig. 3.1 Freezing point of water vs. salt content

3.2 ACOUSTICAL PROPERTIES OF WATER

Because water has a higher density than air, sound travels 4.5 times faster in water, at a velocity of approximately 1,450 to 1,500 m/s. The speed of sound increases slightly with increased salt content and depth, and also with increased temperatures. Higher energies are needed to generate sound under water (as compared with sounds generated in air), but on the other hand, travel distance increases remarkably. The conduction of sound depends mainly on its frequency. Higher frequencies are deadened more intensively than lower ones. Further, a diver's neoprene hood is an effective barrier for frequencies above 1 kHz. Sound generated in an air-filled helmet or full face mask is not transmitted to the surrounding water due to the high absorption of sound.

Sometimes distinct contiguous layers of water caused by sudden differences in temperature or salinity, known as thermoclines, occur. These thermoclines reflect sound waves and lead to other anomalies in sound propagation. Such anomalies are used, for example, by submarines to hide from sonar. Inexperienced divers can lose their acoustical orientation or be misled by such effects. Humans can localize the direction of a source of sound in the air very precisely by discriminating the difference in time as sound reaches the right and left ears. This ability fails under water due to the higher speed of sound. For orientation, the intensity of a sound source can be used successfully.

Transmission of sound is based on a series of pressure waves; these waves also pass through the body of a submerged diver. When high-intensity sources such as sonar or underwater explosions are involved, the pressure waves may result in severe injuries when they pass through open spaces in the body such as the lungs. A special case is an underwater explosion where very intensive pressure waves are generated. The initial shock wave has the highest intensity and is therefore most dangerous. The following pressure waves decrease in intensity. Bottom and side (if they exist) limitations

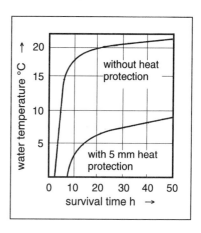

Fig. 3.2 Survival time in water vs. water temperature

cause reflections which interfere with the pressure waves from the initial explosion. The effect of an underwater explosion is influenced, among other factors, by the brisance of the explosive, water depth, bottom condition, and so on.

To avoid the potential dangers of underwater explosions, divers should leave the water. Another possibility is to keep a safe distance from the underwater explosions. To estimate the expected pressure, a relation between mass of explosive and distance from the diver is given in Figure 3.3. [7]

$$p = \frac{13{,}000 \; S^{1/3}}{R} \text{ in psi} \qquad p = \frac{353 \; S^{1/3}}{R} \text{ in bars} \qquad (3.1)$$

S = mass of explosive in lb   S = mass of explosive in kg
R = distance in feet   R = distance in meters

3.3 OPTICAL PROPERTIES OF WATER

In the course of human evolution, the eye has adapted to the visibility conditions on the earth's surface. Very different conditions are found underwater; these greatly influence the diver's ability to see. Because water is much denser than air, objects seen underwater appear blurred—the geometry of our eye precludes the projection of a clear picture of the object on the retina. But the use of a face mask with an air layer between the eye and the face plate solves this problem.

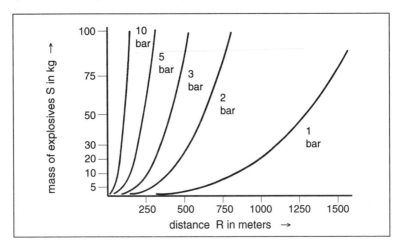

Fig. 3.3 Explosion pressure vs. distance and weight of charge [7]

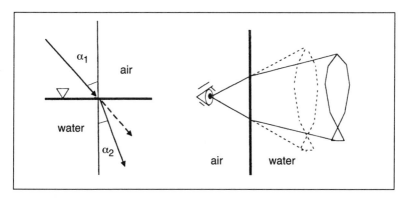

Fig. 3.4 Refraction relations for the materials combination air/water

Another effect, known as refraction, must be taken into account. When light enters a dense medium like water, the light rays are bent because the speed of light is reduced in denser media. The relation of different travel speeds in different media is called the refractive index (n). This refractive index is defined as the sinus of the angle of incidence (α_1) divided by the sinus of the reflexion angle (α_2).

$$n = \frac{\text{travel velocity in air}}{\text{travel velocity in water}} = \frac{\sin \alpha_1}{\sin \alpha_2} = \frac{4}{3} \tag{3.2}$$

The refractive index in 3.2 is valid for the combination air/water. This index is constant for a given material combination, and each combination is described by its own refractive index. The material combination air/glass, e.g., has the refractive index (n) of 1.5.

As a consequence, objects underwater seem to be nearer to the diver, only 3/4 of the actual distance from him, and they appear 1.33 times larger than they are in reality. These effects must be taken into account in underwater photography and in other situations.

Another concern is the scattering and diffusion of light due to dissolved particles that reduce visibility in the water. In extreme cases, depending on the concentration of such particles, visibility can be reduced to zero. The visibility of colors under water also changes. White light consists of 7 or 8 colors of the spectrum, each characterized by its electromagnetic wavelength. The visible spectrum lies between low frequency infrared with wavelengths of approximately 0.8 micrometers and high frequency ultraviolet with wavelengths of roughly 0.38 micrometers. As water depth increases, the low frequency colors like red and orange are filtered out first, while the higher frequency colors, such as green and blue, disappear at greater depths, as illustrated in reference [7]. Depth is not the only factor responsible for color changes and light absorption; salinity, the kind and sizes of particles suspended in the water, and so on, also affect color perception. At greater depths, all colors disappear and only differences in brightness can be distinguished. The eye can differentiate objects under poor visibility conditions much better than it can see colors. An artificial light source is required for taking pictures or videos underwater. Selection of the spectrum of the light source must take into account the different depths at which colors are absorbed.

CHAPTER 4

Properties of Air

Of all the breathing gases used in diving, air is the most important. For that reason air is discussed separately in this chapter. The earth is surrounded by a mantle of air necessary for the evolution of life.

Atmospheric air consists of gases including: nitrogen N_2, 78.08%; oxygen O_2, 20.95%; argon Ar, 0.93%; carbon dioxide, CO_2, 0.03%; and other, 0.01%. This remaining 0.01% consists of different rare gases, including hydrogen, ozone, vapor, etc. Air has a mean density of ρ = 1.293 g/*l*.

The mantle of air extends from the earth's surface to 1500 km into space. The composition of atmospheric air, with the main components oxygen and nitrogen, is the same up to an altitude of approximately 100 km. The weight of the air column acting on the earth's surface creates a pressure of 1.013 bars or 1013 mbars at sea level, the atmospheric pressure. Seventy-five percent of the mass of the

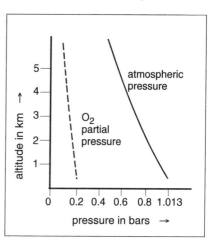

Fig. 4.1 Atmospheric pressure distribution vs. altitude

air mantle is concentrated in a 10 km layer near the earth's surface. The atmospheric pressure at sea level of 1.013 bars decreases with increasing altitude. The same pattern is valid for the temperature distribution. The reduction of atmospheric pressure versus altitude is described, with some simplification, by the following barometric formula:

$$p\,(H) = p_0 \exp\,(\,\text{-}k \times H\,) \tag{4.1}$$

with p_0 = atm. pressure at sea level
         H = altitude in km
         k = thermodynamical constant

At an altitude of 10 km or 33,000 feet, the normal cruising altitude for transatlantic flights, the atmospheric pressure is only 0.26 bars, and the temperature is approximately -50°C.

Atmospheric air contains vapor; the portion of vapor in the air depends on temperature. The higher the temperature, the more vapor the air can absorb until saturation (100% humidity) is reached. The relation of actual humidity to saturated air at a given temperature level is the relative humidity, expressed as a percentage. When saturated air is cooled down, the air cannot hold all of the vapor and some is condensed to water. Fig. 4.2 shows that saturated air at 35°C containing 5.5 vol% of vapor will reduce its humidity content to only 0.6 vol% when the air is cooled to 0°C.

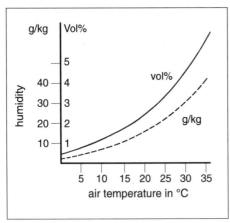

Fig. 4.2 Humidity of atmospheric air vs. air temperature

         Mixed Gas Diving

CHAPTER 5

Diving Gases and Their Properties

5.1 INTRODUCTION

Due to the physiological limitations on humans breathing atmospheric air, divers must use artificial breathing mixtures at greater depths. The composition of these mixtures is determined mainly by depth of the dive and bottom time.

The most important component of any breathing gas is oxygen, necessary for metabolism which produces energy for maintaining the body's functions. The demand for oxygen by different organs of the body varies and depends, among other factors, on the type of physical work being done. Similarly, there are differences in the sensitivity of the body's organs to sudden interruptions of the oxygen supply. The time within which irreversible damage will occur varies from a few minutes in the case of the brain or spinal cord to several hours for tissues like fat or bone, which have a much smaller oxygen demand.

Supplying oxygen to the human body begins with the respiration process via the lungs. The lungs are responsible for the gas exchange in which oxygen is transported by the red blood cells to all body tissues via the circulatory system. The carbon dioxide produced as a waste product of the metabolic process is transported back to the lungs, where it is exhaled. The exchange of oxygen and carbon dioxide takes place via the fine membranes of the alveoli or air sacks, which are the main structures in the lungs. The surface of the alveoli forms a total area of 100 to 200 m^2. The function of the lungs is to reduce the oxygen content of the inhaled breathing gas and to enrich the carbon dioxide during exhalation. Nitrogen is not involved in the metabolic process; its only function is to rarefy the oxygen in the air.

When air is inhaled under raised pressure conditions, effects occur which may lead to severe health problems. The diver must know about these problems for his own safety, and he must also know the physiological limitations of his diving gases. In the following sections, the components of breathing gases used in commercial diving are introduced to the extent that the adverse effects which may occur will be understood. More details on the complex respiration processes and interactions are given in references [5, 8, and 10], among others.

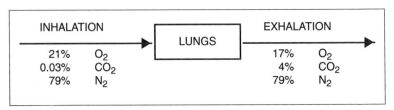

Fig. 5.1 Principle of gas exchange during respiration

5.2 OXYGEN

Oxygen is a colorless, odorless, tasteless gas with the atomic number 8 and an atomic weight of 16. Under normal conditions oxygen exists in a diatomic state, which means that two atoms form an oxygen molecule (O_2). It is the most abundant element on earth. Without oxygen, no burning would be possible, and without oxygen no human life would exist on earth.

Oxygen has a density $\rho = 1.429\ g/l$ under normal conditions. The boiling point is -183°C, its heat conductivity 26.4 mW/m·K (milliwatts per meter and Kelvin). Approximately 21% of atmospheric air is oxygen, corresponding to an oxygen partial pressure of 0.21 bars.

Increased partial pressures and longer exposure times lead to oxygen poisoning. Depending on the level of partial pressure, two kinds of poisoning effects are known—neurological and pulmonary. Partial pressures of 2.5 bars or more can lead to poisoning of the central nervous system (CNS), manifested by symptoms such as twitching of facial muscles, tunnel vision, dizziness, nausea and convulsions. At high pressure levels, these symptoms occur after just a few minutes of exposure time.

Sensitivity to oxygen poisoning varies among individuals and depends, among other factors, on the person's physical condition. A diver can tolerate a higher O_2 level at rest than after heavy manual work.

To check for special oxygen sensitivity, O_2 tolerance tests are carried out. The diving candidate breathes oxygen under a partial pressure of 2.8 bars for half an hour. If there are any symptoms of O_2 poisoning, the candidate should be rejected for work as a commercial diver.

Compared to neurological O_2 toxicity, the first effects of pulmonary toxicity occur at lower partial pressures, depending on exposure time. Breathing oxygen-enriched mixtures over a period of 24 hrs with partial pressures below 1 bar may lead to poisoning of the lungs. Increasing pressure reduces the exposure time that will cause the same lung damage. Symptoms of pulmonary oxygen toxicity start with sensations of burning during inspiration, and choking; symptoms progress to continuous choking and increasing pain during inspiration. The lungs' tissues are progressively damaged and finally death will occur due to an insufficient oxygen supply (see Fig. 5.2).

Today an oxygen partial pressure of 0.5 bars is accepted as the upper limit that can be breathed over long periods of time without any adverse effects. For that reason, the partial pressure during saturation dives must not exceed 0.5 bars except for limited operations; for shorter periods, a slightly higher partial pressure can be tolerated.

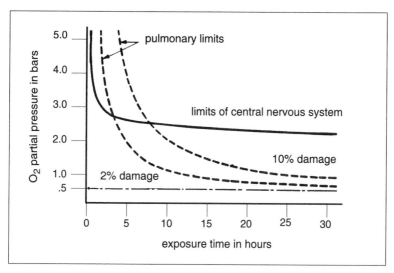

Fig. 5.2 O_2 toxicity vs. partial pressure and exposure time

For surface-supplied air diving operations, which are limited in general to approximately 50 msw, the O_2 partial pressure is 1.26 bars. According to Fig. 5.2, an exposure time of roughly 8 hrs is necessary to cause 2% lung damage. Because for decompression safety the bottom time for air dives is limited to approximately 1 hr at 50 msw, the possibility of oxygen poisoning for these dives can usually be excluded. However, during treatment procedures in a chamber, where high O_2 pressures are necessary, neurological poisoning may occur, especially when the diver is exhausted after heavy work.

For economic reasons, oxygen-enriched O_2/N_2 mixtures, known as nitrox, are used. The higher oxygen portion in this breathing gas increases the risk of oxygen poisoning. If a nitrox mix of 40/60 with 40% O_2 is used at the same depth of 50 msw, the oxygen partial pressure is raised to 2.4 bars. This pressure, in combination with heavy underwater work, increases the risk of oxygen poisoning considerably. Tolerable exposure times under increased oxygen partial pressure conditions are published in references [7, 9, and 133], among others (see also Fig. 5.3). For nitrox operations, an O_2 partial pressure of approximately 1.4 bars offers a reasonable precaution against the risk of oxygen poisoning.

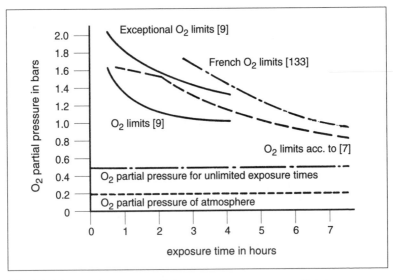

Fig. 5.3 Tolerated oxygen partial pressures vs. exposure times

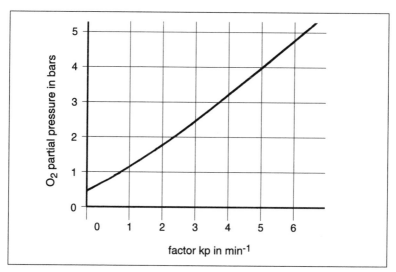

Fig. 5.4 Factor kp vs. oxygen partial pressure [5]

Diving with pure oxygen in a closed circuit (used only in special military actions) naturally creates a high risk of neurological oxygen poisoning. The maximum depth for such operations is limited to 8 msw. Tolerable exposure times for pure oxygen diving are published, for example, in reference [9]. But pure oxygen is used widely for decompression and therapeutic treatment. For these procedures, oxygen levels and exposure times change accordingly (see Fig. 5.5); therefore, it is difficult to determine the effects of oxygen alone. For estimating the accumulated effects of pulmonary oxygen toxicity, a concept of comparative dose UPTD has been introduced. The unit UPTD (Unit Pulmonary Toxic Dose) is by definition the effect of breathing oxygen under 1 bar conditions for one minute. The UPTD is the product of exposure time (t) in minutes times a factor (kp), which depends on the oxygen partial pressure, as stated in reference [5] (see Fig. 5.4).

$$UPTD = kp \times t \qquad (5.1)$$

To determine the total UPTD of a given treatment procedure, the single UPTDs of the corresponding oxygen treatment stages are calculated and added. As an example, the total UPTD for USN Treatment Table 6 is given in Table 5.1.

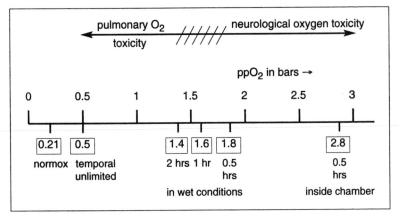

Fig. 5.5 Oxygen partial pressures and tolerable exposure times

For decompression or for treatment of light symptoms of decompression sickness (DCS Type I), the total UPTD should not exceed 600 UPTD. For treatment of all other symptoms of decompression sickness (DCS Type II), the tolerable dose should not be more than 1,400 UPTD.

5.3 NITROGEN

Nitrogen is, like oxygen, a colorless, odorless, tasteless gas. It has the atomic number 7 and an atomic weight of 14. It exists in a diatomic state (N_2) under normal conditions. Compounds of nitrogen, especially amino acids, are the basis for the evolution of higher life forms.

Table 5.1 Total UPTD of U.S. Navy Treatment Table 6

Depth range (m)	O_2-partial press. (bars)	kp (min^{-1})	Exposure time (min)	UPTD
18	2.8	3.57	60	214
18 ... 9	2.4	3.04	30	91
9	1.9	2.36	120	283
9 ... 0	1.5	1.78	30	53
				Σ 64

Table 5.2 Effects of raised N_2 partial pressure on man [7]

N_2 Partial Pressure	Effects on Man
2 .... 4 bars	Mild impairment of performance on unpracticed tasks; mild euphoria
4 bars	Delayed response to visual and auditory stimuli
4 .... 6 bars	Laughter and loquacity that may be overcome by self control; overconfidence; calculation errors
6 bars	Sleepiness; hallucinations; impaired judgment
6 .... 8 bars	Convivial group atmosphere; talkative; uncontrolled laughter approaching hysteria
8 bars	Severe impairment of intellectual performance; manual dexterity less affected
8 .... 10 bars	Gross delay in response to stimuli; diminished concentration; mental confusion
10 bars	Severe impairment of practical activity and judgment; memory defects; euphoria; almost total loss of intellectual and perceptive faculties; hallucinations; unconsciousness

Nitrogen has a density $\rho = 1.2504$ g/l under normal conditions. The boiling point is -194.6°C, and its heat conductivity is 25.9 mW/m·K. The portion of nitrogen in the air is about 79%, corresponding to a partial pressure of 0.79 bars. Nitrogen is not involved in metabolism and is physiologically an inert gas. Increasing the nitrogen partial pressure induces symptoms of narcosis or anesthesia, known as nitrogen narcosis, with effects similar to those of alcohol consumption.

The first effects of nitrogen narcosis appear at a depth of roughly 30 msw corresponding to an N_2 partial pressure of 3.16 bars. The narcotic effects grow more pronounced with increasing partial pressures. At a depth of 60 msw intellectual concentration decreases markedly and responses to visual and auditory stimuli are noticeably delayed. For the narcotic effects at increasing depths, see Table 5.2. The narcotic effects disappear immediately when ascending to a shallower depth. Because of the narcotic effects of nitrogen, air diving is limited to a depth of 50 msw in most countries.

There are different hypotheses to explain the narcotic effects of nitrogen. One hypothesis is based on the swelling of nerve cells by narcotic gases. And there is a certain correlation between narcotic effects and the solubility of narcotic gases in the tissues of nerve cells, the socalled lipids.

Table 5.3 Comparison of narcotic potential of different diving gases

Gas	Symbol Weight	Molecule	Lipid Sol.	Narcotic Pot. Ratio to N_2	Narcotic
Helium	He	4			0.235
Neon	Ne	20			0.274
Hydrogen	H_2	2			0.541
Nitrogen	N_2	28			1.0
Argon	Ar	40	↓	↓	2.326
Krypton	Kr	83.8			7.143

Table 5.3 gives a comparison of the narcotic potential of gases which are available as rarefaction media in breathing mixtures for diving. For deep diving operations, nitrogen is generally replaced by helium due to its low narcotic potential. Neon or hydrogen can also be considered, since their narcotic potential is also lower than that of nitrogen.

5.4 AIR AND NITROX

Air and nitrox both consist of the elements oxygen and nitrogen. While air has a constant oxygen/nitrogen ratio of 21%/79%, mixes with different ratios of O_2/N_2 are known as nitrox (*nitr*ogen/*ox*ygen).

Air is the cheapest and most widely used diving gas; it is available all over the world in unlimited quantities, and it can be used immediately. Air has a density $\rho = 1.293$ g/l and its boiling point is -194°C. Its heat conductivity is about 26 mW/m·K. The physiological effects of air under raised pressure conditions are determined mainly by the narcotic potential of nitrogen, see Chapter 4 for properties of air.

Nitrox is an oxygen/nitrogen mix with a composition different from that of air. For economic reasons nitrox mixtures with higher oxygen contents are used, as longer bottom times respectively shorter decompression times compared to air diving can be achieved, see Chapter 9.6. However, the risk of oxygen poisoning must be considered very carefully. The physiological properties of a given nitrox mix are determined by the amounts of oxygen and nitrogen in the mixture under raised pressure conditions.

5.5 CARBON DIOXIDE

Carbon dioxide, CO_2, is a colorless and odorless gas with a molecular weight of 44.01. Approximately 0.033% of the atmosphere is carbon dioxide; it results, among other things, as a waste product of human and

Table 5.4 Effects of CO_2 Concentrations on Man [28]

CO_2-Conc. (Vol.%)	CO_2-P.P. (bars)	Effects on man
2	0.02	Beginning of intensification of breathing
3	0.03	First signs of discomfort
4	0.04	Increase in breathing frequency
4....5	0.04...0.05	After a fast rise in CO_2, a strong feeling of discomfort occurs, as does sweating, headache, buzzing in the ears, pounding heart, and an increase in blood pressure After a slow rise in CO_2, adaptation is possible, but not comfortable
5	0.05	Sweating, difficulty in breathing, fear, strong headache
6	0.06	If sudden, death is possible; if slow, adaptation is just tolerable
6...10	0.06...0.10	Adaptation tolerable up to 1 hr, but abilities greatly reduced
8...10	0.08...0.10	Considerably increased rate of breathing and pulse frequency, difficulty in breathing, dizziness, vomiting, apathy, unconsciousness, blue coloring of skin, cessation of breathing
20	0.20	Fast death

animal metabolism. Carbon dioxide has a density $\rho = 1.977$ g/l under normal conditions, which means that it is heavier than air. The boiling point is about -78.5°C, and its heat conductivity approximately 16.4 mW/m·K. Carbon dioxide dissolves easily in liquids.

From a physiological point of view, CO_2 primarily controls the breathing center. A raised carbon dioxide level in the blood leads to an intensification of breathing until normal conditions are achieved again. If the concentration of CO_2 increases because of insufficient ventilation, which may occur during heavy work when using helmets with large dead spaces, carbon dioxide poisoning occurs (see also Table 5.4). Exposure time is vital in considering the possible physiological effects of raised carbon dioxide concentrations. For short exposure times of about one hour, concentrations up to 3% under 1 bar conditions ($ppCO_2 = 30$ mbars) can be tolerated without damage.

For long exposure times, such as saturation dives, the carbon dioxide concentration must be limited to 0.5%, 5 mbars. Therefore, continuous monitoring of carbon dioxide concentrations during saturation operations is vital.

5.6 HELIUM

Helium is a colorless, odorless, and tasteless rare gas with the atomic number 2 and an atomic weight of 4. It is $5.24 \cdot 10^{-4}$ of the atmosphere, and it is a monatomic gas. Helium has a density $\rho = 0.179$ g/l under normal conditions and is therefore 7.24 times lighter than air. Its boiling point is -269°C, only 4°C above absolute zero. Its heat conductivity is 150 mW/m·K, 6 times higher than that of air. The technical handling of helium is somewhat problematical due to its low density and volatility. Mixed gas supply systems offshore must be virtually helium-tight to avoid large gas losses. This places considerable demands on the components of such systems.

The narcotic potential of helium is much smaller than that of nitrogen (Table 5.3). Therefore helium is used instead of nitrogen at greater depths, where dive operations exceed the air limits of 50 to 60 msw. For deep-dive operations worldwide, mixes of helium and oxygen are the basis for mixed gas diving. Corresponding to the gas components helium and oxygen, these mixtures are known as helox or heliox.

Because of helium's physical properties, some technical and physiological problems must be considered. The low density of helium causes not only technical problems in relation to the tightness of components in mixed gas systems, but also distorts the diver's voice. This phenomenon is known as the Donald-Duck effect. Human vocal cords are adapted to the density of air and the voice is distorted beyond recognition in media with lower densities. To guarantee sufficient communication between diver and topside personnel, electronic devices known as unscramblers must be used. These devices electronically divide the helium-affected speech and bring the amplitudes of the single speech segments back to their original levels (see Fig. 5.6).

Another important consideration is the body's heat loss while breathing heliox. Under atmospheric conditions, the heat loss while breathing air is only approximately 10% of the total heat generated by the body. This loss rises slightly with increasing air dryness, as heat is necessary for the vaporization of moisture in the respiratory tract, until saturation is achieved, as stated in reference [11].

Compression of the breathing gas increases its heat conductivity due to higher gas density. In the special case of heliox, with the high heat conductivity of helium, the body's heat loss is much higher than when breathing air. Breathing cold heliox draws more heat from the body core than the body can generate to maintain its core temperature. This problem cannot be overcome by using hot water suits, which only keep the diver's skin warm. The cold breathing gas cools the body core down to an intolerable temperature within a short time. The decrease of the normal body temperature from 37°C (98.6°F) by only a few degrees Centigrade causes not only severe health problems but may be fatal.

Depending on the relative humidity of the breathing gas, the critical depth lies between 250 and 280 msw. The critical depth is the depth where the generated body heat is in equilibrium with the heat removed by the cold breathing gas at the same temperature as the surrounding water, as defined in reference [12]. At greater depths, without any countermeasures such as heating the gas, more heat is removed via the breathing gas than the body can supply. Consequently, the body's core temperature decreases, causing hypothermia. Recent investigations on heat protection problems have been described in, for example, in reference [130]. To avoid hypothermia, the breathing gas must be heated in correspondence with the working depth. Fig. 5.7 gives an idea of tolerable temperatures of breathing gases used in the diving industry.

During deep diving operations divers must live for long periods in chambers supplied with heliox bottom gases. To maintain comfortable living conditions, the chamber temperature must be kept constantly at

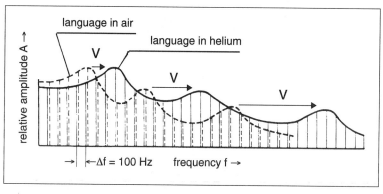

Fig. 5.6 Distortion of voice in a helium atmosphere

approximately 30°C. It must be noted that the margin for comfort is roughly 1 degree Centigrade, requiring very exact temperature control. Even a difference of only 1 degree Centigrade may cause intolerable temperature conditions inside the chamber.

At greater depths, helium causes a physiological problem known as High Pressure Nervous Syndrome, or HPNS. If divers go deeper than 200 msw and, if additionally, high compression rates are used, disorders of the central nervous system (CNS) may occur. These disorders are manifested by symptoms such as tremors of the hands and torso, visual disorders, micro sleep, dizziness, and nausea. Other abnormal reactions have also been noticed, for example, brain waves which changed significantly in cases of HPNS, according to reference [10].

To understand the complex HPNS processes, a simple technical picture may be helpful. The nerves, consisting of nerve cells as conductors and the surrounding lipids as insulation, are exposed to an increasing pressure. This results in compression of the lipids and the insulation, causing "short-circuits" of the CNS. A high lipid solubility means a large swelling of the lipid tissues with increasing cell volume, which counteracts the effects of compression. Table 5.3 shows the correlation between lipid solubility and the narcotic potential for different

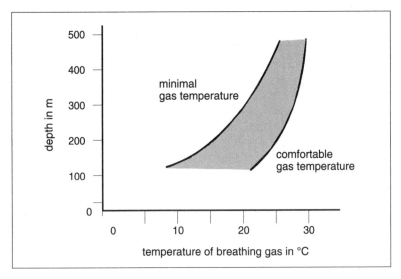

Fig. 5.7 Tolerable temperatures of breathing gas vs. depth

diving gases. The solubility of helium in lipid tissues is clearly lower than that of other gases, resulting in less swelling. Raised ambient pressures cause compression of the nerve cell membranes; in the case of helium, the swelling effects are too small to compensate for the pressure effects. To overcome HPNS effects, narcotic gases with corresponding high lipid solubility are added to increase the nerve cell volume. Based on these findings, in U.S. deep-diving operations 5 to 10% nitrogen is added to the heliox mix to suppress HPNS effects, as stated in reference [10, 13]. The mixture with the additional nitrogen is known as trimix. Using trimix, a test dive down to 686 m was completed as part of the ATLANTIS III project at Duke University. In Germany, trimix with 5% nitrogen was used successfully, without any HPNS symptoms, for all dives down to 600 m in the underwater simulator GUSI at Geesthacht.

5.7 HYDROGEN

Hydrogen is a colorless, odorless, tasteless gas with the atomic number 1 and an atomic weight of 1. Hydrogen exists in a diatomic state (H_2) under normal conditions. It is a very active gas present in most chemical compounds. It is the basis of our universe, which consists of more than 99% hydrogen. Hydrogen has a density $\rho = 0.090$ g/l under normal conditions and is therefore the lightest element on earth. Its boiling point is -253°C, and its heat conductivity is 181 mmW/m·K—7 times higher than that of air and on the same order of magnitude as that of helium.

Hydrogen reacts violently with oxygen at concentrations of more than 4 vol% oxygen. To avoid oxyhydrogen reactions, O_2 concentrations must be well under 4 vol% (see Fig. 5.8). Physiologically, hydrogen acts as an inert gas; its narcotic potential lies between that of nitrogen and that of helium, with about half of nitrogen's potential. Due to this higher narcotic potential, HPNS effects are suppressed successfully.

Hydrogen's low density makes hydrogen mixes suitable as breathing gases for very deep diving operations, where the density of the gases cannot be neglected. The problems of body heat loss and voice distortion for hydrogen are similar to those of helium. Hydrogen's diffusion coefficient is comparable to helium's, but its solubility in oil or water is more or less the same as nitrogen's.

Ten deep-diving operations have been successfully performed by the French diving company Comex during the HYDRA experiments. They used oxygen/hydrogen mixtures, known as hydrox, and oxygen/hydrogen/

helium mixtures, known as hydreliox, for a depth range of 200 to 534 msw, as stated in reference [14]. In November 1992, the U.S. dive record of 686 m was broken by Comex during the HYDRA 10 experiment. The record dive to 701 m was performed in their chamber system at Marseille, France. The total dive took 47 days, using hydreliox (H_2-He-O_2) as the breathing gas, according to reference [129]. The oxygen partial pressure was kept at 0.4 bars constantly, corresponding to an O_2 content of about 0.5%. The remaining 99.5% of the breathing gas consisted of hydrogen and helium.

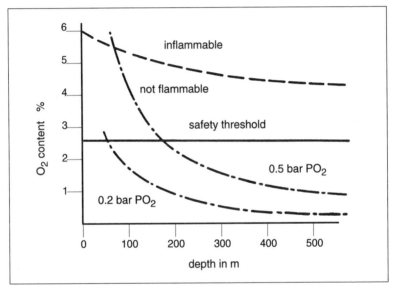

Fig. 5.8 Inflammability thresholds of hydrogen

CHAPTER 6

Gas Laws

6.1 IDEAL GAS LAW

The gas laws describe the physical correlations among the volume, pressure, and temperature of gases and the properties of gas mixtures. The laws are valid for ideal gases only, where there are no interactions among the gas molecules or between the molecules and their container. The ideal gas law states

$$p\,V = n\,R\,T \tag{6.1}$$

V, p, and T correspond to volume, pressure, and temperature, where pressure and temperature are given in *absolute* values. Little (n) is the mass of the matter involved, and (R) is the general gas constant.

$$R = 8.3144.10^{-2} \quad \frac{\text{bar m}^3}{\text{kmol K}}$$

Real gases often show different characteristics and may vary widely from ideal gases. But for real gases under low pressure and temperature conditions, the ideal gas law can be applied with sufficient accuracy. Approaching the range of critical temperatures, where the gaseous phase changes into the liquid phase, noticeable differences from the ideal gas law occur even at low pressures. The same is true for real gases under high pressure, where for some kinds of gases enormous variance from the ideal gas law can be seen.

To apply the ideal gas law to real gases, a correction factor Z is introduced for each gas. This individual factor Z depends on the pressure and temperature of the particular gas. When Z is exactly 1, the ideal gas law is correct. If the factor Z is less than 1, the compressibility of the real gas is higher, given the same pressure and temperature conditions. In that case, for example, the volume of a given gas in a tank may be larger than the result of the ideal gas law calculations. When the factor Z is greater than 1, the correspondences are just the other way round, according to reference [61].

6.2 DERIVED GAS LAWS

The ideal gas law in Fig. 6.1 can also be written as

$$\frac{p \cdot V}{T} = n \cdot R$$

Because the mass of matter (n) and the gas constant (R) for a gas under consideration are constant, the ideal gas law can now be written as

$$\frac{p \cdot V}{T} = \text{const}$$

Comparing two gas conditions, 1 and 2, leads to the general gas law

$$\frac{p_1 \cdot V_1}{T_1} = \frac{p_2 \cdot V_2}{T_2} \tag{6.2}$$

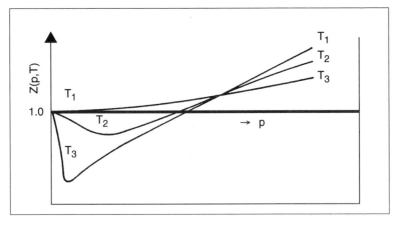

Fig. 6.1 Correction factor Z(p,T) vs. pressure and temperature

6.2.1 Boyle's Law

Considering two gas conditions, where the temperature is constant, so that $T_1 = T_2$, the general gas law changes to Boyle's law

$$p \cdot V = \text{const} \quad \text{or} \quad p_1 V_1 = p_2 V_2 \qquad (6.3)$$

6.2.2 Charles' Law

Considering two gas conditions, where volume or pressure is constant ($V_1 = V_2$ or $p_1 = p_2$), the general gas law changes to Charles' law

$$\frac{V}{T} = \text{const} \quad \text{or} \quad \frac{V_1}{T_1} = \frac{V_2}{T_2} \qquad (6.4)$$

In the case of a constant volume

$$\frac{p}{T} = \text{const} \quad \text{or} \quad \frac{p_1}{T_1} = \frac{p_2}{T_2} \qquad (6.5)$$

6.2.3 (Partial Pressure Law) Dalton's Law

Dalton's law states that in a mixture of ideal gases, the partial pressure of each gas component is the same as the pressure would be if the single component were alone and occupied the total volume. The total pressure of a mixture is therefore the sum of the partial pressures of each gas component.

$$p = pp_1 + pp_2 + pp_3 + \ldots\ldots\ldots\ldots\ldots + pp_n \qquad (6.6)$$

21/79 AIR 1 bar	=	21% OXYGEN 0.21 bar	+	79% NITROGEN 0.79 bar

The correlation among total pressure, partial pressure, and the concentration of a given gas component (k) is shown clearly by the following formula, known as the T-formula:

$$\frac{pp_k \text{ in bars}}{p \text{ in bars} \mid \text{Conc.k}} \qquad (6.7)$$

The T-formula written out

$$pp_k = p \cdot Conc.\ k \quad \text{in bars} \tag{6.7a}$$

$$p = \frac{pp_k}{Conc.\ k} \quad \text{in bars} \tag{6.7b}$$

$$\text{Concentration k} = \frac{pp_k}{p} \tag{6.7c}$$

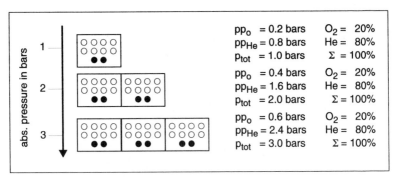

Fig. 6.2 Partial pressures of a 20/80 heliox mix

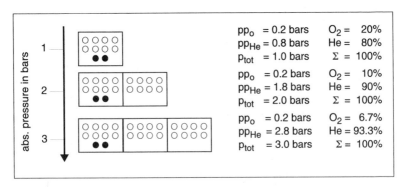

Fig. 6.3 Partial press. of 20/80 heliox with constant O_2 partial pressure

6.2.4 Henry's Law

Henry's law describes the solubility of gases in liquids. The solubility depends mainly on the ambient pressure of the gas in contact with the liquid on the partial pressure of a particular gas component. Other parameters influencing gas solubility are temperature, contact area, and the solubility coefficient of the gas in the liquid. For practical considerations, Henry's law will be dealt with only qualitatively, although its consequences are of great importance in diving.

Because the human body consists mainly of water, the solubility of gases in water plays an essential role in the uptake and release of inert gases by the body's tissues. It is important for the diver to know that the deeper he dives, the more gas is dissolved in his body. Ambient pressure and the amount of dissolved gas are directly proportional. The principle of gas uptake and release is shown in Fig. 6.4.

Increasing the ambient pressure, corresponding to diver's descents to greater depths, causes further dissolution of gas molecules in liquid. According to Henry's law, the amount of dissolved gas in the liquid increases from G_0 to G_1 (Fig. 6.4).

During the diver's ascent, the ambient pressure decreases. Because the liquid cannot dissolve as many gas molecules at lower pressures, gas is released, corresponding to the new ambient pressure. The amount of gas in the liquid is now reduced from G_1 to G_2, where the excess gas is released as bubbles. These bubbles may induce decompression sickness and may cause very severe health problems.

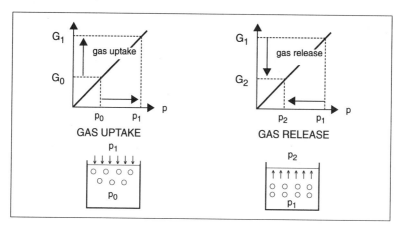

Fig. 6.4 Principle of gas uptake and release according to Henry's law

6.3 PRACTICAL APPLICATIONS OF GAS LAWS

The physical relationships among pressure, volume, and temperature discussed in this chapter will be demonstrated by practice-oriented examples.

Example 1: A diver ascends freely from 5.5 msw to the surface. How much will his lung volume increase, if he does not release the air?

Application of Boyle's law

condition 1 at 5.5 msw: $V_1 = 100\%$ $p_1 = msw/10 + 1 = 1.55$ bars

condition 2 at surface: $V_2 = ?$ $p_2 = 1$ bar

$$V_1\, p_1 = V_2\, p_2 \quad V_2 = V_1 \frac{p_1}{p_2} = 100\% \; \frac{1.55}{1} = 155\%.$$

Answer: The lungs will theoretically expand to 155% of their original volume. In practice the lungs would tear.

Example 2: A diver's lungs have a vital capacity of 6 l and a residual volume of 1.5 l. How deep can he free dive from the surface to achieve just the residual volume?

Application of Boyle's law

condition 1 at surface: $V_1 = 6\,l$ $p_1 = 1$ bar

condition 2 at depth: $V_2 = 1.5\,l$ $p_2 = ?$

$$p_1\, V_1 = p_2\, V_2 \quad p_2 = p_1 \frac{V_1}{V_2} = 1\text{ bar} \; \frac{6\,l}{1.5\,l} = 4\text{ bars}.$$

Conversion of absolute pressures into water depths:

$$msw = (p - 1)10 = (4 - 1)10 = 30\text{ m}.$$

Answer: The diver can go down to a maximum depth of 30 msw.

Example 3: A diver descends to 50 msw in 10 msw steps. At which step does greatest relative change of volume occur?

Application of Boyle's law for the single steps

condition 1 from surface: $V_1 = 100\%$ $p_1 = 1$ bar

condition n (step (n-1)10): $V_n = ?$ $p_n = n$ bars, n = 2, 3, 4, 5, 6

$$V_1\, p_1 = V_n p_n \quad V_n = V_1 \frac{p_1}{p_n} = 100\% \frac{1}{n} \text{ in percent}$$

diving step 10 msw	$n = 2$	$V_2 = 100\% \; 1/2 = 50\%$
diving step 20 msw	$n = 3$	$V_3 = 100\% \; 1/3 = 33\%$
diving step 30 msw	$n = 4$	$V_4 = 100\% \; 1/4 = 25\%$
diving step 40 msw	$n = 5$	$V_5 = 100\% \; 1/5 = 20\%$
diving step 50 msw	$n = 6$	$V_6 = 100\% \; 1/6 = 17\%$

Answer: The greatest relative change of volume occurs at the first step (see Fig. 6.5).

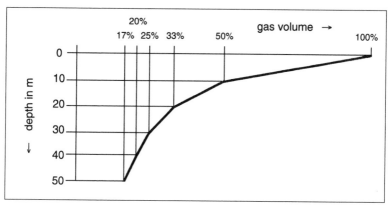

Fig. 6.5 Relative volume differences vs. depth

Example 4: A lift bag with a volume of 0.25 m³ is filled to 30% with air at a depth of 40 msw. How many liters of air are released when it reaches the surface?

Application of Boyle's law

condition 1 at 40 msw:	$p_1 = 5$ bars	$V_1 = 250\,l \times 30\% = 75\,l$
condition 2 at surface:	$p_2 = 1$ bar	$V_2 = ?$

$$p_1 V_1 = p_2 V_2 \quad V_2 = V_1 \frac{p_1}{p_2} = 75\,l \; \frac{5 \text{ bars}}{1 \text{ bar}} = 375\,l$$

Answer: The theoretical volume of the lift bag would be 375 *l* at the surface. Because the bag's volume is only 250 *l*, the difference of 375 *l* - 250 *l* = 125 *l* is released at the surface.

Example 5: A lift bag is filled to 40% with air at a depth of 35 msw. The safety valve opens at 20% overpressure. At which depth does the valve open when ascending?

Application of Boyle's law   (6.3)
condition 1 at 35 msw: $V_1 = 40\%$ $p_1 = 4.5$ bars
condition 2 at opening depth $V_2 = 120\%$ (20% overpressure) $p_2 = ?$

$$p_1 V_1 = p_2 V_2 \quad p_2 = p_1 \frac{V_1}{V_2} = 4.5 \text{ bars} \frac{40\%}{120\%} = 1.5 \text{ bars}$$

Conversion of absolute pressures into water depths:

$$msw = (p - 1)10 = (1.5 - 1)10 = 5 \text{ m}$$

Answer: The safety valve of the lift bag is activated at a depth of 5 m.

Example 6: At the boundary of two layers of water the temperature jumps from 10°C to 15°C. How does a volume of 1 l change, moving from the colder layer to the warmer one?

Application of Charles law $p_1 = p_2$ (6.4)
condition 1 of cold layer: $V_1 = 1\ l$ $T_1 = 10 + 273 = 283$ K
condition 2 of warm layer: $V_2 = ?$ $T_2 = 15 + 273 = 288$ K

$$\frac{V_1}{T_1} = \frac{V_2}{T_2} \quad V_2 = V_1 \frac{T_2}{T_1} = 1\, l \frac{288 \text{ K}}{283 \text{ K}} = 1.0177\ l$$

Answer: Moving the volume from the cold to the warm layer means a volume increase of 1.77%. A temperature change of just 1°C at a temperature level of 0° Centigrade increases the volume by 1/273 or 0.366%.

Example 7: A tank of 8 l is compressed to 200 bars overpressure at ambient temperature (15°C). During the compression, it heats up by 50°C. What pressure does the gauge show after the tank cools down to ambient temperature?

Application of Charles law   (6.5)
Volume of tank is constant, $V_1 = V_2$
condition 1 (after compression)

$$p_1 = 200 + 1 = 201 \text{ bars} \qquad T_1 = (15 + 50) + 273 \qquad T_1 = 338 \text{ K}$$

condition 2 (after cooling down) $\qquad p_2 = ? \qquad T_2 = 15 + 273 = 288 \text{ K}$

$$\frac{p_1}{T_1} = \frac{p_2}{T_2} \quad p_2 = p_1 \frac{T_2}{T_1} = 201 \text{ bars} \frac{288 \text{ K}}{338 \text{ K}} = 171.27 \text{ bars}$$

Answer: The pressure of 171.27 bars is the absolute pressure, while the gauge reading gives the overpressure reduced by the atmospheric pressure of 1 bar. So the reading is 171.27 bars - 1 bar = 170.27 bars after cooling down.

Example 8: A volume of 6 *l* has an ambient temperature of 5°C at a depth of 150 msw. What volume can be expected at the surface, where the temperature is 27°C?

Application of the general gas law $\hspace{4cm}$ (6.2)
condition 1 at 150 msw: $V_1 = 6\,l \quad p_1 = 16 \text{ bars} \quad T_1 = 5 + 273 = 278\text{K}$
condition 2 at surface: $\quad V_2 = ? \qquad p_2 = 1 \text{ bar} \qquad T_2 = 27 + 273 = 300\text{K}$

$$\frac{p_1 V_1}{T_1} = \frac{p_2 V_2}{T_2} \quad V_2 = V_1 \frac{p_1 T_2}{p_2 T_1} = 6\,l \frac{16 \times 300}{1 \times 278} = 103.6\,l$$

Answer: At the surface the volume will be 103.6 l.

Example 9: A diver performs heavy work at 45 msw and consumes 60 *l*/min of air. Theoretically, how long can he work, when a tank of 50 *l* with a gauge reading of 190 bars is available at the surface?

To answer this question, all volumes must be converted into surface volumes, using Boyle's law.

condition 1 at 45 msw: $\qquad V_1 = 60\,l\,/\text{min} \qquad p_1 = 5.5 \text{ bars}$
condition 2 at surface: $\qquad V_2 = ? \qquad\qquad\quad p_2 = 1 \text{ bar}$

$$p_1 V_1 = p_2 V_2 \quad V_2 = V_1 \frac{p_1}{p_2} = 60\,l\,/\text{min} \frac{5.5}{l} = 330\,l\,/\text{min}$$

Determination of available air supply in surface volumes:

condition 1 at start: $\qquad V_1 = 50\,l \qquad\qquad p_1 = 191 \text{ bars}$
condition 2 at surface: $\qquad V_2 = ? \qquad\qquad\quad p_2 = 1 \text{ bar}$

Because the diver works at 45 msw corresponding to 5.5 bars ambient pressure, he can only use the difference between 191 bars and 5.5 bars in absolute pressures or 190 bars and 4.5 bars in overpressures. It must be mentioned that this is a theoretical consideration, as a residual pressure of some bars must always remain in the tank.

$$p_1 V_1 = p_2 V_2 \quad V_2 = V_1 \frac{p_1}{p_2} = 50 \, l \, \frac{191 - 5.5}{1} = 9{,}275 \, l$$

The theoretical working time: $\quad t = \dfrac{9{,}275 \, l}{330 \, l / \min} = 28.1 \min$

Answer: The theoretical working time at 45 msw will be approximately 28 minutes. In addition, the working time must be determined while taking into account that a residual volume of 40 bars must be kept in the tank and that the helmet's regulator needs a working pressure of 8 bars. The available air supply is now

$$V_2 = V_1 \frac{p_1}{p_2} = 50 \, l \frac{191 - 5.5 - 40 - 8}{1} = 6{,}875 \, l$$

Answer: The air supply allows a working time t of 6,875 l/330 = 20.8 min.

Example 10: A compressor at the surface delivers 10 m^3 air per hour. Is this capacity sufficient to supply a diver at 40 msw with 40 *l*/min?

Conversion of air supply into surface volumes according to Boyle's law.
condition 1 at 40 msw: $\quad V_1 = 40 \, l$/min $\quad p_1 = 5$ bars
condition 2 at surface: $\quad V_2 = ? \quad p_2 = 1$ bar

$$p_1 V_1 = p_2 V_2 \quad V_2 = V_1 \frac{p_1}{p_2} = 40 \, l/\min \, \frac{5}{1} = 200 \, l/\min$$

The demand at the surface is 200 *l*/min × 60 min/h = 12 m^3/h

Answer: The compressor's capacity of 10 m^3/h is not sufficient to supply the diver.

Example 11: Air with 21% oxygen and 79% nitrogen is used for a dive down to 50 msw. What are the partial pressures of O_2 and N_2?

Application of Dalton's law (6.7a)
The total pressure of 6 bars and concentration of components are known.

$ppO_2 = p \times conc. O_2 = 6\ bars \times 0.21 = 1.26\ bars$

$ppN_2 = p \times conc. N_2 = 6\ bars \times 0.79 = 4.74\ bars$

$p = ppO_2 + ppN_2 \qquad \Sigma = 6.00\ bars$

Answer: The partial pressures of oxygen and of nitrogen are 1.26 bars and 4.74 bars respectively at 50 msw.

Example 12: For the French record dive to 701 msw the oxygen partial pressure was limited to 0.4 bars. What was the O_2 concentration of the breathing gas?

Application of Dalton's law (6.7c)
The total pressure of 71.1 bars and the O_2 partial pressure are known.

$$Conc.\ O_2 = \frac{ppO_2}{p} = \frac{0.4\ bars}{71.1\ bars} = 0.0056$$

Concentration in %: $0.0056 \times 100\% = 0.56\% O_2$

Conc. in parts per million (ppm) $0.0056 \times 10^6\ ppm = 5600\ ppm\ O_2$

Answer: The O_2 concentration was 0.56% or 5,600 ppm.

Example 13: An emergency gas must not exceed an oxygen partial pressure margin between 0.16 and 1.25 bars. What is the depth range of an emergency gas with 8% oxygen?

Application of Dalton's law (6.7 b)
The partial pressures and the O_2 concentration are known.

$p = 0.16\ bars/0.08 = 2\ bars \qquad D = (p - 1)10 = 10\ msw$

$$p = \frac{ppO_2}{conc.\ O_2}$$

$p = 1.25\ bars/0.08 = 15.63\ bars \quad D = (p - 1)10 = 146.3\ msw$

Answer: The emergency mix with 8% oxygen can be used between 10 msw and 146.3 msw.

Example 14: During a chamber dive at 360 msw a CO_2 concentration of 130 ppm is monitored. What is the CO_2 partial pressure inside the chamber?

Application of Dalton's law   (6.7a)
The total pressure of 37 bars and the CO_2 concentration are known.

$ppCO_2 = p \times conc.CO_{22}$ $ppCO_2 = 37$ bars $\times 130\ 10^{-6} = 4810\ 10^{-6}$ bars
   $= 4.81$ mbars

Answer: The CO_2 partial pressure in the chamber is 4.81 millibars.

Example 15: An underwater laboratory is stationed at 20 msw and contains, for fire reasons, a nitrox mixture ($ppO_2 = 0.3$ bars, rest N_2). Which is the theoretical depth for decompression using air tables? (See Chapter 9.6 for more details.)

Application of Dalton's law:
   Step 1: Calculate the actual nitrogen partial pressure.
   Step 2: Calculate the water depth which corresponds to the actual
        N_2 partial pressure when using air as breathing gas.

Step 1: $p = 3$ bars $ppN_2 = p - ppO_2 = 3 - 0.3 = 2.7$ bars

The actual N_2 concentration:

$conc.N_2 = ppN_2/p = 2.7/3.0 = 0.9; \rightarrow 90\%\ N_2$

Step 2: The actual N_2 partial pressure and the N_2 concentration
        of air are known.

$p_{air} = ppN_2/conc.N_2$ $p_{air} = 2.7$ bars$/0.79 = 3.42$ bars

Conversion into water depth msw $= (p_{air} - 1)10 = 24.2$ msw

Answer: Using air tables for decompression, a theoretical depth of 24.2 msw must be used instead of the actual depth of 20 msw.

CHAPTER 7

Gas Management

7.1 INTRODUCTION

Gas management includes all activities related to the handling and distribution of gases for diving—the analysis of demand for intended operations, gas transport, and mixing of gases, as well as the supervision of quality, monitoring, and distribution. For some gas management tasks (e.g., determination of gas quantities for diving operations or for mixing gases) some basic knowledge of mathematics and physics is necessary. Also the handling and storage of gases under pressure requires knowledge of a number of safety regulations. In this chapter, safety rules and regulations for the storage and handling of inflammable, explosive, or toxic gases and gases under pressure will be introduced. The mathematical basics for gas calculations will also be discussed.

For recommended gas quantities for diving operations offshore, the industry published a guidance note in 1983 in reference [15].

7.2 LEGAL BASIS OF HANDLING COMPRESSED GASES

To protect their citizens, almost all countries have issued rules to eliminate potential dangers from technical installations and from handling dangerous materials. One aspect of this legislation is the handling of compressed gases. In Germany, the legal document is the *Druckbehälter Verordnung,* also known as reference [16] (Pressure Vessel Regulation). Derived from reference [16], *Technische Regeln Druckgase* (TRG) (Technical Regulations on Gases under Pressure) is available, with detailed requirements, e.g., for breathing mixtures in reference [17] or the operation of filling stations in reference [18].

To guarantee the safe handling of compressed gases, additional rules and regulations must be followed; these are issued by the German professional trade association in references [19, 20, 21] for accident prevention. Detailed regulations are available for handling gases, including oxygen, and other activities.

Further regulations, known as DIN Standards, deal with design criteria for the technical components of pressure systems, which can be found in [22, 23]. The DIN Standards, stating the established rules for technology, will soon be changed into European EN Standards in the interests of EC standardization. For diving related legislation, see Chapter 13.

7.3 COLOR CODING OF PRESSURE TANKS

For easier identification of the contents of gas cylinders, color coding systems are used. Unfortunately there is no international agreement about color coding yet. Most countries have their own color coding systems, which differ widely. It is important to understand that the color code is no guarantee that a tank contains the gas indicated by the code. Reliable information about the contents and other data are given only by the identification markings on the gas cylinder. In Germany, for example, the above mentioned *Technical Rules on Gases Under Pressure* (TRG), referred to as reference [17], stipulates the following color coding:

Table 7.1 Color Coding of Gas Cylinders According to TRG

Gas	Color code
Oxygen	blue
Nitrogen	green
Acetylene	yellow
Inflammable or toxic gases	red
Nonflammable gases like air	gray

In the U.S. another color code system is used. According to reference [9], oxygen is marked green, nitrogen gray, and air black. In the North Sea area, a color coding system has been established in reference [24] which is valid in the British and Norwegian sector; it has also been adopted by other institutions such as the German Classification Society, Germanischer Lloyd, as shown in reference [25] (see Table 7.2). The French diving industry also uses the North Sea standard, including the color coding, as the basis for its diving activities.

In the offshore industry, the North Sea standard has been adopted widely by internationally operating diving companies. It represents the highest safety standard in diving. The International Maritime Organization (IMO), in its code of safety for diving systems, recommends this color coding, as stated in reference [134]. So standardization of color coding is beginning.

It should be remembered, however, that the color code gives only a first clue as to the gas contents of a cylinder or a bank. More reliable data are given by the identification markings stamped on the shoulder of the cylinder. These data include information on tank volume, rated pressure and test pressure, material specification, manufacturer identity, inspection date, etc. But all that information does not eliminate the possibility of filling a tank with improper gases. Therefore, each breathing gas should be analyzed before connecting it to the diver's supply system.

Table 7.2. Color Coding in the North Sea Area [24]

Gas	Cylinder body	Cylinder top
Helium	brown	brown
Oxygen	black	white
Oxygen/Helium	brown	brown & white quarters
Nitrogen	gray	black
Oxygen/Nitrogen (Air)	gray	black & white quarters
Oxygen/Nitrogen/Helium	brown	black & white & brown sections
Calibration gases	pink	pink

7.4 PURITY OF GASES

For gases or gas mixtures, purity standards must be considered in relation to their use, e.g., as breathing gases in diving or as calibration gases in chemistry or general engineering. It is clearly understood that purity standards for calibration gases must be extremely high. To characterize the purity level, the purity grade percentage is described by the number of nines. So 3.0 = 99.9%, 4.0 = 99.99%, 5.0 = 99.999%, and 5.5 = 99.9995%.

The purity of a gas depends on the production method used. It is obvious that handling extremely pure gases requires special facilities and equipment. Fortunately, such extreme purity standards are not necessary for breathing mixtures. On the other hand, minimum standards must be maintained. Impurities in a gas, which can be tolerated under atmospheric conditions, lead to intolerable concentrations with severe consequences for the diver's health during compression.

Air is the breathing medium most used in diving all over the world. Therefore, special attention must be paid to its purity. In Germany, for example, purity standards for air are stated in DIN Regulation 3188, according to reference [26] (see Table 7.3). In Table 7.3, different national purity standards for air are compared.

Table 7.3 Different Purity Standards for Air

Component Stand. DIN 3188	German Standard US Navy	U.S. Stand. BS 4275	Brit. French Stand. issued 1992	
Oxygen (%) more than 16	20 ... 21	20 ... 22	21 ± 0.5	
CO_2 (ppm)	800	1000	500	1667
CO (ppm)	30	20	5	8
Hydrocarbons (mg/m^3)	0.3	25 ppm	0.5	0.5

For other diving gases, the British diving industry, for example, has an agreement with the suppliers, issued in 1984, on purity standards for diving gases they produce, according to reference [27]. These recommendations for purity standards are widely accepted (see Table 7.4). In the U.S., purity standards are available for the most-used diving gases—oxygen, nitrogen, and helium. These standards differentiate among different criteria. Type I is only valid for gaseous media and class I means oil-free gases. For diving, only oil-free gases are of concern.

For oxygen, three grades are used: Grade A—Aviator's breathing; Grade B—Industrial and medical; and Grade C—Technical. For oxygen, grades A and B differ only in their moisture content. Both grades have a purity standard of at least 99.5% oxygen, and both grades can be used for diving.

For nitrogen, three grades are also used: Grade A—99.95% purity; Grade B—99.5% purity; and Grade C—99.5% purity. As in the case of oxygen, nitrogen grades B and C differ only in their moisture content. In general, moisture is no problem in diving, so all three grades are usable.

For helium, only Grade A, with a purity of approximately 99.999%, is available with no oil and no moisture.

Table 7.4 Purity Standards of Diving Gases [27]

Contaminant	Oxygen	Helium	Nitrogen
Nitrogen (ppm)	1000	200	-
Oxygen (ppm)	-	50	50
Carbon dioxide (ppm)	10	10	10
Carbon monoxide (ppm)	1	1	1
Neon (ppm)	10	10	10
Argon (ppm)	4000	25	25
Hydrogen (ppm)	10	10	10
Methane (ppm)	25	5	5
Other Hydrocarbons (ppm)	3	1	1
Moisture (ppm)	25	25	25

7.5 GAS ANALYSIS

7.5.1 Introduction

Analysis of diving gases and continuous monitoring of breathing gases are vital for safe diving. Especially in saturation diving, an efficient and reliable gas analysis is important. Due to long-term exposures, even small deviations from nominal values can lead to severe health problems for the diver. The first concern is monitoring oxygen concentrations, followed by control of carbon dioxide. As already mentioned, a check of oxygen concentrations of each breathing gas is essential before the gas is connected to the diver's supply. In the past, some severe accidents occurred because improper breathing gases were used. It may also be necessary to consider other contaminants. For example, contaminants may get into the breathing gas during activities such as hyperbaric welding.

There are different analyzers for use during specific applications, depending on the kind of gas to be analyzed and the expected concentrations. Analyzers used offshore must fulfill some basic requirements:

- be suitable for operation within a pressure chamber;
- have sufficient accuracy under field conditions;
- be reliable under rough conditions;

- be easy to handle and maintenance-free, as far as possible;
- have a guaranteed energy supply; and
- guarantee that continuous monitoring is possible.

There are very complex and accurate analyzers available, more suited for laboratory use. In the field under rough conditions, these systems are less useful. Analyzers must be calibrated at regular intervals. In practice, this is done every 8 to 24 hours using special calibration gases.

7.5.2 Analyzers

There are a number of analyzers available which are able to analyze one gas only or several gases at the same time, depending on the intended task. Here only the measurement principles of analyzers used in diving are introduced. More details are available from manufacturers, among others; also, the operating instructions contain detailed information on specific analyzers (see also the table of gas analysis equipment in reference [9]).

Electro-chemical Principle. This principle is used for measuring oxygen. Using the chemical reactions of oxygen in a fuel cell (electrolytic cell), an electric current is generated proportional to the amount of oxygen. The advantages of this measuring principle are its ease of use, direct reading of oxygen partial pressures, its independence from any auxiliary energy, and its insensitivity to variable measuring positions. The disadvantage is that the fuel cell will be consumed during operation and must be replaced.

Paramagnetic Principle. This principle, also employed for measuring oxygen quantities, uses the paramagnetic characteristic of oxygen. A magnetic field changes its properties in the presence of oxygen. The field change is proportional to the amount of oxygen and is converted into a measurable signal. Analyzers based on the paramagnetic principle give very accurate results. But this type of analyzer needs a power source and it is very sensitive to variations in measuring positions.

Infrared Absorption Principle. The infrared absorption principle is used for measuring carbon dioxide in the field. This principle is based on the absorption of infrared radiation by carbon dioxide. The absorption is proportional to the CO_2 concentration. A reference cell contains a calibrated reference gas which is compared with the actual gas in the measuring cell. This measuring procedure is very sensitive to moisture and impurities in the actual gas, which can falsify the results enormously.

Principle of Gas Chromatography. Gas chromatography is a very versatile method for analyzing gas mixtures. In filters, the gas sample is separated into its single components. Each gas component passes a detector, where a measuring signal is generated, depending on the kind and amount of the gas component. Considerable technical equipment is necessary, but gas chromatography's accuracy and sensitivity offer versatile applications in gas analysis.

Mass Spectrometry. The method of mass spectrometry is similar to gas chromatography; it is a very accurate and versatile procedure for analyzing all gases and gas mixtures. The measuring principle is based on the ionization of gas molecules by radiation with electrons in a vacuum chamber. The ionized molecules will be accelerated by magnetic and electric fields and deflected corresponding to the mass of the molecules. The charges of the deflected ions are proportional to the kind and amount of gas molecules and proportional to the concentration of gas being analyzed. The disadvantage of this method is also the considerable amount of technical equipment necessary for gas analysis. Therefore, gas chromatography and mass spectrometry are methods used mainly under laboratory conditions.

Principle of Colorimetric Detection (Test Tube). The principle of colorimetric indications of gas concentrations by means of test tubes (Draeger tubes) is simple and cheap, but has limitations in accuracy. An exact dosage of the gas is released into the test tube, which contains a chemical filling. The gas reacts with the chemical in the tube, changing its color. To identify different substances, specific chemical reactions are used. The color change is proportional to the gas concentration and can be read from a calibrated scale on the tube. The result is valid only under atmospheric conditions. In a hyperbaric environment in a chamber, the reading must be corrected to get the actual concentration. For each kind of gas or substance, a special tube is available, which can be used only once. Because the chemical filling loses its reaction potential over time, the use of these test tubes is temporally limited.

7.6 OXYGEN HANDLING AND CLEANING

Depending on depth and operational use, each breathing gas contains oxygen in concentrations of less than 1% up to 100% oxygen. For offshore operations, pure oxygen is stored in banks on board ships (DSV) or rigs or other places at the diving site. This oxygen is used for mixing the correct breathing gases. Due to the danger of explosion when handling pure oxygen or oxygen-enriched mixtures, a number of safety precautions must be taken.

Compressed oxygen is the most dangerous gas to handle in commercial diving. For that reason, safety standards must be strictly followed (e.g., as stated in references [9, 21, 29]). To avoid dangerous concentrations of oxygen in closed spaces, effective ventilation is essential. Therefore oxygen storage banks are preferably installed in the open. The distribution of highly pressurized oxygen should be avoided due to the potential of its exploding. It is common practice in the field to regulate oxygen directly at the manifold of the storage bank to a level of approximately 40 bars before it is distributed.

Special attention must be paid to components like hoses and fittings that are in contact with oxygen. The materials must be oxygen compatible. For that reason, for example, valves with Teflon sealings must be excluded and only metal sealings used for oxygen-proof valves.

For opening and closing oxygen tanks, only stem valves are allowed on the high-pressure side instead of the normal ball valves. Due to the rapid opening and closing of ball valves, pressure peaks can be induced in the system, followed by temperature peaks. A sudden rise in temperature may trigger an explosion in the O_2 system.

Oxygen lines should be separated from all other lines, especially from those containing inflammable substances. All pipes, valves, hoses, etc. of an oxygen system must be used for oxygen only and correspondingly marked. Special attention must be paid to the cleanliness of O_2 pipings and fittings. Due to the risk of explosions, the system must be absolutely free of oil and grease. Lubrication with silicon grease is not allowed for oxygen systems, but there are special oxygen compatible lubricants available. In addition to oil, grease, and dirt, metal burrs and slivers, including stainless steel slivers, may be sources of contamination. They may get into the oxygen system, for example, during maintenance and repairs, and they are extremely dangerous under increased pressures. Only slight energies are necessary to ignite an oxygen explosion. Sources of ignition can be heat generated by rapid pressurization, friction heat caused by high flow rates, electrostatic sparks, and mechanical impacts.

It is vital to know that new equipment is not oxygen clean; slivers or other contaminants may remain in valves, fittings, etc. Only specially-marked and packed parts are oxygen clean and can be used without additional cleaning. In all other cases, the components must be cleaned according to company procedures or recommendations such as those given in reference [29]. The metal parts of a component (hardware) are cleaned with special solvents, some of which are toxic. Therefore, precautions are necessary when using these solvents. For cleaning software such as Neoprene O-rings, rubber, etc., alkaline detergents are used. The cleaning itself must be done in a very clean place and plastic gloves must be worn. To dry the cleaned parts, only certified oil-free air or nitrogen can be used. The cleaned parts must be sealed immediately and must be correctly marked.

Never start checking and testing newly installed oxygen equipment at the rated pressure. Moving gases like oxygen is usually done by using the pressure differences between the charged storage tank or bank and the consumer station, a procedure known as cascading. But in other cases, oxygen must be pumped and this procedure requires special equipment. Two types of pumps have been introduced offshore for oxygen compression, the piston pump, known as the Haskel pump, and the membrane pump, known as the Corblin pump. The main feature of the Haskel pump is its air motor, an air-driven piston pump. A smaller piston, mechanically connected but completely separate from the air motor, completes the oxygen pumping. The main feature of the Corblin pump is a flexible metal membrane that compresses the oxygen inside the compression chamber. The pump is electrically driven. In both pumps, the compression chamber is completely separate from the remaining pump area.

7.7 PHYSICAL-MATHEMATICAL BASICS OF GAS MANAGEMENT

This section deals with the basics of gas demand calculations and gas mixing, illustrated by practice-oriented examples in section 7.8.3.

7.7.1 Volume Calculations

Different kinds of containers are available for gas storage. The following compilation gives an overview of containers used in the industry. Often a container consists of partial volumes, for example, of a cylinder and two hemispheres.

Cylinder	Diameter D	$V = \pi/4\ D^2L = 0.785\ D^2L$
	Length L	
Sphere	Diameter D	$V = \pi/6\ D^3 = 0.524\ D^3$
Hemisphere	Diameter D	$V = \pi p/12\ D^3 = 0.262\ D^3$
Semi-ellipsoid	Diameter D	$V = \pi/4\ D^2\ 0.7h = 0.545\ D^2h$
	Greatest height h	

Cylindrical container with hemispherical ends

Cyl. Diameter D $\qquad$ $V = \pi/4\ D^2\ (\ L + 2/3\ D\ )$
Cyl. Length L

Cylindrical container with elliptical ends

Cyl. Diameter D $\qquad$ $V = \pi/4\ D^2\ (\ L + 1.4\ h\ )$
Cyl. Length L

7.7.2 Gas Demand Calculations

For the calculation of the gas content FGV (Free Gas Volume) under surface conditions, Boyle's law is applied (see Chapter 6).

$$V_1\ p_1 \qquad = \qquad V_2\ p_2$$
(surface condition) $\qquad\qquad$ (storage condition)

V_1 = gas content (FGV) under surface conditions

p_1 = atmospheric pressure (1 bar)

V_2 = tank volume

p_2 = absolute pressure of tank

Normally the content of a tank is related to atmospheric pressure, meaning that the residual volume under 1 bar conditions remains in the tank. This residual volume can be used only theoretically under vacuum conditions.

If a tank of volume V, charged at absolute pressure p, is emptied into the atmosphere, its free gas volume (FGV) is

$$FGV = V \times (p - 1) \qquad \text{in volume units} \qquad\qquad (7.1)$$

To determine the diver's gas demand, the Respiratory Minute Volume (RMV), which depends on different parameters, must be known. Besides the diver's physical condition and his experience, the kind of physical work he will be doing determines the RMV.

The time-dependent gas demand is

$$FGV\ (t) = n\ RMV\ p\ t \quad \text{in volume units} \qquad\qquad (7.2)$$
with $\qquad$ n = number of divers
$\qquad$ RMV = respiratory minute volume in l/min
$\qquad$ p = absolute pressure at underwater site in bars
$\qquad$ t = diving time in minutes

The respiratory minute volume (RMV) at the underwater working place is depth-independent; it depends only on the diver's physical underwater work. The RMV is roughly 10 l/min at rest and rises for very heavy work to 80 l/min and more (see Fig. 7.1). The oxygen demand necessary for metabolism is 0.5 l/min at rest and approximately 3.0 l/min for very heavy work.

In reference [30], a statistical investigation of the diver's average respiratory minute volume in the North Sea is described (see Fig. 7.2). The result shows that the mean value lies between 30 and 40 liters of air per minute.

The German diving regulations stated in reference [31], use the following RMV figures for determining air reserves:

Scuba   30 l/min
Surface supplied diving   60 l/min

To determine the amount of a single gas component in a mixture, the total gas amount must be multiplied by the single component's concentration.

$$FGV (k) = V\, p\, conc.k \quad \text{in volume units} \tag{7.3}$$

where   V = volume of the container in m^3
           p = absolute pressure in bars
           conc.k = concentration of component k in%/100

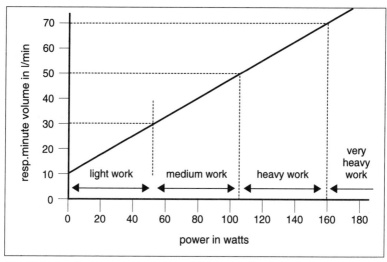

Fig. 7.1 Respiratory minute volume (RMV) vs. physical power

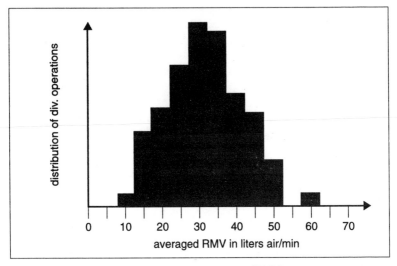

Fig. 7.2 Averaged Respiratory Minute Volume (RMV)

Example: A habitat of 15 m^3 is compressed to 200 msw; it contains a heliox mix of 2.5/97.5. How much oxygen does the habitat contain?

The heliox consists of 2.5% oxygen and 97.5% helium. Using (7.3) the amount of oxygen is

$$20 = \frac{200 \ msw}{10} \ m \, / \, ATM$$

FGV (O$_2$) = 15 m^3 × 21 × 2.5/100 = 7.875 m^3 O$_2$

Answer: The habitat contains a total of 15 × 21 = 315 m^3 heliox with an oxygen portion of about 7.9 m^3.

Volume Calculation at Variable Pressures. In the decompression phase of a saturation dive, the total pressure in the chamber is decreased according to the decompression profile. For physiological reasons, the O$_2$ partial pressure is kept constant over the decompression period. This requires that the O$_2$ concentration be continuously changed (see Fig. 7.3). To calculate the necessary oxygen volume, the variable O$_2$ concentration must be considered.

FGV (O$_2$) = V p conc.O$_2$ (p)   (7.3a)

According to (6.7c), the concentration of O_2 = ppO_2/p, where ppO_2 is constant. Differentiating both sides of formula (7.3a) gives

$$d\,FGV\,(\,O_2\,) = V \times p \times d\,conc.O_2\,(p)$$

Using (6.7c) $d\,FGV\,(O_2) = V \times ppO_2 \times dp/p$

After integration $FGV\,(O_2) = V \times ppO_2 \times ln\,(p)$ (7.4)

with V = chamber volume in m^3
  ppO = required oxygen partial pressure in bars
  ln (p) = natural logarithm of initial chamber pressure

In equation (7.4) it is assumed that the O_2 partial pressure is constant during the whole decompression phase until surfacing. This is an estimation on the safe side. Fig. 7.3 shows the increasing oxygen concentration with decreasing depths at a constant partial pressure level. If during decompression different partial pressures are applied, equation (7.4) must be subdivided according to the partial pressure used in the corresponding depth range. Of course, equation (7.4) can also be applied to other gas components.

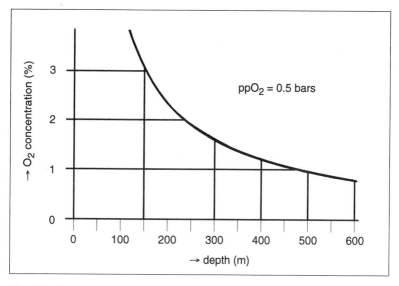

Fig. 7.3 Oxygen concentration vs. depth at constant partial pressure

Example: Decompression starts at 250 msw in a living chamber with a volume of 22 m^3. How much oxygen is necessary for the decompression to the surface without considering the metabolic demand of the divers, when the partial pressure shall be maintained at 0.45 bars?

Input data: p initial is 26 bars. The natural logarithm of 26 is 3.26.
According to (7.4), FGV (O$_2$) = 22 m^3 × 0.45 × ln (26) = 32.3 m^3 O$_2$

Depth of Pressurization (DOP). When a chamber is pressurized with a particular press gas, the depth of pressurization (DOP) is the depth at which the desired partial pressure of the gas component k is achieved.

$$DOP = \frac{pp_{k \text{ desired}} - pp_{k \text{ existing}}}{\text{conc.k of press gas}} \, 10 \text{ in m} \qquad (7.5)$$

$pp_{k \text{ desired}}$ = desired partial pressure of component k
$pp_{k \text{ existing}}$ = existing partial pressure of component k
conc. k = concentration of component k in the press gas, expressed in%/100

Example: A diving bell is pressurized from the surface to 150 msw with heliox 4/96. The O$_2$ partial pressure is limited to 0.6 bars.

$ppO_2 \text{ desired}$ = 0.6 bars
$ppO_2 \text{ existing}$ (surface) = 0.21 bars
oxygen concentration of press gas = 4%

$$DOP = \frac{0.6 \text{ bars - } 0.21 \text{ bars}}{0.04} \, 10 = 97.5 \text{ m}$$

Answer: Starting from the surface, the bell is pressurized to 97.5 m with heliox where the desired oxygen partial pressure of 0.6 bars is just achieved. Further pressurization from 97.5 msw to 150 msw must be continued with pure helium.

A modified calculation of the DOP according to (7.5) is necessary when instead of pure helium, a "lean mixture" with a minimum concentration of 2% oxygen is used (see reference [32]). Now the desired O$_2$ partial pressure must be achieved with two heliox mixtures of different concentrations.

$$DOP = \frac{(pp_{k\ desired} - pp_{k\ exist.}) - D/10\ conc.\ k\ of\ lean\ mix}{10\ in\ m} \quad (7.6)$$

conc. k press gas - conc. k lean mixture

D = desired depth in m
lean mix = mixture with a minimum O_2 conc. of 2%

Example: For the previous example, the DOP will be determined now with the same press gas, heliox 4/96, and as the lean gas a heliox mixture of 2/98.

$pp O_2$ desired = 0.6 bars $pp O_2$ existing(surface) = 0.21 bars
O_2 conc. of press gas = 4% O_2 conc. of lean gas = 2%

$$DOP = \frac{(0.6\ bars - 0.21\ bars) - 150/10 \times 0.02}{0.04 - 0.02} 10 = \frac{0.39 - 15 \times 0.02}{0.02} 10 = 45\ m$$

Answer: The first phase of pressurization is performed from the surface to 45 msw with the press gas heliox 4/96. From 45 msw down to the desired depth of 150 msw, the bell is pressurized with the lean mix of heliox 2/98. Checking the oxygen partial pressures:

portion of surface partial pressure:	1 bar × 0.21	= 0.21 bars
portion of lean mix (2/98):	(15 - 4.5) × 0.02	= 0.21 bars
portion of press gas (4/96):	4.5 bars × 0.04	= 0.18 bars
		= 0.60 bars

7.7.3 Practical Examples

Example 1: The gauge pressure of an air tank of 2 m^3 reads 200 bars. How much air does the tank contain?

According to (7.1)

$$FGV = V \times p_{gauge} = 2\ m^3 \times 200 = 400\ m^3\ air$$
$$FGV_{absolute} = V \times p_{abs} = 2\ m^3 \times 201 = 402\ m^3\ air$$

Answer: When the tank is emptied under atmospheric conditions, 400 m^3 of air are available. If the tank is emptied under vacuum conditions, 402 m^3 are available. The residual volume of 2 m^3 always remains in the tank under atmospheric conditions.

Example 2: A bank consists of 10 cylinders; each is 2 m^3. The bank is filled with trimix (O_2, N_2, He) and the pressure gauge reads 180 bars. The oxygen partial pressure of the bank is 0.5 bars, the nitrogen portion is 5%, and the remaining gas is helium. How much of each component gas is available?

One hundred and eighty bars gauge reading means an absolute pressure of the bank of 181 bars. The total amount of trimix in the bank is

$$FGV_{abs.} = 10 \times 2m^3 \times 181 = 3620 \text{ m}^3$$
$$p_{abs.} = ppO_2 + ppN_2 + ppHe$$

ppO_2 is given	=	0.50 bars	
$ppN_2 = p$ conc.$N_2 = 181$ bars x 0.05	=	9.05 bars	
$ppHe = 181$ bars - 0.5 - 9.05		= 171.45 bars	
		Σ = 181.00 bars	

The single gas components result: $FGV(k) = FGV_{abs} \times pp_k/p_{abs.}$

Oxygen:	$FGV(O_2) = 3620$ m^3 × 0.5/181	= 10 m^3
Nitrogen:	$FGV(N_2) = 3620$ m^3 × 9.05/181	= 181 m^3
Helium:	$FGV(He) = 3620$ m^3 × 171.45/181	= 3429 m^3
		Σ = 3620 m^3

Answer: The bank contains 10 m^3 of oxygen, 181 m^3 of nitrogen, and the remaining 3429 m^3 is helium.

Example 3: Two surface-supplied divers work for 40 mins at a depth of 45 msw. How much air is necessary, considering a 50% reserve?

According to German regulations in reference [31] for surface-supplied diving, a RMV of 60 l/min must be maintained. Using (7.2)

$FGV(t) = n$ RMV p t + 50% reserve = 2×60 l/min × 5.5 × 40 min × 1.5
= 39,600 liters or 39.6 m^3 air

Answer: An air supply of 39.6 m^3, which includes a reserve of 13.2 m^3 (50%), must be available at the dive site.

Example 4: A diver works for 4 h at 150 msw. His RMV is 40 l/min. The working pressure of his helmet must be 15 bars over ambient pressure. There is a bank at the dive site consisting of 32 cylinders, each cylinder having a volume of 50 l and a pressure reading of 190 bars. Is the gas supply sufficient, and what reserve is available?

The absolute pressure at the diver's work site is

p = msw/10 + 1
p = 150/10 + 1 = 16 bars

To determine the usable FGV, the available amount of gas must be reduced by the ambient pressure p_{amb} and the working pressure p_{work} of the helmet, as these amounts cannot be used for breathing.

FGV_{usable} = n FGV_{cyl} (p_{bank} - p_{amb} - p_{work}) = 32 × 50 l (191 - 16 - 15)

FGV_{usable} = 1.6 m^3 × 160 = 256 m^3 gas

Diver's gas demand for 4 h (240 min) according to (7.2):

FGV(t) = n × RMV × p × t = 1 × 40 l/min × 16 × 240 min = 153.6 m^3

Reserve in % = $\dfrac{FGV_{usable} - FGV(t)}{FGV(t)}$ 100% = $\dfrac{256 - 153.6}{153.6}$ 100% = 67%

Answer: The usable gas supply of 256 m^3 is sufficient for the intended dive and includes a reserve of 67%.

Example 5: A diver works at 250 msw and has a bale-out tank of 8 l, charged at 200 bars. How long can he breathe from his emergency supply, when the working pressure of his helmet is 10 bars over ambient pressure and a RMV of 30 l/min is considered?

The absolute pressure at the dive site is

p = msw/10 + 1 = 250/10 + 1 = 26 bars.

The usable FGV under ambient and working pressures is

FGV_{usable} = V_{cyl} (p_{cyl} - p_{amb} - p_{work}) = 8 l (201 - 26 - 10) = 1320 l

Using (7.2)   t = $\dfrac{FGV_{usable}}{RMV × p}$ t = $\dfrac{1320 \, l}{30 \, l/min × 26}$ = 1.7 min

Answer: The supply is sufficient for only 1.7 min or 100 seconds.

Example 6: Two 50 l tanks, charged at 200 bars, will be used for filling 2 × 7 l Scuba cylinders. Which method is recommended—

a) simultaneous filling with both tanks or
b) successive filling (cascading)?

Because filling is performed in a closed system, the volumes before filling must be equal to the volumes after filling.

$$V_1\,p_1 + V_2\,p_2 \quad = \quad (\,V_1 + V_2\,)\,p_{total}$$
before filling   after filling

Method a (simultaneous filling with both tanks)
The calculation is performed here in gauge pressures (p - 1). It could also be done in absolute pressures p.

Input data: $V_1 = 2 \times 50\ l = 100\ l \quad p_1 = 200$ bars
       $V_2 = 2 \times\ 7\ l = \ 14\ l \quad p_2 = \ \ \ 0$ bars

$$p_{total} = \frac{V_1 p_1 + V_2 p_2}{V_1 + V_2} \quad p_{tota} = \frac{100\ l \times 200 + 14\ l \times 0}{100\ l + 14\ l} = 175.44 \text{ bars}$$

Using method a, the Scuba cylinders can be charged at 175.44 bars.

Method b (cascading)
Using the cascading method, the first 50 l tank alone charges the Scuba cylinders.

Step 1: $V_1 = 1 \times 50\ l \quad\quad p_1 = 200$ bars
    $V_2 = 2 \times 7\ l \quad\quad p_2 = \ \ 0$ bars

$$p_{total} = \frac{50\ l \times 200 + 14\ l \times 0}{50\ l + 14\ l} = 156.25 \text{ bars}$$

Step 2: $V_1 = 1 \times 50\,1 \quad\quad p_1 = 200$ bars
    $V_2 = 2 \times 7\,1 \quad\quad p_2 = 156.25$ bars

$$p_{total} = \frac{50\ l \times 200 + 14\ l \times 156.25}{50\ l + 14\ l} = 190.43 \text{ bars}$$

Answer: The cascading method allows the Scuba cylinders to be charged at 190.43 bars, while using method a (simultaneous filling), the Scuba cylinders can only charged at 175.44 bars.

Example 7: A spherical bell with an inner diameter of 2.25 m will be pressurized from surface to 360 msw with heliox 3/97. The oxygen partial pressure is limited to 0.45 bars. What is the gas demand for pressurization?

Volume of bell $\quad\quad V = \pi/6 \times D^3 \quad\quad V = 0.524 \times 2.25^3 = 5.97 \ m^3$

DOP according to (7.5):

Input data: $\quad\quad ppO_2 \ _{desired} = 0.45 \quad\quad O_2 \ conc. \ of \ press \ gas = 3\%$
$\quad\quad\quad\quad\quad\quad ppO_2 \ existing = 0.21$

$$DOP = \frac{ppO_2 \ _{des.} - ppO_2 \ _{exist.}}{O_2\text{-conc. press gas}} \ 10; \ DOP = \frac{0.45 \ bars - 0.21 \ bars}{0.03} \ 10 = 80m$$

The bell pressurization starts with heliox 3/97 down to 80 msw, where the desired O_2 partial pressure of 0.45 bars is achieved. The pressurization to 360 msw is continued with pure helium.

Heliox demand: $FGV = V \times DOP/10 \ = 5.97 \ m^3 \times 80/10 \quad\quad = 47.8 \ m^3$
Helium demand: $FGV = V(D\text{-}DOP)/10 = 5.97 \ m^3 (360\text{-}80)/10 = 167.2 \ m^3$

Total gas volume: $FGV = V \times D/10 = 5.97 \ m^3 \times 360/10 \quad\quad = 215.0 \ m^3$

Answer: For pressurizing the bell to 360 msw, 47.8 m^3 of heliox 3/97 and 167.2 m^3 of pure helium are necessary.

Example 8: Example 7 is changed so that instead of pure helium a lean mixture with an oxygen content of 2%, according to reference [32], is used.

DOP according to (7.6) =

$$\frac{(\ 0.45 - 0.21\ ) - 360m/10 \times 0.02}{0.03 - 0.02} = \frac{0.24 - 0.72}{0.01} \ 10 \ =$$

The result shows a negative DOP; the lean mix with 2% O_2 has too much oxygen. Which mix can be used to achieve the desired partial pressure of 0.45 bars just at the desired depth D of 360 msw? Equation (7.5) is converted to

$$conc. \ k = \frac{pp_k \ _{desir.} - pp_k \ _{exist.}}{D} \ 1000 \ in \ \% \quad\quad\quad\quad (7.7)$$

Using (7.7) the oxygen concentration of the press gas must be:

$$\text{conc. } O_2 = \frac{0.45 \text{ bars} - 0.21 \text{ bars}}{360 \text{ m}} \; 1000 = 0.667\% \text{ oxygen}$$

Checking partial pressures:

O_2 portion at surface 1 bar × 0.21	= 0.21 bars
press gas portion 36 bars × 0.0667	= 0.24 bars
	Σ = 0.45 bars

Answer: The pressurization of the bell is performed from the surface to the desired depth of 360 msw using the press gas heliox 0.67/99.33. The amount of heliox is: FGV = V × D/10 = 5.97 m^3 × 360/10 = 215 m^3.

Example 9: The bell in example 7 will be pressurized to D = 240 msw from the surface with a trimix. What concentration of the trimix must be used when the desired oxygen partial pressure is 0.5 bars and the nitrogen concentration in the mix is 5%?

According to (7.7) the oxygen concentration of the press gas amounts to

$$\text{conc. } O_2 = \frac{ppO_{2 \text{ desir.}} - ppO_{2 \text{ exist.}}}{D} \; 1000$$

$$= \frac{0.5 \text{ bars} - 0.21 \text{ bars}}{240 \text{ m}} \; 1000 = 1.2\%$$

The required nitrogen concentration of 5% at depth corresponds to a partial pressure, according to (6.7a) of

$$ppN_2 = 24 \text{ bars} \times 0.05 = 1.2 \text{ bars}$$

$$\text{conc. } N_2 = \frac{ppN_{2 \text{ desir.}} - ppN_{2 \text{ exist.}}}{D} \; 1000$$

$$= \frac{1.2 \text{ bars} - 0.79 \text{ bars}}{D} \; 1000 = 1.7\%$$

The rest of the trimix is helium; the amount is calculated as

100% - 1.2% - 1.7% = 97.1%.

Answer: The trimix used for bell pressurization from the surface consists of 1.2 % oxygen, 1.7% nitrogen, and 97.1% helium.

Example 10: A chamber system has a total volume of 98 m³ and is pressurized to 600 msw with mixed gas. The leakage rate is 2%/d for 9 days at 600 msw and 15 days at 360 msw. The reserve gas is 50% of the pressurized volume. The working pressure is at least 15 bars over ambient pressure. How much gas is necessary, and how many storage tanks with a volume of 2 m³, charged at 200 bars, must be kept ready?

The following amounts of gas are necessary:

Pressurization:	FGV = 98 m³ × 61	5,978 m³
Leakage rate at 600 msw:	FGV = 98 m³ × 61 × 0.02 × 9d	1,076 m³
Leakage rate at 360 msw:	FGV = 98 m³ × 37 × 0.02 × 15d	1,088 m³
Reserve:	FGV = 98 m³ × 61 × 50%	2,989 m³
	FGV_{total}	Σ 11,131 m³

The usable gas volume of a storage tank according to (7.1), considering the ambient pressure of 61 bars and working pressure of 15 bars over ambient pressure, results in FGV_{usable}=2 m³×(201-61-15)=250 m³/tank.

The number n of necessary storage tanks is determined to be

$n = FGV_{total}/FGV_{usable}$

$n = 11,131 m³/250 m³$ per tank = 44.52 tanks   → 45 storage tanks

Another possibility for determining the number of storage tanks is to calculate on the basis of gross volumes.

Gross volume of storage tank:

$FGV_{tk\ gross} = 2\ m³ × 201 = 402\ m³/tank$

$$FGV_{gross} = FGV_{net}\ \frac{p}{p - p_{amb} - p_{work}}$$

$$= 11,131\ m³\ \frac{201}{201 - 61 - 15} = 17,899\ m³$$

number of storage tanks $n = FGV_{gross}/FGV_{tk\ gross}$

$n = 17,899\ m³/402\ m³$ per tank = 44.52 tanks

Example 11: For 4 different gases (air, oxygen, heliox 2/98, and helium) the DOP (Depth of Pressurization) shall be determined. The pressurization starts from the surface and the desired O_2 partial pressure must not exceed 0.5 bars.

$$\text{press gas air} \quad DOP = \frac{0.5 \text{ bars} - 0.21 \text{ bars}}{0.21} \; 10 = 13.8 \text{ m}$$

$$\text{press gas oxygen} \quad DOP = \frac{0.5 \text{ bars} - 0.21 \text{ bars}}{1.0} \; 10 = 2.9 \text{ m}$$

$$\text{press gas heliox 2/98} \quad DOP = \frac{0.5 \text{ bars} - 0.21 \text{ bars}}{0.02} \; 10 = 145 \text{ m}$$

$$\text{press gas helium} \quad DOP = \frac{0.5 \text{ bars} - 0.21 \text{ bars}}{0} \; 10 = \text{infinite !}$$

Because the press gas helium contains no oxygen, its O_2 concentration is zero. Dividing by zero results, mathematically, in infinity. When a press gas contains no oxygen, it is impossible to raise the oxygen partial pressure.

7.8 GAS MIXING
7.8.1 Introduction

For diving at greater depths and for longer operational times, artificial breathing mixtures are used. The main components of the breathing gas are usually oxygen and helium; sometimes nitrogen is added. The French have used hydrogen very successfully as well as a combination of hydrogen and helium for deep diving operations.

Although suppliers could deliver each kind of premixed gas in every desired composition, normally the diving operators, for economic reasons among others, prepare their own breathing mixtures from standard gases.

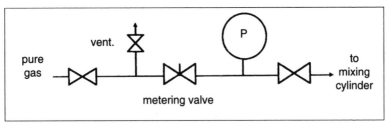

Fig. 7.4 Mixing facility for mixing by partial pressure

The following methods are available for mixing gases: mixing by partial pressure; mixing by volume; mixing by weight; and continuous-flow mixing.

Mixing by partial pressure is the method usually used, and it is the preferable method offshore. The technical equipment is very simple and consists of an accurate pressure gauge and a few valves; one valve must be a metering valve for exact measuring of the gases (see Fig. 7.4).

For mixing gases, some safety precautions must be considered:

- To avoid moisture entering the storage tanks, a minimum overpressure should be kept in the tanks.
- All gases should be analyzed prior to mixing; the oxygen concentration, especially, must be checked. Purity standards must be maintained and gases must be continuously monitored.
- Pipes and hoses must be kept clean, including fittings, especially those used for handling of pure oxygen or oxygen-enriched mixtures.
- Smoking and open fires are strictly prohibited in the mixing area.
- Protective clothing should be worn, especially when handling oxygen.
- For homogenous mixing of gases in the cylinder, allow at least 6 hours or roll the cylinders for at least 1 hour.

7.8.2 Mixing Formulae

Some useful formulae for mixing gases are introduced here. For the calculations, absolute pressures or gauge pressures can be used, but the pressures must not be combined. Because for gas mixing, only gauge readings are usually available, gauge pressures will be used here.

a) Mixing of pure gases into an empty tank

$$p_k = p \times conc.k \tag{7.8}$$

with p_k = partial pressure (gauge) of component k in bars

p = desired final pressure in bars

conc.k = desired concentration of component k in%/100

Example: A heliox 16/84 is needed, charged at 200 bars into an empty tank.

The partial pressures adjusted at the pressure gauge are the following

$$pO_2 = 200 \text{ bars} \times 0.16 \qquad = \ 32 \text{ bars}$$
$$pHe = 200 \text{ bars} \times 0.84 \qquad = 168 \text{ bars}$$
$$\overline{\phantom{pHe = 200 \text{ bars} \times 0.84 \qquad }\ \ \Sigma = 200 \text{ bars}}$$

Answer: The filling starts with the light gas. The empty tank is charged with helium at a gauge pressure of 168 bars. In the next step, oxygen is added until the desired final pressure of 200 bars is achieved.

b) Adjusting a mix under initial pressure of a component

Here the tank already contains a gas component k, charged at the pressure p_k. After adjusting the mix to the desired concentration, the final pressure p_{mix} results.

$$p_{mix} \ = p_k/conc.k \qquad \text{in bars} \qquad\qquad (7.9)$$

with p_{mix} = final pressure of the mix in bars

$\qquad p_k$ = initial pressure of component k in bars

$\quad$ conc.k = desired concentration of component k in %/100.

Example: A heliox mixture 16/84 is needed. The tank already contains pure helium, charged at 120 bars. How much oxygen must be added, and what will the final pressure of the mix be?

$$p_{mix} = pHe/conc.He \ = \ 120 \text{ bars}/0.84 \ = \ 142.9 \text{ bars}$$

Answer: The final pressure of the mix is 142.9 bars, and 142.9 - 120 = 22.9 bars of oxygen must be added. Checking the O_2-conc:

$$conc.O_2 = pO_2/p_{mix} = 22.9/142.9 = 0.16 \ \rightarrow 16\% \ O_2$$

c) Changing a mix to a desired concentration and a desired final pressure

$$p_{mix} \qquad = p_{mix \ exist.} + (\ p_{k \ desir.} - p_{k \ exist.} \ ) \qquad\qquad (7.10)$$

with p_{mix} $\ $ = final pressure of the mix in bars

$p_{mix \ exist.}$ = existing pressure of the initial mix in bars

$\quad p_{k \ desir.}$ = desired pressure of component k in bars

$\quad p_{k \ exist.}$ = existing pressure of component k in bars

If the term in brackets, $(p_{k\ desir.} - p_{k\ exist.})$ is negative, then the existing pressure of the mix, $p_{mix\ exist.}$, must first be reduced by the amount

$$P_{reduc.} = \frac{|\ p_{k\ desir.} - p_{k\ exist.}\ |}{conc.k_{\ exist.}} \text{ in bars} \qquad (7.11)$$

Example a: A tank is charged at 150 bars and contains a heliox mixture of 16/84. A new mix of heliox 20/80 is needed, and the rated pressure of 200 bars must be achieved. What actions must be taken to get the desired mix?

desired pressure of oxygen: $pO_{2\ desir.}$ = 200 bars × 0.2   = 40 bars
existing pressure of oxygen: $pO_{2\ exist.}$ = 150 bars × 0.16   = 24 bars

Difference   = 16 bars

$p_{mix} = p_{mix\ exist.} + (\ pO_{2\ desir.} - pO_{2\ exist.}\ )$

p_{mix} = 150 bars + (40 bars - 24 bars) = 150 + 16 = 166 bars

Answer: Sixteen bars of oxygen are added to the heliox mix of 16/84, charged at 150 bars, resulting in a final pressure of 166 bars. To get the desired final pressure of 200 bars, the difference of 200 - 166 = 34 bars of pure helium must be added.

Example b: Example a) shall be changed so that a heliox 20/80 exists, charged at 150 bars, and a mix of 16/84 is needed at the rated tank pressure of 200 bars.

desired pressure of oxygen: $pO_{2\ desir.}$ = 200 bars × 0.16   = 32 bars
existing pressure of oxygen: $pO_{2\ exist.}$ = 150 bars × 0.20   = 30 bars

Difference   = 2 bars

$p_{mix} = p_{mix\ exist.} + (\ pO_{2\ desir.} - pO_{2\ exist.}\ )$

p_{mix} = 150 bars + (32 bars - 30 bars) = 150 + 2 = 152 bars

Answer: Two bars of oxygen are added to the heliox mix 20/80, charged at 150 bars, resulting in a final pressure of 152 bars. To get the desired final pressure of 200 bars, the difference of 200 - 152 = 48 bars of pure helium must be added.

Example c: In this example all the other conditions are the same as in example b, except that the existing pressure of the mix is 180 bars instead of 150 bars.

desired pressure of oxygen: $pO_{2\ desir.}$ = 200 bars × 0.16   = 32 bars
existing pressure of oxygen: $pO_{2\ exist}$ = 180 bars × 0.20   = 36 bars
_____
                                         Difference   = - 4 bars

The result is negative, which means that the oxygen pressure is 4 bars too high. As a consequence, the existing pressure of the mix must be reduced (see 7.11).

$$P_{reduc} = \frac{\overline{|\ pO_{2\ desir.} - pO_{2\ exist.}\ |}}{conc.O_{2\ exist.}} = \frac{\overline{4\ bars}}{0.20} = 20\ bars$$

Answer: In the first step, the existing pressure of the 20/80 mix must be reduced by 20 bars from 180 bars to 160 bars. In the second step, the difference of 200 - 160 = 40 bars of pure helium must be added. Checking the oxygen pressure:

$pO_{2\ desired}$ = 200 bars × 0.16 = 32 bars
$pO_{2\ existing}$ = 160 bars × 0.20 = 32 bars

d) Mixing two mixtures of different concentrations

With two mixtures, mix 1 and mix 2, of different concentrations of component k, the desired concentration can only be achieved when it is between the concentrations of mix 2 and mix 1.

conc. k (mix 2) > conc. k (desired) > conc. k (mix 1)
$$p\ (mix\ 1) = p_{mix\ desir.}\ \frac{\overline{in\ bars}}{conc.k\ (mix\ 2) - conc.k\ (mix\ 1)} \qquad (7.12)$$

Example: Two heliox mixtures, 5/95 and 20/80, are available. A heliox 16/84 is needed. The rated tank pressure of 200 bars must not be exceeded.

Input data: conc. O_2 (mix 2) = 0.20   conc. O_2 (mix 1) = 0.05
              conc. $O_{2\ desired}$ = 0.16 $p_{mix\ desired}$ = 200 bars

$$p\ (mix\ 1) = 200\ bars\ \frac{\overline{0.20 - 0.16}}{...} = 200\ bars\ \frac{\overline{0.04}}{...} = 53.3\ bars$$

Answer: 53.3 bars of mixture 1 (5/95) are put into an empty tank. The remaining 200 - 53.3 = 146.7 bars of mixture 2 (20/80) is added. Checking the O_2 partial pressures:

mix 1	= 53.3 bars × 0.05	= 2.66 bars
mix 2	= 146.7 bars × 0.20	= 29.34 bars
desired mix	= 200 bars × 0.16	= 32.00 bars

When instead of the desired final pressure, $p_{mix\ desir.}$, the initial pressure of one of the mixtures is given, (7.12) is converted to

$$p_{mix} = p\,(mix1)\,\frac{conc.k\,(mix\,2) - conc.k\,(\,mix\,1)}{conc.k\,(mix\,2) - conc.\,k_{desir.}} \text{ in bars } (7.13)$$

Example: Two heliox mixtures, 3/97 (mix 1) and 16/84 (mix 2), are available. A mixture of 12/88 heliox is needed. Mix 1 is charged at 100 bars. What is the final pressure of the desired mix, when the rated tank pressure of 200 bars must not be exceeded?

Input data: conc. O_2 (mix 2) = 0.16 conc. O_2 (mix 1) = 0.03
conc. $O_{2\ desired}$ = 0.12 p (mix 1) = 100 bars

$$p_{mix} = 100 \text{ bars } \frac{0.16 - 0.03}{0.16 - 0.12} = 100 \text{ bars } \frac{0.13}{0.04} = 325 \text{ bars}$$

Starting with mix 1 (3/97), charged at 100 bars, 325 - 100 = 225 bars of mix 2 (16/84) are needed to achieve the desired mixture of 12/88. But because the rated tank pressure of 200 bars is far exceeded, the existing pressure of mix 1 must be reduced (7.12).

$$p\,(mix1) = p_{mix\ desir.}\,\frac{conc.O_2\,(mix\,2) - conc.\,O_{2\ desir.}}{conc.\,O_2\,(mix\,2) - conc.\,O_2\,(mix\,1)}$$

$$p\,(mix1) = 200 \text{ bars } \frac{0.16 - 0.12}{0.16 - 0.03} = 200 \text{ bars } \frac{0.04}{0.13} = 61.5 \text{ bars}$$

Answer: The existing pressure of 100 bars of mix 1 (3/97) must be reduced by 100 - 61.5 = 38.5 bars, and the remaining 200 - 61.5 = 138.5 bars of mix 2 (16/84 heliox) is added. Checking the O_2 partial pressures:

mix 1	= 61.5 × 0.03	= 1.84 bars
mix 2	= 138.5 × 0.16	= 22.16 bars
desired mix	= 200 × 0.12	= 24.00 bars

The calculations have been done to determine oxygen concentrations, as oxygen is the most critical component of a breathing gas. But it is obvious that the given formulae can be used analogically for any other component.

7.8.3 Practical Examples

The mixing formulae introduced in 7.8.2 will be applied to practice-oriented examples, to determine, mainly, oxygen concentrations for different breathing gases. For the calculations, gauge pressures are used, as is usual for gas mixing.

Example 1: A bank contains heliox 16/84 and is charged at 80 bars. How much helium must be added to rarefy the mixture to 5/95 heliox, given the rated bank pressure of 200 bars?

According to (7.10) $\quad p_{mix} = p_{mix\ exist.} + (pO_{2\ desir.} - pO_{2\ exist.})$

Input data:
$$pO_{2\ desired} = 200\ bars \times 0.05 \quad = 10.0\ bars$$
$$pO_{2\ existing} = 80\ \underline{bars \times 0.16} \quad = \underline{12.8\ bars}$$
$$Difference \quad = -2.8\ bars$$

The negative difference shows that for the desired final pressure of 200 bars, 2.8 bars of oxygen is too much in the existing mix. The existing pressure of 80 bars must be reduced according to (7.11).

$$P_{reduc.} = \frac{difference}{conc.\ O_{2\ exist.}} = \frac{2.8\ bars}{0.16} = 17.5\ bars$$

Answer: The pressure of the existing heliox mix 16/84 must be reduced by 17.5 bars to 80 - 17.5 = 62.5 bars. The remaining 200 - 62.5 = 137.5 bars is filled with pure helium. Checking the O_2 partial pressures:

$$pO_{2\ desired} = 200\ bars \times 0.05 = 10\ bars$$
$$pO_{2\ existing} = 62.5\ bars \times 0.16 = 10\ bars$$

Example 2: Two heliox mixes, mix 1 (6/94) charged at 100 bars, and mix 2 (20/80) charged at 120 bars, are available. The desired gas mix is 16/84. The rated bank pressure is 200 bars. How should the mixing be done for optimal use of the existing mixes?

Input data: conc.O_2 (mix 2) = 0.20   conc.O_2 (mix 1) = 0.06
              conc.O_2 $_{desired}$ = 0.16
                  p (mix 2) = 120 bars   p (mix 1) = 100 bars

The final pressure according to (7.13) and using the pressure of mix 1 = 100 bars results in

$$p_{mix} = 100 \text{ bars } \frac{0.20 - 0.06}{0.20 - 0.16} = 100 \text{ bars } \frac{0.14}{0.04} = 350 \text{ bars}$$

The final pressure using the full pressure of mix 1 is 350 bars, which exceeds the rated pressure of the bank by 75%. The final pressure is determined by using the full pressure of mix 2. Formula (7.13) is converted to (7.14) for mix 2.

$$p_{mix} = p \text{ (mix 2)} \frac{\text{conc.k (mix2) - conc.k (mix1)}}{\text{conc.k}_{desired} \text{ - conc.k (mix1)}} \text{ in bars} \qquad (7.14)$$

According to (7.14)

$$p_{mix} = 120 \text{ bars } \frac{0.20 - 0.06}{0.16 - 0.06} = 120 \text{ bars } \frac{0.14}{0.10} = 168 \text{ bars}$$

Answer: For optimal use of the existing mixtures, mix 2 is chosen and 168 - 120 = 48 bars of mix 1 are added. Checking the O_2 partial pressures:

mix 1 = 48 bars × 0.06   =   2.88 bars
mix 2 = 120 bars × 0.20   = 24.00 bars
───
desired mix = 168 bars × 0.16 = 26.88 bars

Example 3: A bank contains nitrox 40/60 charged at 140 bars. The oxygen portion will be reduced by adding pure nitrogen. What kind of nitrox can be prepared, when the rated pressure of the bank is 200 bars?

The actual O_2 partial pressure is pO_2 = 140 bars × 0.4 = 56 bars. Pure nitrogen is added until the rated pressure of 200 bars is achieved.

The new O_2 concentration = 56 bars/200 bars = 0.28;
in%: 0.28 × 100% = 28%.

Answer: The new mix is nitrox 28/72, charged at 200 bars.

7.9 GAS DEMAND CALCULATIONS FOR A COMPLETE DIVING OPERATION

A diving system consists of two living chambers (DDCs) of 18 m³ each, a transfer chamber (DTC) of 9 m³ and a bell (PTC) of 5 m³ (see Fig. 7.5). A saturation dive will be carried out for 24 days at 240 msw with 6 divers in the system. The oxygen partial pressure must not exceed 0.5 bars. The leakage rate will be 0.5 m/h. The built-in-breathing system (BIBS) must supply all divers for a minimum of 4 hours; the RMV will be 20 *l*/min. As reserve, sufficient gas must be available to pressurize the total system to the storage depth of 240 msw. The working depth is 260 msw. In 24 hrs, 3 bell runs are performed. Each of the two divers in the bell works for 3.5 hrs in free water, having an average RMV of 35 *l*/min. The oxygen partial pressure of the bell is slightly higher than for the rest of the system and will be between 0.55 and 0.65 bars. The decompression rate is simplified to *1* m/h from storage depth to surface. For treatment gases, the O_2 partial pressure will be between 1.5 and 2.6 bars. For emergency gases, the O_2 partial pressure will be between 0.16 and 1.25 bars. The supply of treatment gases will be sufficient for a treatment period of 2 × 4 hrs per diver, given a RMV of 20 *l*/min. The emergency gas supply will be sufficient for 24 hrs per diver, given a RMV of 20 *l*/min. The residual bank pressure must be at least 20 bars over ambient pressure.

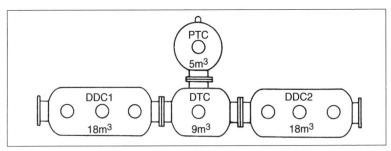

Fig. 7.5 Chamber configuration of a simple saturation diving system

To determine the kind and quantities of diving gases necessary, the calculations will be done for the three operational phases: a) chamber operation; b) bell operation; and c) treatment operation.
Further differentiation leads to the following steps:

a) chamber operation:
  compression phase;
  gas loss by leakages;
  oxygen demand for divers;
  oxygen demand during decompression;
  BIBS gases; and
  reserve of chamber gas;
b) bell operation:
  compression gases;
  divers' gas demand at working depth;
  bell's emergency supply; and
  reserve gas for bell; and
c) treatment operation:
  treatment gas mixes; and treatment gas demands.

a) Chamber operation

Compression phase:
The total volume of the chamber system as shown in Fig. 7.5:

$$V = 2 \times 18 \text{ m}^3 + 1 \times 9 \text{ m}^3 + 1 \times 5 \text{ m}^3 = 50 \text{ m}^3$$

Composition of bottom gas given that $ppO_2 = 0.5$ bars

$$\text{conc.}O_2 = ppO_2/p_{bottom} = 0.5 \text{ bars}/25 \text{ bars} = 0.02 \quad \rightarrow 2\% \; O_2$$

For suppression of HPNS-effects (see Chapter 5), 5% nitrogen is added.

Composition of bottom mix: $2\% \; O_2 / 5\% \; N_2 / 93\% \; He$

The chamber system is pressurized to 240 msw from the surface. As the press, gas a mixture that achieves the desired oxygen and nitrogen partial pressures just at bottom depth will be used.

Desired oxygen partial pressure: $= 0.50$ bars
Desired N_2 partial pressure:

$$ppN_2 = p_{bot} \times \text{conc. } N_2 = 25 \text{ bars} \times 0.05 = 1.25 \text{ bars}$$

The concentration of the press gas according to (7.7) is:

$$\text{conc.}O_2 = \frac{0.5 \text{ bars} - 0.21 \text{ bars}}{240m} \, 1000 = 1.208\% \rightarrow 1.2\% \; O_2$$

$$\text{conc.}N_2 = \frac{1.25 \text{ bars} - 0.79 \text{ bars}}{240m} \, 1000 = 1.91\% \rightarrow 1.9\% \; N_2$$

Checking the partial pressures:

Oxygen:	1 bar × 0.21	= 0.210 bars
	24 bars × 0.012	= 0.288 bars
	Σ	= 0.498 bars
Nitrogen:	1 bar × 0.79	= 0.790
	24 bars × 0.019	= 0.456 bars
	Σ	= 1.246 bars

The press gas consists of $\rightarrow$ 1.2% O_2 / 1.9% N_2 / 96.9% He
The amount of press gas needed, according to (7.1):

$$FGV = V \, (\, p - 1 \,) = 50 \, m^3 \, (\, 25 - 1 \,) = 1200 \, m^3$$

The total compression time, including stops for pressure adaptation, according to Chapter 11.1, is approximately 4 hours.

Gas loss by leakage:
The leakage rate is assumed to be 0.5 m/h, corresponding to a daily pressure loss of 12 msw/d resp. 1.2 bars/d.

Total loss per day: $FGV(\, day \,) = 50 \, m^3 \times 1.2 = 60 \, m^3$ bottom gas
Total loss for 24 days: $FGV(\, total \,) = 60 \, m^3 \times 24 \, d = 1440 \, m^3$

The daily loss of 60 m^3 from leakage and lockings corresponds to 5% of the total chamber volume and is a conservative approximation. The same leakage rate is assumed for the compression and decompression phases. Because the compression lasts only 4 hours and the bottom pressure of 25 bars is achieved at the end of the compression phase, this leakage portion is neglected.

The decompression period is determined to be

decompression time t = bottom depth/decompression rate
t = 240 msw/ 1 m/h = 240 h or 10 days

Because the decompression rate is 1 m/h and 24 m/d and the leakage rate is 12 m/d, the leakage supports decompression.

Oxygen demand of divers during bottom phase:
According to 7.7.2 the oxygen demand for each diver in the chamber is 0.5 l/min. It is assumed that all divers are inside the chamber, and the time for bell runs is neglected. This is an approximation on the safe side.

O_2 demand = 6 divers × 0.5 l/min × 60 min/h × 24 h/d × 24 d = 103.7 m^3

Oxygen demand of divers during decompression phase (10 d):

The oxygen demand is determined by two factors:
   i)   demand necessary for metabolism; and
   ii)   demand to maintain the desired partial pressure.
   i) O_2 demand =

      6 divers × 0.5 l/min × 60 min/h × 24 h/d × 10 d = 43.2 m^3
   ii) $FGV(O_2)$ =
      $V\, pp_{O2} \ln (p_{bottom}) = 50 \text{ m}^3 \times 0.5 \times \ln (25) = 80.5 \text{ m}^3$

The total oxygen demand for metabolism: 103.7 + 43.2 = 147 m^3

BIBS gases:
In case of contamination of the chamber atmosphere or unbreathable chamber gases, the divers are supplied by the built-in breathing system (BIBS). According to AODC in reference [15], the supply must be sufficient for 4 hours at bottom depth, assuming a RMV of 20 l/min for each diver. The amount of BIBS gas necessary is calculated according to (7.2):

FGV = 6 divers × 20 l/min × 25 x 60 min/h × 4 h = 720 m^3 bottom gas

The BIBS system also distributes the emergency gases in case the normal supply system fails. First the concentration of emergency gases must be determined for the whole depth range, taking into account the given oxygen partial pressure limitations of 0.16 bars resp. 1.25 bars.

To determine emergency gas concentrations, Dalton's law (6.7) is used, starting with the lower limit of 0.16 bars from the surface.

Step 1: given: ppO_2 = 0.16 bars; p = 1 bar;
O_2 conc = ? O_2 conc. = 0.16 bars/1 bar = 0.16.   → 16% O_2

Step 2: given: ppO_2 = 1.25 bars; conc. = 16% O_2
maximum depth = ? p = 1.25 bars/0.16 = 7.81 bars   → 68 msw

Step 3: given: ppO_2 = 0.16 bars; p = 7.8 bars;
O_2 conc. = ? O_2 conc. = 0.16 bars/7.8 bars = 0.0205   → 2% O_2

Step 4: given: ppO_2 = 1.25 bars; conc. = 2% O_2;
maximum depth = ? p = 1.25 bars/0.02 = 62.5 bars   → 615 msw

The following emergency gases are chosen:

emergency gas: heliox 16/84   depth range: surface ... 68 msw;   and
heliox 2/98 or bottom gas 2/5/93   68 msw ... 240 (615) msw.

The amount of emergency gases needed for 24 h is determined according to (7.2):

heliox 16/84: FGV = 6 divers × 20 l/min × 7.8 × 60 min/h × 24 h = 1348 m^3
heliox 2/98: FGV = 6 divers × 20 l/min × 25 × 60 min/h × 24 h = 4320 m^3

Reserve gases:
According to reference [15], the minimum amount of reserve gas must allow pressurization of the total system. So the following gases are kept in reserve:

compression gas (1.2 O_2/1.9 N_2/96.9 He):   1200 m^3
bottom gas (2 O_2/5 N_2/93 He):   1440 m^3
oxygen for metabolism: 147 m^3
oxygen for decompression: 81 m^3

Compilation of gases for chamber operation:

compression gas (1.2/1.9/96.9):
1,200 m^3 + 1200 m^3 (reserve)   → 2,400 m^3
bottom gas (2/5/93):
1,440 m^3 (leakage) + 1440 m^3 (reserve)   → 2,880 m^3
BIBS gas (2/5/93)   →   720 m^3

emergency gas (2/5/93)	$\rightarrow$ 4,320 m^3
emergency gas (heliox 16/84)	$\rightarrow$ 1,348 m^3
oxygen: 147 m^3 (metabolism) + 147 m^3 (reserve)	$\rightarrow$ 294 m^3
oxygen: 81 m^3 (decompression) + 81 m^3 (reserve)	$\rightarrow$ 62 m^3

b) Bell Operation

Pressurization of bell:

The desired oxygen partial pressure in the bell must be between 0.55 and 0.65 bars for a bell depth of 260 msw. This results in an O_2 concentration of:

conc.O_2 = 0.55 bars/27 bars = 0.02;
conc.O_2 = 0.65 bars/27 bars = 0.024

For simplicity, the lower limit of 2% O_2 is chosen, so that the bell gas corresponds to the bottom gas (2 O_2/5 N_2/93 He).

Bell compression:

Three bell runs per day total 72 bell runs (B/R) for the 24-day diving operation. The depth difference per bell run is

(260 msw - 240 msw)/10 = 2 bars
FGV = V_{bell} × depth diff. × number of B/R = 5m^3 × 2 × 72 = 720m^3

Divers' gas demand at working depth:

During each bell run, two divers work for 3.5 *h* each outside the bell at the working depth of 260 msw. The average RMV is assumed to be 35 *l*/min (see 7.7.2).

FGV = n × RMV × p × t × B/R =
FGV = 2 divers × 35 *l*/min × 27 × 3.5 h × 60 min/*h* × 72 = 28,577 m^3

This enormous gas demand is the result of the open circuit operation, where bell gas is exhaled directly into the environment or the exhaled gas is carried back to the surface via a push/pull system for reclaiming. The other possibility is using a closed circuit apparatus, where only the divers' consumed oxygen is replaced (see Chapter 9).

Bell emergency supply:

According to Norwegian regulations, the emergency supply must be sufficient to provide gas for each diver for a minimum of 30 min at working depth, assuming a RMV of 50 l/min. The operational pressure must be at least 8 bars over ambient pressure, and the pressure loss due to leakage is assumed to be 2.5 bars in 8 hours. The bell emergency supply, according to (7.2), results in:

$$FGV = n \times RMV \times p \times t = 2 \text{ divers} \times 50 \ l/\text{min} \times 27 \times 30 \text{ min} = 81 \text{ m}^3$$

Gas loss by leakage:

$$FGV = V_{bell} \times p' = 5 \text{ m}^3 \times 2.5/8 \text{ h} = 12.5 \text{ m}^3/8 \text{ h}$$

Determining the number of storage tanks for the bell emergency supply:
The storage tanks have a volume of 50 l, charged at 200 bars.

gross volume (8 bars over amb. press.)

$$= 81 \text{ m}^3 \ \frac{200}{200 - 26 - 8} = 97.6 \text{ m}^3$$

gross volume (2.5 bars over amb. press.)

$$= 12.5 \text{ m}^3 \ \frac{200}{200 - 26 - 2.5} = 14.6 \text{ m}^3$$

gross volume of bell emergency gas (2/5/93)

$$= 97.6 \text{ m}^3 + 14.6 \text{ m}^3 = 112.2 \text{ m}^3$$

gross volume of one storage tank

$$FGV = 50 \text{ l} \times 200 = 10 \text{ m}^3$$

number of emergency gas tanks

$$n = 112.2 \text{ m3}/10 \text{ m}^3 = 11.22 \text{ tanks} \ \rightarrow 12$$

Bell reserve:
According to reference [15], the reserve must be sufficient for one bell run

bell compression: $FGV = V_{bell} \times \text{depth diff.} = 5 \text{ m}^3 \times 2 = 10 \text{ m}^3$
divers' demand: $FGV = n \times RMV \times p \times t =$
$FGV = 2 \text{ divers} \times 35 \ l/\text{min} \times 27 \times 3.5 \text{ h} = 397 \text{ m}^3$

Total amount of bell reserve gas: $= 407 \text{ m}^3$

Compilation of gases for bell operation:

bell compression to working depth (2/5/93)	720 m^3
divers' demand (2/5/93)	$28,577 \text{ m}^3$
bell reserve (2/5/93)	407 m^3
emergency supply (2/5/93)	12 tanks of 50 l

c) Treatment Operation

Necessary treatment mixes:

The given limits of the oxygen partial pressure for treatment gases are between 1.5 bars as the lower limit and 2.6 bars as the upper limit. The calculation starts from the surface, beginning with pure oxygen.

Step 1: given: $ppO_2 = 2.6$ bars; $conc.O_2 = 100\%$;
maximum depth = ? $p = 2.6$ bars/1.0 = 2.6 bars $\rightarrow$ 15 msw

Step 2: given: $ppO_2 = 1.5$ bars; $p = 2.5$ bars;
$conc.O_2 = ?$ $conc.O_2 = 1.5$ bars/2.5 bars = 0.6 $\rightarrow$ 60% O_2

Step 3: given: $ppO_2 = 2.6$ bars; $conc.O_2 = 0.60$;
maximum depth = ? $p = 2.6$ bars/0.60 = 4.33 bars $\rightarrow$ 32 msw

Step 4: given: $ppO_2 = 1.5$ bars; $p = 4.2$ bars
$conc. O_2 = ?$ $conc.O_2 = 1.5$ bars/4.2 bars = 0.357 $\rightarrow$ 36% O_2

Step 5: given: $ppO_2 = 2.6$ bars; $conc. O_2 = 0.36$
maximum depth = ? $p = 2.6$ bars/0.36 = 7.22 bars $\rightarrow$ 60 msw

Step 6: given: $ppO_2 = 1.5$ bars; $p = 7.0$ bars;
$conc.O_2 = ?$ $conc.O_2 = 1.5$ bars/7.0 bars = 0.214 $\rightarrow$ 24% O_2

To get reasonable mixes, the O_2 concentration is rounded up to 24% O_2.

Step 7: given: $ppO_2 = 2.6$ bars; $conc.O_2 = 0.24$;
maximum depth = ? $p = 2.6$ bars/0.24 = 10.8 bars $\rightarrow$ 95 msw

Step 8: given: $ppO_2 = 1.5$ bars; $p = 10.5$ bars;
$conc.O_2 = ?$ $conc.O_2 = 1.5$ bars/10.5 bars = 0.143 $\rightarrow$ 14% O_2

Step 9: given: $ppO_2 = 2.6$ bars; $conc.O_2 = 0.14$;
maximum depth = ? $p = 2.6$ bars/0.14 = 18.57 bars $\rightarrow$ 175msw

Step 10: given: $ppO_2 = 1.5$ bars; $p = 18.5$ bars;
$conc.O_2 = ?$ $conc.O_2 = 1.5$ bars/18.5 bars = 0.081 $\rightarrow$ 8% O_2

Step 11: given: $ppO_2 = 2.6$ bars; $conc.O_2 = 0.08$;
max depth = ? $p = 2.6$ bars/0.08 = 32.5 bars $\rightarrow$ 315 msw

Treatment gases and their applied depth range:

treatment gas depth range

100% O_2	surface	...	15 m	
heliox 60/40	15 m	...	32 m	
heliox 36/64	32 m	...	60 m	
heliox 24/76	60 m	...	95 m	
heliox 14/86	95 m	...	175 m	
heliox 8/92	175 m	...	240 m	

To determine the amount of treatment gases necessary according to (7.2), it is assumed that each diver can be treated for 8 h on the basis of an average RMV of 20 l/min. The maximum pressure of each depth range is used.

$$FGV = 6 \text{ divers} \times 20 \ l/min \times 8 \ h \times 60 \ min/h \times p_{max} = 57.6 \ m^3 \times p_{max}$$

pure O_2 (to 15 msw)	$FGV = 57.6 \ m^3 \times 2.5$	$=$	$144 \ m^3$
60/40 (to 32 msw)	$FGV = 57.6 \ m^3 \times 4.2$	$=$	$242 \ m^3$
36/64 (to 60 msw)	$FGV = 57.6 \ m^3 \times 7.0$	$=$	$404 \ m^3$
24/76 (to 95 msw)	$FGV = 57.6 \ m^3 \times 10.5$	$=$	$605 \ m^3$
14/86 (to 175 msw)	$FGV = 57.6 \ m^3 \times 18.5$	$=$	$1,066 \ m^3$
8/92 (to 240 msw)	$FGV = 57.6 \ m^3 \times 25.0$	$=$	$1,440 \ m^3$

Determination of the number of tanks necessary:

To determine the number of storage tanks needed, all volumes must be given in surface volumes. Therefore some of the results must be converted accordingly. The calculated volumes are net volumes, which must be converted into gross volumes, taking into account that the residual pressure in the tanks must be at least 20 bars over ambient pressure. The tanks are charged at 200 bars and have a volume of 1 m^3 each; each contains a free gas volume of 200 m^3.

Conversion from net into gross volume:

$$\text{gross volume} = \text{net volume} \ \frac{200 \text{ bars}}{200 \text{ bars} - p_{ambient} - p_{residual}}$$

compression gas (1.2/1.9/96.9) = 2,400 m^3

$$\text{gross volume} = 2,400 \ m^3 \ \frac{200}{200 - 24 - 20} = 3,077 \ m^3$$

Mixed Gas Diving

number of tanks n = 3,077 m^3/200 m^3 = 15.4 $\rightarrow$ 16

chamber bottom gas (2/5/93)

$$= 2,880 \text{ m}^3 + 720 \text{ m}^3 + 4,320 \text{ m}^3 = 7920 \text{ m}^3$$

gross volume = 7,920 m^3 $\dfrac{200}{200 - 24 - 20}$ = 10,154 m^3

bell bottom gas (2/5/93) = 720 m^3 + 28,577 m^3 + 407 m^3 = 29,704 m^3

gross volume = 29,704 m^3 $\dfrac{200}{200 - 26 - 20}$ = 38,577 m^3

total amount of bottom gas

gross volume = 10,154 m^3 + 38,577 m^3 = 48,731 m^3

number of tanks n = 48,731 m^3/200 m^3 = 243.7 $\rightarrow$ 244

number of squads (1 squad contains 12 tanks) = 244/12 $\rightarrow$ 21

emergency gas (16/84) = 1348 m^3

gross volume = 1348 m^3 $\dfrac{200}{200 - 6.8 - 20}$ = 1,557 m^3

number of tanks n = 1,557 m^3/200 m^3 = 7.8 $\rightarrow$ 8

The oxygen demand for the divers' metabolism is independent of depth and has been determined at storage depth. The demand must be converted into surface volumes to get the FGV according to 7.7.2. To be on the safe side, the O_2 demand for metabolism during decompression is also calculated at the storage depth of 240 msw.

FGV(O_2) = V(metabolism + reserve) × p = 294 m^3 × 25 = 7,350 m^3

oxygen = 7,350 m^3 (metabolism) + 162 m^3 (decompression)
+ 144 m^3 (treatment) = 7,656 m^3

gross volume = 7,656 m^3 $\dfrac{200}{200 - 24 - 20}$ = 9,815 m^3

number of tanks n = 9,815 m^3/200 m^3 = 49.07 $\rightarrow$ 49

treatment gas (60/40) = 242 m^3

gross volume = 242 m^3 $\dfrac{200}{200 - 3.2 - 20}$ = 274 m^3

number of tanks n = 274 m³/200 m³ = 1.37 → 2

treatment gas (36/64) = 404 m³

gross volume = $404 \text{ m}^3 \dfrac{200}{200 - 6 - 20}$ = 465 m³

number of tanks n = 465 m³/200 m³ = 2.32 → 3

treatment gas (24/76) = 605 m³

gross volume = $605 \text{ m}^3 \dfrac{200}{200 - 9.5 - 20}$ = 710 m³

number of tanks n = 710 m³/200 m³ = 3.55 → 4

treatment gas (14/86) = 1,066 m³

gross volume = $1,066 \text{ m}^3 \dfrac{200}{200 - 17.5 - 20}$ = 1312 m³

number of tanks n = 1,312 m³/200 m³ = 6.56 → 7

treatment gas (8/92) = 1,440 m³

gross volume = $1,440 \text{ m}^3 \dfrac{200}{200 - 24 - 20}$ = 1846 m³

number of tanks n = 1846 m³/200 m³ = 9.23 →10

Compilation of all operational gases:

Kind of gas	Number of tanks (1 m³)	
Compression gas (1.2/1.9/96.9)	16	
Bottom gas (2.0/5.0/93.0)	244	21 squads (12 tanks)
Oxygen	49	
Emergency gas (heliox 16/84)	8	
Treatment gas (heliox 60/40)	2	
Treatment gas (heliox 36/64)	3	
Treatment gas (heliox 24/76)	4	
Treatment gas ˙ (heliox 14/86)	7	
Treatment gas (heliox 8/92)	10	

CHAPTER 8

Basics of Hydromechanics

8.1 WATER PRESSURE

Water pressure increases linearly with increasing depth. As stated in Chapter 2, a water depth WD of 10 msw means a water pressure increase of approximately 1 bar. The total pressure p is the sum of the water pressure pw, the atmospheric pressure p_{atm} of 1 bar and an overpressure p_o as an additional pressure acting on the surface (see Fig. 8.1). The total pressure results in

$$p = p_w + p_{atm} + p_o = WD/10 + p_{atm} + p_o \quad \text{in bars} \tag{8.1}$$

A typical application of hydromechanics in diving is the Buffalo-system used for dividing pressure chambers into a dry part and a wet part. Fig. 8.2 shows the principle of the system which consists of two shifted, semihigh bulkheads which allow passage from the dry part into the wet part and vice versa. To keep equilibrium between the wet and dry parts, the pressures at the free surface level must be equal.

While the gas pressure p_{gas} is constant from the bottom to the top of the chamber (assuming that the mass of the gas can be neglected) the water pressure p_w forms a triangular load over the chamber with the maximum pressure at the bottom. There are three typical pressure conditions, one at the top of the chamber, one at the free water level, and one at the chamber bottom (see Fig. 8.2).

P_{gas} P_{water}

	P_{gas}	P_{water}	
top of chamber	D/10	0	$p_{gas} > p_w$
depth D at free water level	D/10	D/10	$p_{gas} = p_w$
bottom of chamber = WD	D/10	WD/10	$p_{gas} < p_w$

These conditions will not alter if the atmospheric pressure p_{atm} or an overpressure p_o is be added at both sides. In these cases, the system will keep its equilibrium.

To estimate the horizontal resp. vertical forces affecting chamber and chamber equipment such as doors, locks, port holes, etc., it is necessary to determine the representative component of the water pressure p_w. This pressure component p_w, multiplied by the area A, results in the total force H in the case of horizontal water pressures (see Fig. 8.3), and V in the case of vertical pressures. The horizontal force H is thought of as attacking at the center of the area A. This is a simplification because the horizontal force acts exactly at the center of pressure, which differs a little from the center of the area. But to estimate pressure effects, the center of the area may be used.

The horizontal force H is given by

$$H = p_w \times A = D/10 \times A \quad \text{in N} \tag{8.2}$$

with p_w = pressure component in Pa for Pascal or bars

     A = area in m^2

     D = depth to the center of area A in m

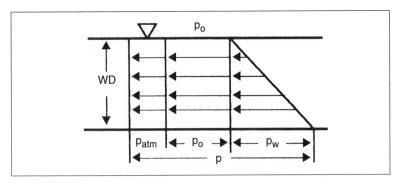

Fig. 8.1 Portions of total pressure

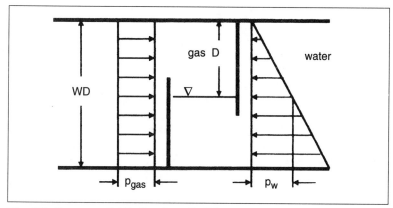

Fig. 8.2 Pressure distribution for a Buffalo-system

The vertical force V is calculated by multiplying the maximum pressure component $p_{wmax} = WD/10$ by the given area A. An example shows how to determine forces induced by water pressure.

Example: The hull of a vessel has a rectangular leak of b = 2.5 and h = 4 m. The upper edge of the leak is 3.6 m below water level. What horizontal force will act on the sealing of the leak when the flooded room is pumped out?

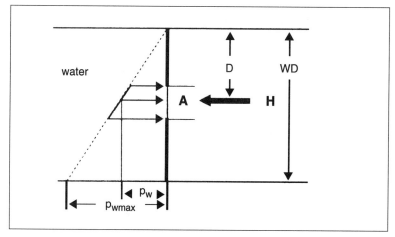

Fig. 8.3 Horizontal force H acting on a given area A

Area A of the leak is $A = b \times h = 2.5\ m \times 4.0\ m = 10\ m^2$

The distance from the center of the area to the water level results in:
$D = 3.6\ m + h/2 = 3.6\ m + 4/2\ m = 5.6\ m$

The horizontal force H according to (8.2):
$H = p_w \times A = D/10 \times A = 0.56\ bar \times 10\ m^2 = 560\ kN$

Answer: A force of 560 kN acts on the rectangular leak, attacking at the center of the leak area. It is a trapezoidal load with its minimum pressure component, $p_{wmin} = 0.36$ bars, at the upper edge of the leak and the maximum pressure component, $p_{wmax} = 0.76$ bars, at the lower edge.

8.2 OUTFLOW OF LIQUIDS

When handling chamber systems, the operating crew must be able to estimate the time necessary for emptying chambers that are filled with liquids. Outflow calculations must differentiate between containers with large surfaces compared to the outflow area (see Fig. 8.4a) and containers with limited surfaces (Fig. 8.4b). In the first case, the relevant pressure height D can be assumed as constant for the outflow process. In the case of limited surfaces, the pressure height D(t) is time-dependent and decreases with elapsed time. Normally, the atmospheric pressure acts on the surface as well as on the outflow area A_1. So the pressure effects due to the atmospheric environment are equal. In closed containers, an overpressure or underpressure over the surface may exist; this will greatly effect the outflow.

Outflow calculations are based on the application of Bernoulli's formula. For the configuration with an infinite surface, meaning a constant pressure height, and neglecting constriction effects, the outflow velocity v is:

$$v = \sqrt{2\ g\ D} \quad \text{in m/s} \tag{8.3}$$

If there is an additional overpressure p_o on the surface, the outflow velocity increases to:

$$v = \sqrt{2\ (\ g\ D + p_o/\rho_{liquid}\ )} \quad \text{in m/s} \tag{8.4}$$

with   g = earth's acceleration, approximately 10 m/s^2
        D = pressure height over the center of the outflow area in m
        p_o = overpressure over surface in Pa
        ρ_{liquid} = density of liquid in kg/m^3

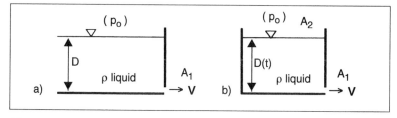

Fig. 8.4 Containment configurations to demonstrate the outflow for
a) infinite surface   b) limited surface A_2

The outflow volume rate is

$$V = A_1 \times v \qquad \text{in m}^3/\text{s} \tag{8.5}$$

The outflowing mass of liquid is

$$m = A_1 \times v \times \rho_{liquid} \qquad \text{in kg/s} \tag{8.5a}$$

In the case of a limited surface, shown in the configuration 8.4b, the pressure height decreases with the outflow. The outflow time for totally emptying a container with an open surface A_2 results in

$$t = A_2/A_1 \sqrt{2\,D/g} \qquad \text{in s} \tag{8.6}$$

For a closed container, an additional overpressure p_0 over the surface can be used to reduce the outflow time. It is assumed that the overpressure is kept constant until the container is completely emptied.

$$t = A_2/A_1 \left(\sqrt{2/g\,(D + p_0/\rho_1 g)} - \sqrt{2\,p_0/\rho_1\,g^2} \right) \qquad \text{in s} \tag{8.7}$$

Example: A lock L = 50 m in length and B = 15 m in width is filled to a height of 4.4 m with water. At the bottom of the lock gate there is a leak of 0.5 m². When will the lock be completely emptied?

To determine the outflow time, (8.6) is used.
Surface of the lock $A_2 = L \times B$; $A_2 = 50 \text{ m} \times 15 \text{ m} = 750 \text{ m}^2$
A_1 is given = 0.5 m²

$$t = A_2/A_1 \sqrt{2\,D/g} = 750/0.5 \sqrt{2 \times 4.4/10} = 1500 \sqrt{0.88} = 1407 \text{ s}$$

Answer: The lock is emptied in about 1400 seconds, roughly 23.5 min.

Now assume that the lock is emptied into a vacuum, which has the same effect as an additional pressure of 1 bar on the lock's surface. After how much time would the lock now be emptied, if the other conditions are the same? To use (8.7), the density of the liquid must be known. The lock is filled with fresh water which has a density of 1000 kg/m^3; $p_0 = 1$ bar $= 10^5$ N/m^2.

$$t = 750 \text{ m}^2/0.5 \text{ m}^2 \left(\sqrt{2/10 \, (D + 10^5/1000 \times 10)} - \sqrt{2 \times 10^5/1000 \times 10^2} \right)$$

$$t = 1500 \left(\sqrt{0.2 \, (4.4 + 10)} - \sqrt{2} \right) = 1500 \, (\, 1.697 - 1.414 \,) = 425 \text{ s}$$

Answer: The effect of the additional pressure of 1 bar reduces the outflow time from 1400 s to 425 s, or approximately 7 min, a reduction to less than one third of the time.

In the case of a rectangular or square cross section, the surface A_2 is constant for a constant length during the whole outflow process. In other cases, with cylindrical or completely irregular cross sections, the surface A_2 changes with the decreasing pressure height D. In such cases, the cross section must be subdivided into rectangles to represent the actual cross section as well as possible, and the calculation is done step by step (see reference [132]). For a cylindrical tank with the diameter d = h and the length L, an analytical solution is available.

$$t = 4 \, L/3 \, A_1 \, \sqrt{d^3/2 \, g} \tag{8.8}$$

Another possibility for a first approximation is to convert the cylindrical cross section into a rectangle with the same pressure height h and the same cross section area as the given circle.

Area $A = \pi/4 \times d^2 = d \times b$
$b = \pi/4 \times d$

When emptying a filled tank, it is necessary to ventilate the space over the free surface. Otherwise a vacuum is formed which prevents further outflow. In that case, equilibrium is achieved between the pressure column h of the liquid and the atmospheric pressure.

$$h \times \rho_{\text{liquid}} \times g = p_{\text{atm}} \tag{8.9}$$

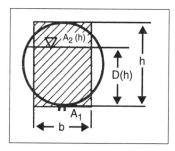

Example: An upright standing cylindrical tank of 3.5 m diameter and a height of 12 m is completely filled with olive oil ($\rho_l = 920$ kg/m³). There is a small leak at the bottom, and the tank is not ventilated. How much olive oil runs out?

According to (8.9) $h = \dfrac{p_{atm}}{\rho_{liquid} \times g} = \dfrac{10^5 \text{ N/m}^2}{920 \text{ kg/m}^3 \times 10 \text{ m/s}^2} = 10.87 \text{ m}$

When $h = 10.87$ m from the bottom is reached, the outflow stops because the pressure column h of the olive oil and atmospheric pressure p_{atm} are now equal. The difference between the cylinder height and pressure column, 1 2 - 10.87 = 1.13 m, is the lost pressure height. The lost volume is

$V_{lost} = \pi/4 \times 3.5^2 \times 1.13 \text{ m} = 10.9 \text{ m}^3$ of olive oil

Answer: Through the leak at the bottom of the tank 10.9 m³ of olive oil are lost, a loss of only 9.4% of the total tank volume. This small loss results from the vacuum formed over the liquid's free surface. If the tank had been ventilated, all of the olive oil would have leaked out.

8.3 ARCHIMEDES' PRINCIPLE

Archimedes' principle, formulated by the Greek mathematician and philosopher Archimedes of Syracus, describes the buoyancy force acting on a body immersed wholly or partially in a liquid or a gas. The buoyancy force is equal to the weight of the liquid or gas displaced by the body.

Weight of the body in air: $\qquad F_W = V\,\rho_b\,g \quad$ in N $\qquad$ (8.10)

Buoyancy of the immersed body: $\;F_B = V\,\rho_l\,g \quad$ in N $\qquad$ (8.11)
Weight of the body in the liquid:

$\qquad F_l = F_W - F_B \qquad\qquad$ in N
$\qquad F_l = V(\,\rho_b - \rho_l)\,g \qquad$ in N $\qquad\qquad$ (8.12)

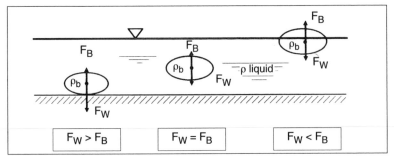

Fig. 8.5 Overview of the different buoyancy conditions

where V = volume of body in volume units
   ρ_b = density of body in kg/m^3

   ρ_l = density of liquid in kg/m^3

   g = earth's gravity in m/s^2 (10 m/s^2)

Using (8.10) the volume is $V = F_W/\rho_b \times g$; replacing V in (8.12) results in the weight of a body immersed in a liquid:

$$F_l = F_W \ \frac{\rho_b - \rho_l}{\rho_b} \ \text{in N} \tag{8.13}$$

According to Fig. 8.5, three different equilibrium conditions are possible. If the weight F_w of the body is more than the buoyancy force F_B, the body sinks to the floor. If the body weight and buoyancy are exactly equal, the body floats in an unstable equilibrium. If the buoyancy force F_B is greater than the body weight F_W, the body buoys up. The displaced mass of liquid corresponds exactly to the body weight F_W. A further correlation between body weight and buoyancy force and their related densities is achieved by combining (8.10) and (8.11).

$$\frac{F_W}{F_B} = \frac{\rho_b}{\rho_l} \tag{8.14}$$

It is important to emphasize that Archimedes' principle is only valid if the water pressure can act on all sides of the body. If, for example, the bottom of a body is embedded partially or completely in the sea floor, Archimedes' principle is not applicable. In this case the body not only loses its buoyancy, but in addition, the water column, including the atmospheric air column over the body, must be considered (see Fig. 8.6).

In this case, the lifting force F_L results in

$$F_L = F_W + A \, (D \times \rho_l \times g + p_{atm}) \text{ in N} \qquad (8.15)$$

F_W = weight of the body in N

A   = horizontal area of the body in m^2

D   = column of liquid over the body in m

p_{atm} = atmospheric pressure in bars or Pa

The lifting force necessary without the assistance of buoyancy is much higher by several orders of magnitude. Therefore, the lifting capacity of most floating cranes is not sufficient to lift embedded objects like ships. In such cases, the embedded object must first be freed by divers to reduce the bottom contact to a minimum. Then, the buoyancy force supports the lifting action and the lifting force is now only a fraction of the force needed to raise the embedded object without buoyancy assistance. This problem of lifting sunken objects is very important for salvage operations.

8.4 PRACTICAL EXAMPLES

For a better understanding of the application of hydromechanics, several practice-oriented examples are given below.

Example 1: A bulkhead has a cylindrical hole of 30 mm diameter at 7.2 m water depth. What is the outflow rate if the water level can be assumed to be constant?

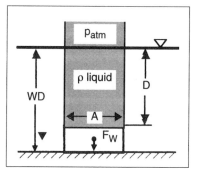

Fig. 8.6 Lifting forces without buoyancy

Given:

pressure height D = 7.2 m

leak area $A_1 = \pi/4 \times 3^2 = 7.06 \text{ cm}^2$

According to (8.3) the outflow velocity is

$$v = \sqrt{2 \times g/D} = \sqrt{2 \times 10/7.2} = 12 \text{ m/s}.$$

According to (8.5) the outflow rate is $V = A_1 \times v$

$$V = 7.06 \text{ cm}^2 \times 1200 \text{ cm/s} \times 60 \text{ s/min} = 508 \text{ } l/\text{min}$$

Answer: The volume rate is 508 l/min, if constriction effects are ignored.

Example 2: The outflow rate of Example 1 is doubled by using an over-pressure on the free surface. What overpressure is necessary?

To double the outflow rate, the velocity v must be doubled because the leak area A_1 remains the same. Using (8.4), the equation is solved for p_o

$$2 \times v = \sqrt{2 (g D + p_o/\rho_1)}$$
$$4v^2 = 2(gD + p_o/\rho_1)$$
$$p_o = \rho_1 (2v^2 - gD)$$
$$p_o = 1000 \text{ kg/m}^3 (2 \times 12^2 - 10 \times 7.2) = 2.16 \text{ } 10^5 \text{N/m}^2$$

Answer: An additional pressure of 2.16×10^5 N/m^2 = 2.16 bars must be built up over the free surface to double the rate from 508 l/min to 1,016 l/ min.

Example 3: A tank car has a cylindrical tank, diameter d = 2 m, L = 6.5 m. The tank is filled with glycerin (ρ_1 = 1200 kg/m^3). There is an outflow valve at the bottom with an inner diameter di = 9 cm. The constriction factor μ is 0.85.

a) In what time is the tank emptied?
b) In what time is the tank emptied when a pressure of 1.5 bars is added?
c) What is the outflow mass at the beginning for cases a) and b)?
d) What is the outflow mass if an additional hose of 9 cm inner diameter and 1 m length is coupled to the outflow valve?

Determination of input data:
Effective outflow area $A_1 = \pi/4 \text{ } di^2\mu$
$A_1 = 0.785 \times 0.09^2 \times 0.85 = 5.4 \text{ } 10^{-3} \text{ m}^2$
pressure height D = 2 m = d

Conversion of the cylindrical tank cross section into a rectangle of same area:

$$b \times d = \pi/4 \times d^2; \qquad b = \pi/4 \times d = 0.785 \times 2 \text{ m} = 1.57 \text{ m}$$

a) The outflow time is determined first with the exact formula for a cylindrical cross section according to (8.8), and for comparison, with the approximation of a rectangle of same area.

Using (8.8)

$$t = 4 \, L/3 \, A_1 \sqrt{d^3/2g}$$

$$t = 4 \times 6.5/3 \times 5.4 \ 10^{-3} \sqrt{2^3/2 \times 10} = 1015 \text{ s}$$

For the approximation using the rectangular area (8.6):

$$A_2 = b \times L = 1.57 \text{ m} \times 6.5 \text{ m} = 10.2 \text{ m}^2$$

$$t = A_2/A_1 \sqrt{2D/g} = 10.2/5.4 \ 10^{-3} \sqrt{2 \times 2/10} = 1194 \text{ s}$$

Answer. The exact solution results in 1015 s or 17 min, and the approximation results in 1194 s or 20 min, an overestimation of 17%.

b) For calculating a solution with an overpressure of 1.5 bars = $1.5 \ 10^5$ N/m², the rectangular approximation is used, as no analytical solution for a cylindrical cross section is available. According to (8.7)

$$t = A_2/A_1 \left(\sqrt{2/g \ (D + p_o/\rho_1 \times g)} - \sqrt{2 \, p_o/\rho_1 \times g^2} \right)$$

$$t = 10.2/5.4 \ 10^{-3} \left(\sqrt{2/10 \ (2 + 1.5 \ 10^5 / 1200 \times 10)} - \sqrt{2 \times 1.5 \ 10^5/1200 \times 10^2} \right)$$

$$t = 1.889 \ 10^3 \left(\sqrt{0.2 \ (2 + 12.5)} - \sqrt{2 \times 1.25} \right) = 230 \text{ s or } 3.83 \text{ min}$$

Answer: The outflow time is now reduced to 230 s, or 3.83 min, which is only 1/5 of the original time. It is assumed that the overpressure acts constantly during the entire outflow process.

c) The outflow mass without overpressure is determined by combining formulae (8.3) and (8.5a), where the maximum outflow occurs at the beginning and reduces to zero at the end.

$$m_{glyc} = \rho_1 \times A_1 \times v = \rho_1 \times A_1 \times \sqrt{2 \times g \times D}$$

$$= 1200 \text{ kg/m}^3 \times 5.4 \ 10^{-3} \text{ m}^2 \ \sqrt{2 \times 10 \text{ m/s}^2 \times 2 \text{ m}} \quad = 41 \text{ kg/s}$$

The outflow mass with the constant overpressure of 1.5 bars is determined by combining (8.4) and (8.5a)

$$m_{glyc} = \rho_1 \times A_1 \times \sqrt{2 \ (g \times D + p_o / \rho_1)}$$

$$= 1200 \text{ kg/m}^3 \times 5.4 \ 10^{-3} \text{ m}^2 \ \sqrt{2(10 \times 2 + 1.5 \ 10^5/1200)} = 110.4 \text{ kg/s}$$

The overpressure increases the outflow rate by a factor of 2.7 from 41 to 110.4 kg/s. The minimum mass outflow is reached when the pressure height D is exactly zero.

$$m_{glyc}(\text{minimum}) = 1200 \times 5.4 \ 10^{-3} \sqrt{2 \times 1.5 \ 10^5 / 1200} = 102.5 \text{ kg/s}$$

The result shows the expected answer, that the effect of the pressure height D is minimal compared to the effect of the overpressure p_o of 1.5 bars. The 2 m height of the glycerin corresponds to a pressure of only 0.24 bars. The minimum outflow rate compared to a) without overpressure is higher by a factor of

$$\sqrt{1.5/0.24} = 2.5 \text{ times higher, leading to } 2.5 \times 41 \text{ kg/s} = 102.5 \text{ kg/s}.$$

d) Using a hose 1 m long with the same diameter as the outflow valve and neglecting the friction in the hose increases the pressure height by 1 m from 2 to 3 m.

The maximum mass outflow is now

$$m_{glyc} = \rho_1 \times A_1 \times \sqrt{2 g \ (D + 1)}$$

$$m_{glyc} = 1200 \text{ kg/m}^3 \times 5.4 \ 10^{-3} \ \sqrt{2 \times 10 \text{ m/s}^2 \times 3m} = 50.2 \text{ kg/s}$$

Answer: Increasing the pressure height using a 1 m hose raises the flow rate by the factor

$$\sqrt{3/2} = 1.225 \text{ or } 22.5\%.$$

Example 4: A lifting bag has a standard volume of 0.75 m³ and is filled at 50 msw ($\rho_{seaw.} = 1013$ kg/m³) to 90% with air ($\rho_{air} = 1.3$ kg/m³). The weight of the lifting bag is 100 N. What is the lifting force of the bag

a) without considering the air with which it is filled?
b) considering the air with which it is filled?

a) lifting force without considering the air with which the bag is filled

Lifting force F_L = Buoyancy - Weight (bag)
$F_L = V\rho_l\, g$ - Weight (bag) = 0.75 m³ × 90% × 1030 kg/m³ × 10m/s² - 100 N
F_L = 6,953 N - 100 N = 6,853 N or 6.853 kN

Answer: The lifting force of the bag without considering the air with which it is filled is 6,853 N or 6.853 kN.

b) lifting force considering the air with which the bag is filled

In this case, the weight of the air filling the bag must be determined and subtracted from the buoyancy force.

F_{air} at 50 msw = $Vp\,\rho_{air}\, g$ = 0.75 m³ × 90% × 6 × 1.3 kg/m³
$\times$ 10m/s² = 53 N

$F_L = F_B$ - Weight (bag) - F_{air} = 6953 N - 100 N - 53 N = 6800 N

Answer: The lifting force, taking into account the air filling the bag, is reduced to 6800 N or 6.8 kN, a reduction of 0.8%. This result shows that under normal conditions the weight of the air filling the bag can be ignored. But under extreme circumstances, the weight of the gas filling the bag must be taken into account, as the next example shows.

Example 5: A bubble of air is at a depth of 8500 msw. What happens to the bubble?

To answer this question, the buoyancy of the bubble and the weight of the air filling it must be compared. It is assumed that the volume of the bubble is 1 *l*.

Buoyancy force $F_B = V\rho_l\, g$ = 1 *l* × 1030 kg/m³ × 10 m/s² = 10.3 N
Weight of air $F_{air} = Vp\,\rho_{air}\, g$ = 1 *l* × 851 × 1.3 kg/m³ × 10 m/s²
= 11.06 N

Answer: The air bubble sinks to the bottom because the weight of the compressed air in the bubble is greater than the bubble's buoyancy.

Example 6: A diver including his suit weights 900 N and has a volume of 75 l. What is his weight in a) sea water ($\rho = 1030$ kg/m^3) and b) in fresh water ($\rho = 1000$ kg/m^3)?

Weight in liquid according to (8.12):

$$F_l = F_W - F_B = F_W - V \times \rho_l \times g$$

a) $F_l = 900$ N - 75l × 1030 kg/m^3 × 10 m/s^2 = 900 N - 772.5 N = 127.5 N

b) $F_l = 900$ N - 75l × 1000 kg/m^3 × 10 m/s^2 = 900 N - 750 N = 150 N

Answer: The diver weighs 127.5 N in sea water and 150 N in fresh water.

Example 7: A rectangular barge with length L = 40 m, beam B = 8 m, and height H = 2 m with a bulk cargo of coal is sunk at 8 mfw. The weight of the barge including cargo is 4800 kN = 4.8 MN. To take into account flooded spaces, 50% of the total weight is added. Density ρ of fresh water is 1000 kg/m^3 or 1 t/m^3.

a) What is the necessary lifting force when the barge is embedded in the bottom?
b) What is the necessary lifting force when the barge is freed?
c) For case b), lifting pontoons with the following dimensions are available: L = 8 m, B = 5 m, maximum draft = 1.2 m. The weight of a pontoon is 260 kN. What draft does the pontoon have due to its weight, and how many pontoons are necessary to lift the sunken coal barge?

The lifting force in the case of an embedded body is determined according to (8.15).

Compilation of input data:

The total weight = weight + add. weight (50%)
= 4.8 MN + 0.5 × 4.8 = 7.2 MN
Bottom area of the barge: A = L × B = 40 m × 8 m = 320 m^2

Pressure p over the barge:
p_{tot} = water column over the barge + p_{atm}
p_{tot} = (WD - H) ρ_l × g + p_{atm}

$$p_{tot} = (\,8\ m - 2\ m\,) \times 1\ t/m^3 \times 10\ m/s^2 + 10^5\ N/m^2 = 160\ kN/m^2$$

Lifting force:

$$F_L = F_W + A \times p_{tot} = 7.2\ MN + 320\ m^2 \times 160\ kN/m^2$$

$$F_L = 7.2\ MN + 51.2\ MN = 58.4\ MN\ or\ 58,400\ kN$$

A lifting force of 58.4 MN is necessary to lift the embedded barge. Most of the necessary lifting force results from the atmospheric pressure, which alone is $10^5 N/m^2 \times 320\ m^2 = 32\ MN$, or 55% of the total lifting force.

b) When the bottom is freed, Archimedes' principle is applicable and the lifting force is now calculated according to (8.10) and (8.11).

Lifting force $\quad F_l = F_W - F_B = F_W - L \times B \times H \times \rho_l \times g$

$$F_l = 7.2\ MN - 40\ m \times 8\ m \times 2\ m \times 1\ t/m^3 \times 10\ m/s^2$$

$$= 7.2 - 6.4 = 0.8\ MN$$

Instead of 58.4 MN, only 0.8 MN, or 800 kN, are necessary to lift the wreck, 1.4% of the force necessary in case a.

c) For lifting the sunken barge, a force of 800 kN is necessary. To calculate the number of pontoons necessary, the lifting capacity of one pontoon must be determined first. In the first step, the draft DR corresponding to the pontoon's weight is calculated. The difference between DR and the maximum draft is the lifting capacity.

To calculate the pontoon's draft DR, the weight F_W must be in equilibrium with the buoyancy force F_B.

$$F_W = F_B = L \times B \times DR \times \rho_l \times g$$

$$DR = \frac{F_W}{L \times B \times \rho_l \times g} = \frac{260\ kN}{8\ m \times 5\ m \times 1\ t/m^3 \times 10\ m/s^2} = 0.65\ m$$

The pontoon's draft DR due to its weight is 0.65 m. As the maximum draft DR_{max} is 1.2 m, the difference is a measure of the pontoon's lifting capacity.

$$F_L = L \times B \times \rho_l \times g \times (\,DR_{max} - DR\,)$$

$$F_L = 8\ m \times 5\ m \times 1\ t/m^3 \times 10\ m/s^2\ (1.2m - 0.65m) = 220\ kN$$

Number of pontoons necessary is

$$n = 800 \text{ kN}/220 \text{ kN} = 3.64 \qquad\qquad \rightarrow 4 \text{ pontoons}$$

Answer: To lift the embedded wreck, a lifting force of 58.4 MN is necessary. If the wreck is washed free, the lifting force is reduced dramatically to only 0.8 MN = 800 kN. Four lifting pontoons are necessary to lift this weight.

Example 8: A body immersed completely in alcohol ($\rho_l = 800 \text{ kg/m}^3$) loses 25% of its weight. What is the density of the body?

Input data:

$$\frac{F_W = 100\%; \quad \rho_{alcohol} = 800 \text{ kg/m}^3}{F_B = \quad 25\%;}$$

According to (8.14)

$$\frac{F_W}{F_B} = \frac{\rho_b}{\rho_l}; \quad \rho_b = \rho_l \, F_W/F_B$$
$$\rho_b = 800 \text{ kg/m}^3 \; 100\%/25\% = 3200 \text{ kg/m}^3$$

Answer: The density of the body is 3200 kg/m^3 or 3.2 t/m^3 (fluorite).

Example 9: A concrete block ($\rho = 2.5 \text{ t/m}^3$) has a weight of 33 kN and lies at a depth of 30 msw ($\rho = 1.03 \text{ t/m}^3$). Lifting bags of 0.5 m^3 are available to lift the block. How many bags are necessary, when 25% of the concrete weight is added to break the block free from the bottom?

According to (8.13) the lifting force is

$$F_L = F_W \; \frac{\rho_b - \rho_l}{\rho_b} + 25\% \, F_W$$

$$F_L = 33 \text{ kN} \, \frac{2.5 - 1.03}{2.5} + 0.25 \times 33 \text{ kN} = 19.4 \text{ kN} + 8.3 \text{ kN} = 27.7 \text{ kN}$$

Lifting capacity of 1 bag:

$$F_B = V\rho_l g = 0.5 \text{ m}^3 \times 1.03 \text{t/m}^3 \times 10 \text{m/s}^2 = 5.1 \text{ kN}$$

The number of lifting bags is

$$n = F_L/F_{bag} = 27.7 \text{ kN}/5.1 \text{ kN} = 5.43 \qquad\qquad \rightarrow 6 \text{ bags}$$

Answer: Six lifting bags are necessary to lift the concrete block.

Example 10: A block of granite ($\rho = 2.2. \text{ t/m}^3$) weights 5 kN and lies at a depth of 25 msw. Thirty percent of the weight is added as the break-free force. What size bag is necessary to bring the granite (+ 25% reserve) to the surface ?

The lifting force according to (8.13) is

$$F_L = 5 \text{ kN} \frac{2.2 - 1.03}{2.2} + 30\% \times 5 \text{ kN}$$

$$F_L = 2.66 \text{ kN} + 1.5 \text{ kN} = 4.16 \text{ kN}$$

$$F_L = 75\% \, F_B = 75\% \, V \times \rho_1 \times g$$

$$V = \frac{F_L}{75\% \times \rho_1 \times g} = \frac{4.16 \text{ kN}}{0.75 \times 1.03 \text{ kg/m}^3 \times 10 \text{ m/s}^2} = 0.539 \text{ m}^3$$

Answer: The lifting bag must be 0.6 m³ or 600 l. This size creates a reserve of 33% instead of 25%.

Example 11: A closed pontoon has a rectangular cross section of B = 5.6 m and H = 3 m. The draft DR in sea water ($\rho_1 = 1025 \text{ kg/m}^3$) is 1.2 m. The pontoon's bottom is damaged and water runs in. It is assumed that the pontoon remains stable. What is its new draft?

The pontoon will flood via the bottom leak until equilibrium is reached between the water level h and compressed air p_1 which cannot escape. The draft DR is increased by the same level h due to the loss of buoyancy caused by the added water. Equilibrium conditions at the pontoon's bottom according to Bernoulli's equation:

$$p_o + (DR + h) \, \rho_1 \times g = p_1 + h \times \rho_1 \times g$$
$$p_o + DR \times \rho_1 \times g = p_1$$

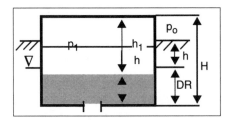

According to Boyle's law $p_o \times V_o = p_1 \times V_1$

$$p_o \times H = p_1 \times h_1 \rightarrow p_o \times H = (p_o + DR \times \rho_1 \times g) h_1$$

$$h_1 = H - h = \frac{p_o H}{p_o + DR\rho_1 g} - h = H (1 - \frac{p_o}{p_o + DR\rho_1 g})$$

Input data:

H = 3.0 m   Draft DR: 1.2 m

$$h = 3.0 \text{ m} (1 - \frac{1 \cdot 10^5 \text{ Pa}}{1 \cdot 10^5 + 1.2 \times 1025 \times 10}) = 3 \text{ m} (1 - 1/1.123) = 0.33 \text{ m}$$

Answer: The new draft is 1.2 m + 0.33 m = 1.53 m

CHAPTER 9

Diving Procedures

9.1 INTRODUCTION

Diving by definition requires staying under ambient pressure conditions of more than 1.1 bars under dry or wet conditions. According to this definition, compressed air workers must be considered divers because they too must follow decompression obligations to get back to the surface safely. Operators of submersibles, submarines, or atmospheric diving systems (ADS) who work under atmospheric pressure conditions are not divers according to the above definition. The inside of a closed pressure hull is independent of the ambient pressure and is always the constant pressure of 1 bar.

Modern diving technology offers different procedures to complete a given underwater task effectively and safely. The dominant parameters in choosing a suitable diving procedure are operational depth and bottom time. Both parameters determine the kinds of breathing gases and the technical diving system that will be required. The apparatuses used for diving procedures vary and include equipment ranging from self-contained underwater breathing apparatus (scuba) to complex diving systems for saturation operations. The choice of the most suitable procedure must take into account both technical demands and economics.

Table 9.1 Diving Procedures

	Autonomous Diving	Surface-supplied Diving	Saturation Diving
Diving gases	O_2 Air Nitrox Mix gas	Air Nitrox Mix gas	Air Nitrox Mix gas
Operational depth in m	< 8 < 45 < 40 < 60	< 60 40 rd. 200 (bell only)	< 15 < 30 701
Decompression	no decompr. stop	depth & time dependent deco	only depth dependent deco
Bottom time	minutes to hours; depth dependent	several hours; depth dependent	several weeks
Supply system by scuba tanks	autonom. supply via hoses	surface supply system	complex chamber

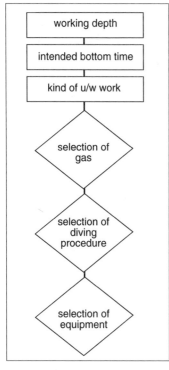

Fig. 9.1 Scheme for the selection of diving procedures and equipment

Table 9.1 gives a rough overview of common diving procedures. The division of diving procedures can follow different criteria, for example, division according to the kind of gas supply: autonomous diving; surface-supplied diving; and saturation diving. Strictly speaking, saturation diving is also a surface-supplied diving technique. But because of the very different diving and decompression procedures, including different technical requirements, saturation diving is dealt with as a separate procedure.

Another possibility is to divide diving procedures according to the gases used: compressed air; nitrox (O_2/N_2 mixtures); mixed gas (mixtures of O_2, He, H_2, etc.); and oxygen.

These divisions should be understood as rough ideas only and not as stringent classifications. In principle nearly all combinations of diving procedures, breathing gases, supplies, etc.

are conceivable. But for technical and economic reasons, only some combinations are of industrial significance. A general scheme for the selection of diving procedures, etc. is given in Fig. 9.1.

9.2 ATMOSPHERIC DIVING SYSTEMS (ADS)

Atmospheric diving systems maintain an atmospheric pressure of 1 bar inside of the system, independent of the ambient pressure outside. Such a system can be a submarine resp. a submersible or a hard suit.

The major advantage of this diving method is that decompression obligations can be completely omitted. At the surface, the operator leaves the ADS immediately. A disadvantage is the limitation on manual work while using an ADS, although much effort has been made to improve the flexibility of these systems. Submersibles and submarines are the classic representatives of 1-bar systems, which exist in a great variety of sizes and types, as

seen in reference [33]. Their depth range goes down to 600 msw and more. Some submersibles are equipped for diver lock-outs. While the pilot of the submersible operates the vessel in an atmospheric compartment, the divers are in bell-like compartments which can be pressurized. After pressure equalization, the divers lock out and afterwards lock in again. It is obvious that the divers must follow decompression procedures according to depth and time, which start in the vessel.

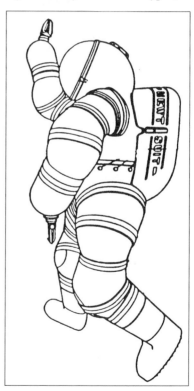

Another ADS is the hard suit, a pressure tight suit with more or less flexible joints, as noted in reference [33]. Modern construction of hard suits is based on steel or aluminum alloys with joints in the arms and legs. Oxygen tanks on the back replace the oxygen used by the operator. Carbon dioxide is removed chemically by a CO_2-absorbent inside the suit. Hard suits

Fig. 9.2 Newly-developed hard suit [34]

are tethered, connected to the surface by an umbilical which contains the energy (necessary for thrusters and lighting) supply and communications equipment. The development of hard suits goes back to the last century, according to reference [33], but real progress was only possible after improvement of joint construction. Common 1-bar systems are the JIM- and SAM-suits. Because movability of the joints decreases with increasing depths, ADS, like WASP and OMAS, replaced leg joints with thrusters. A new development in the 1980s was the NEWT-suit which, according to reference [34], incorporated oil-filled joints that compensated for the ambient pressure (see Fig. 9.2). Twenty joints guarantee reasonable movability.

9.3 AUTONOMOUS DIVING
9.3.1 Introduction

The characteristic feature of autonomous diving is the autonomous gas supply carried by the diver in tanks on his back (scuba). The gas supply is independent of the surface and allows free and flexible operations under water. For that reason, and due to its simple technical demands, this method is standard in sport diving. But autonomous diving is also used very often in commercial diving. This method is a simple and cheap solution for short operations down to depths of approximately 50 msw.

Table 9.2 Diving Times vs. Size of Scuba Tanks

Depth in m	Diving times with 20% reserve in min (RMV = 30 l/min)			
	1400 l	2800 l	3200 l	4000 l
5	25	50	57	71
10	18	37	42	53
20	12	25	28	35
30	9	18	21	26
40	7	15	17	21

On the other hand, only a limited gas supply is available in the scuba tanks, so bottom time is restricted (see Table 9.2). Further limiting factors are operational depth and the diver's personal respiratory minute volume (RMV), dependent on the kind of physical work (see also Fig. 7.1). The gas demand for a constant RMV increases linearly with depth (see Chapter 6). To guarantee safe diving with scuba equipment, regulations and safety recommendations must be followed with respect to depth and bottom times. German regulations allow only no-decompression dives when using scuba. The diver can surface at any time without undergoing decompression stops. The no-decompression limits are depth-dependent (see Fig. 9.3).

According to U.S. and German standards, the diving time to a depth of 10 msw is unlimited, while French standards allow an unlimited stay only to a depth of 7.5 msw. The no-decompression limits, for example, of U.S., French, and German standards differ only slightly. Greater differences exist for the allowed maximum depths for no-decompression dives. German regulations restrict the depth to 45 m, while French and U.S. rules allow 51 m resp. 58 msw (190 feet).

9.3.2 Technical System

In this section, brief comments on technical systems for autonomous diving will be given. Detailed information on technical components are published in, for example, references [7, 28, 33, 38] or given in manufacturers' instructions. The most commonly-used system worldwide is open-circuit

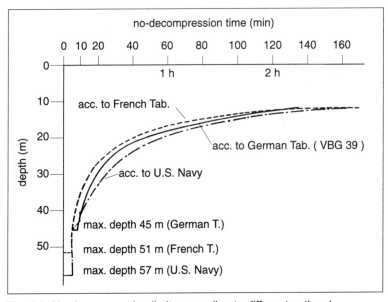

Fig. 9.3 No-decompression limits according to different national regulations

scuba with air as the breathing gas. For special operations with mixed gas or pure oxygen, semi-closed circuit resp. closed-circuit scuba is used.

Standards for diving apparatus in Germany are given in DIN 3179, also known as reference [36], for helmets and scuba gear. In autonomous diving, cylinders in different configurations are used. A single or double tank backpack assembly is standard, but sets of more than two tanks are also used for special operations, e.g., for cave diving.

The cylinders are made of steel or aluminum alloys and meet stringent fabrication specifications issued by relevant national agencies. In Germany, for example, capacity, markings, and color coding of tanks are specified in DIN 3171 or [22]. Inspection intervals for steel tanks are two years according to German regulations (TRG), as seen in reference [18], while for aluminum alloy tanks the inspection must be performed at six-year intervals. In the U.S., qualification tests must be performed every five years for gas cylinders. The rated working pressure is commonly 200 bars in Europe, but there are also tanks designed for a rated pressure of 300 bars. In the U.S., the usual working pressure is lower and rated to 2250 psi, corresponding to about 153 bars.

Classification and safety requirements for scuba tanks are specified in Germany in DIN 58 640, as listed in reference [23]. The minimum capacity of a scuba tank is 1400 l, according to reference [37], which means a tank volume of 7 l based on a rated pressure of 200 bars. A typical scuba system consists of the tank assembly connected by a hose to a regulator. For safety reasons, most tanks have a reserve mechanism integrated into the valve which warns the diver that his supply has reached a critical level. To release the reserve gas in his tank, the diver must activate the reserve mechanism, which allows him to surface safely. In general, the reserve is 20% of the total tank capacity; for a 200-bar tank, the reserve is 40 bars.

The HP-gas from the tank is reduced to the diver's ambient pressure by regulators. Demand regulators are manufactured in one-stage or two-stage configurations. Most common are two-stage regulators which reduce the high pressure gas from the tank in two stages. In the first stage, the HP is reduced to 6 to 10 bars over ambient pressure. The second stage is supplied with this constant intermediate pressure and reduces it in the second step to the diver's ambient pressure. Normally the second stage is combined with a mouthpiece, widely used in sport diving.

Because the mouthpiece can be lost, for example, in very cold water, German safety rules as specified in reference [37], require a full face mask for scientific or commercial diving.

Closed and Semi-Closed Scuba

In Chapter 5 it was mentioned that only 4% of the oxygen in the air is used for the diver's metabolism, while the remaining 79% nitrogen and 17% oxygen are exhaled. In an open circuit, large masses of breathing gas are necessary, even though the diver needs only the oxygen. This oxygen portion is between 0.5 and 3 l/min, depending on the diver's physical exertion. It would be sufficient to replace the oxygen used instead of the total amount of gas, so gas recovery systems, such as closed or semi-closed circuit scuba according to references [33, 38] with pure oxygen or mixed gas, are used. The difference between these systems is that the semi-closed circuit system has a relief valve configured in the exhalation bag. The principle of a complete closed circuit system is shown in Fig. 9.4.

The exhaled gas with enriched carbon dioxide passes through a CO_2-absorbent canister, where CO_2 is removed. The oxygen used is replaced, injected from an oxygen tank into the inhalation bag or counter lung. The inert gas, which is nitrogen in the case of air or helium in the case of mixed gas,

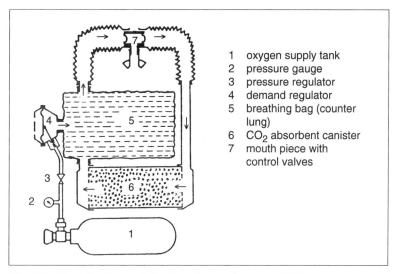

1   oxygen supply tank
2   pressure gauge
3   pressure regulator
4   demand regulator
5   breathing bag (counter lung)
6   CO_2 absorbent canister
7   mouth piece with control valves

Fig. 9.4 Principle of closed circuit scuba using oxygen [38]

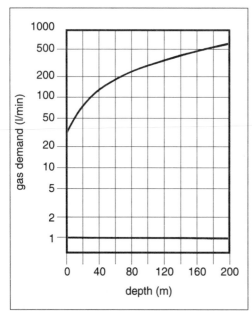

Fig. 9.5 Gas demand for open and closed circuit scuba [38]

remains in the system and is not used in metabolism. A safe control for the amount of oxygen injected is important, but today reliable technical devices are available.

All open systems release exhaled breathing gas into the surrounding water where it ascends as bubbles to the surface. Because these bubbles reveal the diver's location to observers at the surface, the bubbles cannot be tolerated during military operations. Fig. 9.5 shows the difference in gas demand for open and closed circuit scuba. It is based on an oxygen demand of 1 l/min which corresponds in the case of air to a RMV of 25 l/min; the diver uses 1/5 of the oxygen portion. While the oxygen demand of 1 l/min is depth-independent and constant for the closed circuit system, the gas demand increases drastically with depth in the case of an open system. For a water depth of 50 msw, the gas demand goes up to 150 l/min (see Fig. 9.5). A closed circuit scuba system releases no bubbles which could reveal the presence of a diver to observers at the surface, thus such systems are useful for military operations. But the handling of closed circuit scuba requires much technical knowledge and considerable maintenance. A real danger is the possibility of seawater getting into the CO_2 absorbent canister. The water reacts chemically with the soda-sorb and creates an alkaline solution which leads to severe lung damage.

9.3.3 Diving Gases

For economic reasons, compressed air is the standard diving gas worldwide for autonomous as well as for surface-supplied diving.

National regulations on purity standards guarantee the safe use of air for diving operations. But due to the physiological effects of air under raised pressure, its use is limited (Chapter 5). The narcotic effects of nitrogen under increased pressure conditions limit the operational depth to approximately 50 msw. Therefore, in deep diving, air must be replaced by mixed gases. Scuba should be avoided and used only for special applications. One obvious reason is the limited gas supply in open-circuit scuba.

The mixed gas will usually be an O_2-He mixture (heliox). Because the gas must be breathable at the surface, the oxygen content must not fall below 16%. On the basis of a tolerable oxygen partial pressure between 1.4 and 1.8 bars, an operational depth of around 75 to 100 msw is possible. Due to the limited gas supply in the case of open-circuit scuba, a maximum depth of approximately 60 msw should not be exceeded. Using closed or semi-closed circuit scuba, longer dives are possible, but these can be performed only by specially trained personnel. Pure oxygen as a breathing gas in closed-circuit scuba is not used for commercial diving, but is used generally for military actions, according to reference [9]. Due to the tolerable partial pressure of 1.8 bars, the operational depth is restricted to 8 msw (see 5.2). Also, nitrox (O_2-N_2) can be used as a breathing gas for autonomous diving, but for economic reasons depths of more than 40 msw are not feasible.

9.4 SURFACE-SUPPLIED DIVING
9.4.1 Introduction

With the exception of autonomous diving, all diving methods, including saturation diving, are surface-supplied procedures. In surface-supplied diving, breathing gas is supplied to the diver via a hose or an umbilical which also contains communications, hot water, energy, etc. from the surface. Surface-supplied diving with compressed air is the standard commercial procedure worldwide. Restricted gas supplies are not a limiting factor as they are in autonomous diving, but decompression obligations limit dive times. Other restrictions may be, for example, water temperature or kind of underwater work. To get the diver back safely to the surface, depth and time-dependent decompression procedures must be followed. Most countries have their own national decompression tables (see, for example, references [9, 31, 63, 133] and Fig. 9.6).

In Europe, efforts have been made to standardize the different national decompression tables for the EC. Figure 9.6 shows allowable bottom

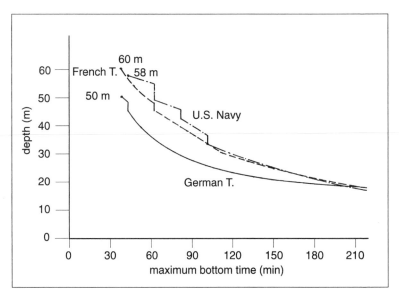

Fig. 9.6 Maximum bottom times for air dives according to national decompression tables

times according to national tables. While U.S. and French standards differ only slightly over the whole depth range, German decompression standards follow a very conservative approach.

9.4.2 Technical System

Technically, using air as the standard breathing gas for diving needs requires only a low pressure (LP) compressor at the surface, connected to the diver via a strengthened rubber or plastic hose (see Fig. 9.7). To guarantee the diver's air supply under all circumstances, two independent supply sources must be available at the surface. As a reserve, a second compressor can be used beside the normal LP compressor or a reserve bank of air cylinders can be installed at the diving site. The amount of reserve gas is regulated by national agencies. For offshore operations, AODC has issued a guidance note on minimum gas quantities, as evident in refrence[15].

In addition to the two independent surface supply systems, each diver carries an individual bale-out tank in case the hose connection is interrupted. The emergency gas in the tank allows the diver's safe return to the surface.

MIXED GAS DIVING

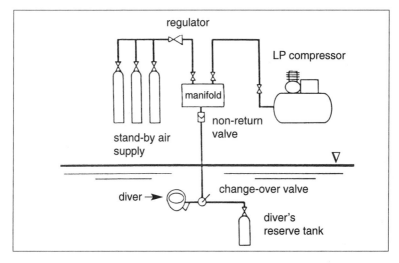

Fig. 9.7 Principle of surface air supply system

According to German regulations in reference [37], the amount of emergency gas must be at least 800 l, meaning a minimum tank capacity of 4 l at a rated tank pressure of 200 bars.

Compressed air is distributed to the divers by means of a manifold or rack box, containing all components such as valves and pressure gauges for distribution, controlling, and monitoring the diver's gas supply (see Fig. 9.8).

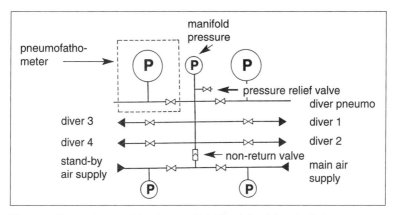

Fig. 9.8 General assembly of a manifold (rack box) for air diving

One part of the rack box is the pneumofathometer, which shows the exact depth of the diver under water using an extra pneumo hose. For determining the diver's depth, the open pneumo hose is blown out from the surface. After closing the pneumo valve topside, equilibrium is achieved between the gas inside the hose and the outer water pressure, giving the depth reading at a pressure gauge.

The pressure of the supply system is approximately 20 bars over ambient pressure, but can be increased if required by the diver. This overpressure is necessary to compensate for friction losses in the hose. The length of the supply hose or umbilical is limited to 80 m. The main part of the umbilical is naturally the gas supply line; this is supplemented by the smaller pneumo hose and communication lines. If the supply hose is not strong enough, a life line is added to the umbilical.

9.4.3 Diving Gases

As in autonomous diving, compressed air is the first choice as the breathing medium for surface-supplied diving using an open circuit system. Unfortunately, the use of air is restricted to depths of about 50 msw due to the narcotic effects of nitrogen. For deeper dives, mixed gases are used; these will be discussed in section 9.7. Nitrox may also be used instead of air; nitrox diving will be discussed separately in section 9.6.

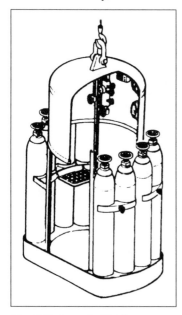

Fig. 9.9 Open bell [39]

9.5 USE OF DIVING BELLS

A special case of surface-supplied diving is the use of open or closed diving bells. Bells are used to transport the diver and his tools to the underwater site without endangering him by exposing him to waves, surface currents, or other unfavorable conditions. A bell also offers protection against unforeseeable events including failure of the gas supply at the work site.

Open Diving Bell

The open diving bell is the simplest bell; it consists of an open cage wherein the upper part is protected by a dome-shaped cover, which is normally transparent (see Fig. 9.9). The diver's head and upper body are in the dry dome area of the bell. He breathes the atmosphere of the dome before he puts his helmet on. The diver may also use the BIBS installed in the bell, for example, for treatment.

To maintain a constant gas volume in the dome during the bell's descent, more gas must be supplied; this can be done via an umbilical from the surface or from gas storage cylinders which are part of the bell's equipment. During ascent, the surplus gas escapes from the dome.

Figure 9.10 shows the principle of the diver's gas supply via a built-in-breathing system (BIBS) in an open bell. In this example, the gas is supplied from the surface; a second line supplies other gases so decompression procedures using heliox or oxygen can be performed easily.

These open bells are used for the transport of two or three divers with their tools and other equipment to the work site. The depth is normally limited to 50 msw, but French rules allow depths to 90 msw, according to reference [133].

Closed Diving Bell

A closed diving bell has the advantages of an open bell with respect to the diver's transport and protection. In addition, it offers pressure and atmosphere adjustments in the bell, independent of the ambient pressure conditions. These adjustments are especially useful for deep diving operations, which could not be performed without closed bells. Design criteria for diving bells are given in detail, for example, in reference [33]. Generally the bell is

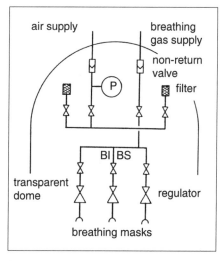

Fig. 9.10 Gas supply scheme of open bell [9]

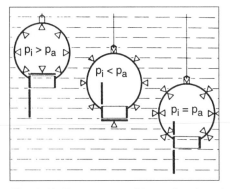

Fig. 9.11 Pressure conditions of a closed bell [33]

supplied from the surface, via an umbilical, with breathing gas, hot water, energy, communications, etc. The bell is subjected to different pressure conditions, shown in Fig. 9.11. When used for saturation diving, the bell is at the storage (working) pressure level on the surface. On its way down, the internal pressure p_i is therefore higher than the ambient water pressure p_a. When the working depth is reached, internal and external pressures are in equilibrium, and the divers lock out. On the way back to the surface, the same conditions occur. Conditions change only when the bell is used, for example, for observations. In that case, the atmospheric pressure p_i inside the bell is lower than the ambient water pressure p_a, which increases accordingly to the depth ($p_i < p_a$).

Each bell is equipped with emergency gas storage to supply the bell autonomously for 12 to 48 hours in case the breathing gas supply is interrupted. Under normal circumstances, the divers breathe the bell atmosphere. But BIBS is available in case the bell atmosphere is contaminated. Different gases are necessary for the divers, e.g., for decompression and therapy procedures in the bell. For safety, at least two divers man a bell; one diver acts as bell man or bell tender, while the other works outside the bell. These functions change after a predetermined time, normally four hours. Most diving bells are designed to carry three divers and their diving gear. When the diver leaves the bell, he is supplied with breathing gas and hot water via an umbilical from the bell (see Fig. 9.12). The length of the umbilical is limited to 30 m, or 100 ft. This restriction may cause problems reaching the work site in the horizontal direction. This situation occurs, for example, when a dive is conducted from a diver support vessel (DSV) to inspect a particular area of a platform structure. As the vessel must stay a safe distance from the platform at the surface, the horizontal distance between the lowered bell and the work location within the structure may be too far for the diver to reach given the length of his umbilical. In that case the solution is a Flying Bell, a bell with additional thrusters that allow a horizontal shifting of the whole bell in the desired direction.

Optimal use of a closed bell requires a chamber system at the surface, to make full use of the potential of bell diving. The bell or personnel transfer chamber (PTC) is connected to the deck decompression chamber (DDC) or living chamber via a deck transfer chamber (DTC).

A variety of operational modes is possible with such a system, using air or mixed gas as the breathing medium. For shallow depths to 50 msw, air is preferably used in the system. In that mode, the closed bell with the divers is lowered to the working area under atmospheric conditions inside the bell. The bell is pressurized at depth until pressure equilibrium is reached. The hatch is now opened and the diver leaves the bell to do his job. On the way back to surface, the hatch stays open so that the expanding air can escape. At the first decompression stop, the hatch is closed and the ascent is continued to the surface where the bell is mated to the DDC. The DDC has been pressurized in the meantime to the bell's pressure level so that the divers can be transferred after the bell and the DDC are connected. Inside the chamber, the decompression is completed under safe and comfortable conditions.

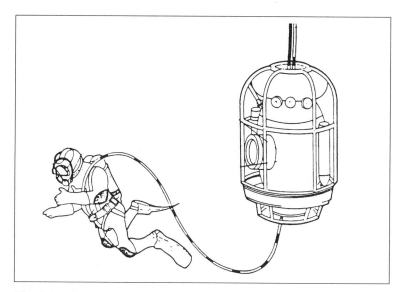

Fig. 9.12. Diver's supply from a diving bell [30]

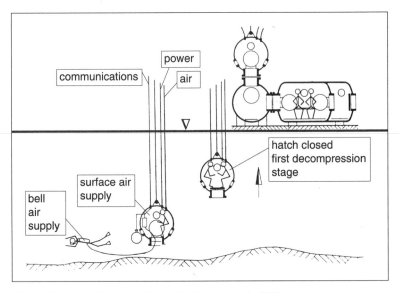

Fig. 9.13 Operation of a closed bell in air mode [33]

If dives are deeper than 50 msw, the breathing gas must be changed and switched over to mixed gas. For short operations, bell bounce diving is an economical choice. For long-term operations, saturation diving is the only choice (see section 9.8).

Bounce diving allows dives to 200 msw, but only for very limited bottom times. The breathing medium is normally heliox (O_2-He), because nitrogen must be replaced by a less narcotic component.

The diving procedure is similar to the bell dive air mode. The closed bell is lowered to the working location (see Fig. 9.13). At depth, the 1-bar atmosphere is replaced by the bottom mix until pressures inside and outside the bell are equal so that the hatch can be opened. When the divers have finished their job and are back in the bell, the hatch is closed and the bell is raised to the surface. Decompression procedures start in the bell, independent of the external water pressure. After surfacing, the bell is mated to the chamber, the divers are transferred, and the decompression is continued inside the DDC.

Theoretically, the decompression procedure in the air diving or mixed gas bounce diving mode can be performed without a surface chamber, using only the closed bell, which is supplied with the necessary gases via the bell's umbilical. But due to the confined space in the bell and other uncomfortable circumstances, the total decompression is done in the bell only in case of emergency. The tolerable heliox mixture is determined by the working depth. During decompression, the composition of the breathing mixes is changed, following complex and time-consuming decompression procedures.

9.6 NITROX DIVING
9.6.1 Introduction

Although nitrox diving is also a surface-supplied diving procedure, it will be discussed separately due to its specific features. Nitrox is a mixture of nitrogen and oxygen, but it usually has a different composition than air. (Air is a nitrox mix with a fixed O_2/N_2 ratio.)

The advantage of using nitrox as a breathing gas is that it normally has a higher O_2 portion than air. Consequently the nitrogen portion must be lower (see Fig. 9.14), reducing decompression times and lengthening bottom times. The higher oxygen concentration may lead to problems with respect to oxygen toxicity; these must be considered carefully when using nitrox.

For every operational depth and every bottom time, an optimal nitrox mixture can be prepared, based on the time-dependent limits of tolerable O_2 partial pressures (see Chapter 5). The more oxygen a nitrox contains, the less nitrogen remains, and less nitrogen means shorter decompression. Although many variable nitrox mixtures are conceivable, only a few fixed mixes are used in practice, e.g., a mix of 32.5/67.5 with 32.5% oxygen and 40/60 with 40% oxygen. When conditions are favorable, an oxygen-enriched mix of 50/50 is sometimes used.

The advantage of nitrox for lengthening bottom times is shown in Fig. 9.15, where nitrox 32.5/67.5 and 40/60 are used. In this figure, the bottom times for air dives are based on German tables for surface-supplied diving, as

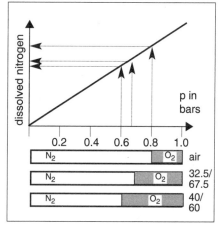

Fig. 9.14 Dissolved nitrogen for different nitrox mixes

seen in reference [31]. The bottom times for the nitrox mixes are converted into equivalent air depths (EAD) (see section 11.4). The allowed bottom time for air according to reference [31], is 65 min at 25 msw. This time is doubled to 130 min by using nitrox 40/60. This example shows that nitrox opens interesting possibilities for commercial and scientific diving.

When using nitrox, the rising O_2 partial pressure must be checked to avoid oxygen poisoning, especially when heavy work must be performed. Tolerable partial pressures of oxygen are given in Chapter 5.

A noticeable gain in bottom times is best achieved at shallower depths. At depths of approximately 35 msw and more, the attainable gain is minimal and economically uninteresting.

9.6.2 Technical System
Nitrox diving is a surface-supplied procedure, very similar to air diving. Therefore the technical system described in section 9.4.2 is in principle

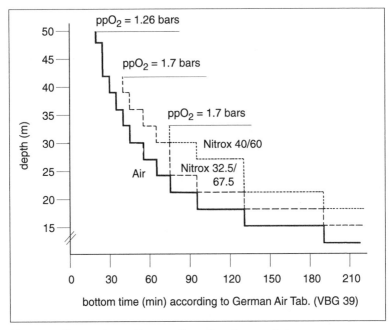

Fig. 9.15 Comparison of bottom times for nitrox and air

also valid for nitrox operations. The diver's supply is produced by a gas mixer, according to reference [40], at the surface, using an air compressor and an oxygen bank which prepares a preset O_2/N_2 mixture. The gas mixer delivers the mix at a pressure of approximately 20 bars. The diver is supplied via a hose which is limited to a length of 80 m, as for air. It is possible to use air as reserve and emergency gas, if a premixed nitrox is not available at the surface.

An advantage of nitrox, from the technical point of view, is the fact that air equipment can usually be used for nitrox diving. But when oxygen-enriched mixes are used, the components of the system must fulfill the previously discussed requirements of oxygen cleanliness (see section 7.6). Operational experiences with nitrox diving are documented, for example, in the Norwegian and German sector, as seen in references [40, 41, 42].

9.7 MIXED GAS DIVING
9.7.1 Introduction

Mixed gases are artificial mixtures; they are used for depths at which air as a breathing gas is not tolerable for physiological reasons. Due to the narcotic effects of nitrogen under raised pressure conditions, air diving is limited to depths between 50 and 60 msw. This limit differs slightly in various national regulations.

In worldwide diving practice, nitrogen is replaced by helium, an expensive gas with the lowest narcotic potential of all inert gases. This heliox or helox O_2/He-mix is the standard diving gas for all deep diving operations. The composition of the heliox depends on the intended depth and bottom time. When the tolerable O_2 partial pressure is fixed according to Fig. 5.3, the operational depth determines the oxygen concentration of the heliox. When the heliox must be breathable at the surface, its oxygen concentration must be at least 16% O_2. If a lower O_2 concentration is necessary for a greater depth, two mixes must be used. The first mix, with a minimum of 16% oxygen, is breathed during the start of the descent. For economic reasons, air is used for the first phase of the dive down to a depth of approximately 10 m to 15 msw. Here the diver stops, and the air is changed completely and replaced by the heliox mixture of the desired O_2 concentration.

9.7.2 Technical System

The technical system for mixed gas diving is similar to that used for air diving with a closed bell (see section 9.4.2). The diver's supply is guaranteed by mixed gas storage, including a compressor as an emergency

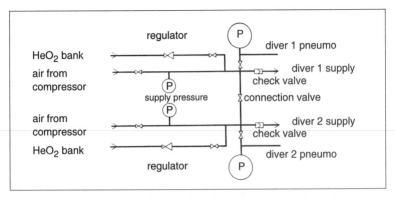

Fig. 9.16 General layout of a rack box for air/mixed gas diving [43]

supply source. Instead of premixed gases, a gas mixer can be used, analogous to mixing nitrox. But in this case the mixer uses pure oxygen and helium to prepare heliox. Figure 9.16 gives the general layout of a distribution panel (rack box) for a mixed gas/air supply. Each diver has two independent supply lines to supply mixed gas as well as air. This alternative is necessary for switching over to air near the surface, where mixes with less than 16% oxygen cannot be tolerated.

The divers are supplied from the surface via a hose, which again is restricted to a length of 80 m. As mixed gases are used at depths greater than 50 msw, only a very limited depth margin is left for operations. It is therefore more reasonable to use diving bells, which are also recommended from a safety point of view. Some countries require the use of diving bells for depths greater than 50 msw. In that case, the supply from the surface is replaced by the shorter supply hose from the bell (see Fig. 9.12). A closed bell is normally combined with a chamber at the surface, as discussed in 9.5.

Bell bounce dives are also possible down to 200 msw, but the required decompression obligations are time-consuming, especially in the case of longer bottom times. Repeated gas changes are necessary to comply with the required decompression procedures. Bell bounce diving may be a reasonable alternative for special deep dive operations of short duration, but in general, saturation diving offers the most economical option for deep diving. Mixed gas diving must take into account the previously discussed problems of distortion of language and heat loss. The special features of helium and its effects on diving have been dealt with in section 5.6.

9.8 SATURATION DIVING
9.8.1 Introduction

Although saturation diving is in principle a surface-supplied diving method, its requirements differ so much from conventional fundamentals and procedures that it is reasonable to discuss it as a specific technique. The technical and personnel requirements for saturation diving cannot be compared with those of any other conventional diving method.

Saturation diving is a relatively new method which was introduced in commercial diving in the 1960s. It should be mentioned that without the introduction of saturation diving, today's achievements in offshore technology would have been impossible.

Saturation diving is based on the simple idea that tissues can dissolve only a limited amount of inert gas under raised ambient pressure, until the tissues are saturated. Then no more gas can be taken up by the tissues. At saturation, exposure time no longer plays a role. From the point of view of decompression, the duration of a saturation dive could theoretically be indefinite; the decompression procedure and decompression time are the same for one day, one week, one month, or one year.

The body is composed of different tissues and each type of tissue becomes saturated after different exposure times. As rule of thumb, it can be assumed that the body is saturated after 12 hours of exposure at a raised pressure level. It is obvious that saturation decompression requires longer decompression times (see Chapter 11).

Another advantage of saturation diving is that it makes excursion operations possible. Starting from the storage or bottom depth, excursions to deeper or lower depths are possible for unlimited durations without any additional decompression obligations when arriving back at storage depth. However, there is only a limited depth margin for excursion dives, depending on the actual storage depth (see section 11.6). Excursion dives are used commercially when the working depth is deeper than the storage depth. The diver leaves his storage depth and goes down to his work site without any decompression obligations when he returns. This saves decompression time when decompression finally starts from the storage depth.

Long-term stays in the chamber system require strict maintenance of environmental parameters such as composition and purity of chamber gas, temperature, etc. The minimum O_2 partial pressure is between 0.16 and 0.2 bars, and due to the long-term effects of oxygen, the upper limit must not exceed 0.5 bars. Based on this tolerable upper limit, the O_2 concentration of the breathing mix is determined by the storage depth (see Fig. 7.3). The oxygen concentration at a storage depth of 600 m is, for example, less than 1% O_2. Not only is the O_2 concentration in the chamber atmosphere continuously monitored, but so is carbon dioxide, a waste product of the human metabolism.

Problems may arise during long-term dives caused, for example, by contamination by unsuitable painting of the chamber, dangerous cleaning substances, or even aftershave products. Contamination by smell or even methane must be considered; the latter has a generation rate of 0.3 to 0.5 l per day and diver, according to reference [54]. Mercury inside the chamber system is a special danger; therefore, no devices containing mercury, such as thermometers, are allowed in the chamber.

Another concern is the divers themselves, who must live for weeks in the very restricted surroundings of the chamber, which may lead to psychological stress. Careful checking of the diver's suitability for saturation dives is essential. Living in a chamber creates hygiene problems. The warm hyperbaric chamber atmosphere with a high humidity level is an ideal environment for multiplying bacteria. Without strict hygiene measures, these bacteria would contaminate the whole chamber system and infect the divers. The ear canal is especially endangered; very painful inflammations may occur and completely disable the diver. Medical treatment also presents problems; well-tested medicines and treatment procedures may result in very different reactions under hyperbaric conditions. Therefore, preventive measures are very important to keep the divers healthy. Daily showers and daily ear prophylaxis, and regular disinfection of living and sanitation areas are only some of the hygiene measures necessary.

Helium's high heat conductivity and the resulting fast body heat loss has been discussed already. Heat loss via breathing in a helium atmosphere is considerable, while heat loss via perspiration is reduced. As a result, the threshold of comfort reverts to a margin of approximately 1°C, requiring very exact temperature control. The temperature level in the chamber must be kept between 30 and 32°C, depending on the depth, according to reference [44].

Helium is the main component of breathing mixes in saturation diving. Its density increases substantially at greater depths, up to 15 g/l, which means a density 12 times higher than that of atmospheric air. Because breathing resistance increases with increased density, the diver must do considerable work to breathe, reducing his physical strength. His strength at 450 msw may be reduced to 30 to 40% of his normal strength, as noted in reference [54].

Saturation dives have been performed for years, the maximum depth achieved being 700 msw. But many phenomena, especially neurological ones, are not yet fully understood. One reason is the lack of sufficient data for very deep dives.

9.8.2 Technical System

Technical and personnel requirements for saturation dives are much more stringent than for any other commercial diving procedure. The technical system must supply the divers and maintain their living conditions for weeks. During the underwater working phase, the divers are supplied from the surface.

The technical concept of the saturation system in Fig. 9.17 is very similar to the chamber system in Fig. 9.13. The saturation system is equipped for divers to stay in the chambers for a longer time.

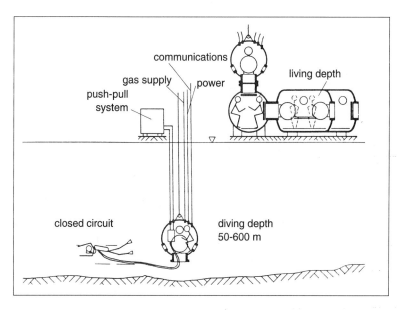

Fig. 9.17 Operation of a closed bell in saturation mode [33]

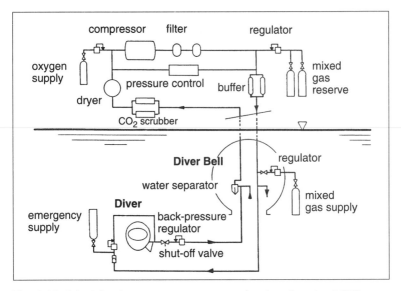

Fig. 9.18 Principle of a gas recovery system (push-pull system) [33]

For deep-diving operations, the mixed gas consists of more than 90% helium. Because helium is very expensive, it is not economical to use an open circuit, where the exhaled gas is lost to the environment, for the diver's supply. Therefore, gas recovery systems are used, with closed circuit supply arrangements at the surface; these are known as push-pull systems.

Premixed heliox is pumped to the bell via the bell's umbilical by means of a compressor. The distribution to the diver occurs via the diver's own umbilical. The diver does not exhale the gas into the surrounding water, but instead it is taken back to the bell and from there to the surface via a return line. Because the diver is not able to force his exhaled gas to the surface with his lungs, he needs technological assistance; hence, the push-pull system. A back pressure regulator in the diver's return line maintains a constant negative pressure to support the diver's breathing. Regulators and other control devices in the system monitor oxygen and carbon dioxide and guarantee that the pressure inside of the diver's helmet is not subjected to intolerable over- or underpressures. Parts of the push-pull system are, for example, redundant CO_2 scrubbers, water separators, buffers, back-up supplies, etc., as listed in reference [33] (see Fig. 9.18). At the surface, the exhaled gas is reconditioned by removing carbon dioxide, adding oxygen, separating water, and heating up the gas before recirculation.

The diver has a bale-out tank as an emergency supply so he can return immediately to the bell in case of problems with his gas supply. His umbilical is limited to a length of 30 m (100 ft.) and contains, in addition to the gas supply and return hose, a hot water line for supplying his hot water suit, a pneumo hose, and communications.

The bellman breathes the bell's atmosphere directly and supervises the diver, who works outside the bell. After approximately four hours, diver and bellman switch and the bellman now works as a diver. After eight hours, when the shift is finished, both divers get back into the bell and close the hatch. The bell returns to the surface and is mated with the chamber system. Because the storage pressure in the chambers and the internal

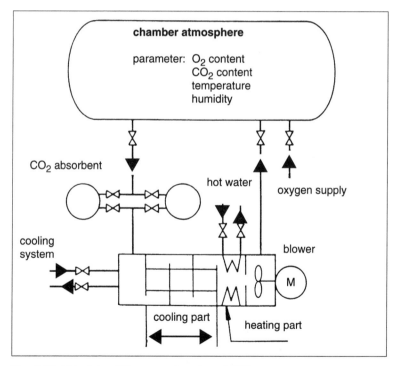

Fig. 9.19 Principle of life support system (LSS)

bell pressure are equal, the first two divers leave the bell and the next two are ready to start the second shift. For a twenty-four hour job, at least six divers must be available. Two divers work their eight-hour shift, while the other four are in the chamber for rest and sleep.

It is vital to provide reasonable living conditions in the chamber because divers must live there for up to several weeks, depending on the job. To maintain living conditions, life-support systems (LSS) must guarantee a breathable chamber atmosphere as well as tolerable temperatures. Therefore, continuous monitoring of the main parameters, such as oxygen and carbon dioxide content, temperature, and humidity inside the chambers, is essential.

The life-support system removes carbon dioxide from the chamber gas by means of CO_2 scrubbers (see Fig. 9.19). Then the gas is cooled

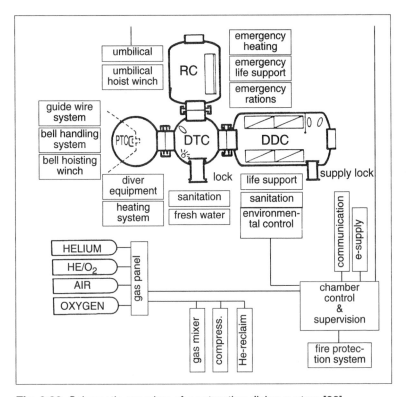

Fig. 9.20 Schematic overview of a saturation diving system [33]

down to condense vapor and remove the water while maintaining a constant humidity level. The gas is heated to 30 to 32° Centigrade to maintain a comfortable chamber temperature. Oxygen, consumed by the divers, is added and the renewed breathing gas goes back into the chamber. In general, each chamber has its own life support system. But for redundancy, each LSS can be connected to any chamber to compensate if a system breaks down.

A saturation system normally consists of more than one living chamber to make the system more flexible. One dive crew can be at storage depth, while another crew in a second chamber is decompressed. It is obvious that this second chamber must be operated separately. Theoretically, saturation dives could be performed for unlimited time periods, but for psychological reasons such dives do not usually exceed four weeks. British and Norwegian guidelines recommend a twenty-four day maximum. When the underwater task requires more time, a second crew must be brought in to continue the work while the first crew is decompressed. A total saturation system consists of different chambers including the bell; it also requires a number of auxiliary systems, such as a control station, life-support, supply and waste management, sanitation, bell handling, and emergency systems with high degrees of redundancy. These requirements lead to relatively complex diving systems, as seen in reference [33] (see also Fig. 9.20).

To handle and safely operate such complex technical systems, well-trained topside personnel as well as experienced divers are vital. Regular emergency drills give all personnel confidence to handle possible emergency situations. Everybody on the team must realize that the divers in the system are dependent on their topside colleagues.

The schematic overview in Fig. 9.20 does not include the hyperbaric rescue system to evacuate the divers if the platform or DSV must be abandoned. In this situation, the saturated divers cannot be decompressed rapidly without endangering the enclosed divers. Therefore, a rescue chamber or a hyperbaric life boat must be on board to accommodate and decompress divers during an evacuation.

Each chamber itself is a relatively complex system; it is shown in Fig. 9.21 (bell of GUSI). The bell is supplied via an umbilical with breathing gas and hot water, but the umbilical also contains the pneumo lines for the bell and the divers as well as lines for measuring and analyzing gas. For simplification, electric and hydraulic lines have been omitted

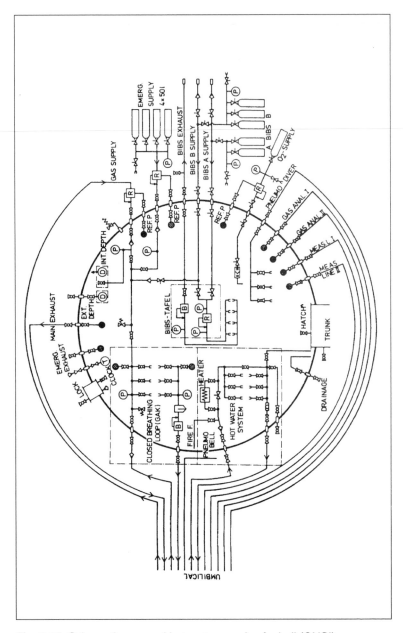

Fig. 9.21 Schematic gas and hot water supply of a bell (GUSI)

in this drawing. The bell also has its own emergency gas storage on the outside, which supplies the bell and the bell's BIBS in case of emergencies or other intolerable events.

An essential part of each bell system is its ballast weight, which can be arranged in different configurations. The fully-equipped bell is designed to float. So additional ballast must be provided to achieve negative buoyancy. The ballast can be released inside of the bell by the divers in case of an emergency. But this is a difficult decision to make because the bell will be completely out of any control as it rises. It is safer to use a second bell, if one is available, to transfer the divers under pressure (TUP). The concepts and designs of different saturation diving systems vary widely to meet the specific needs of the user. Technical solutions of existing saturation systems are given, for example, in references [33, 39].

9.8.3 Diving Gases

In saturation diving, the breathing medium usually employed is mixed gas (Table 9.1). It should be mentioned that air and nitrox are sometimes used, mainly for scientific tasks in underwater habitats at shallower depths. Air has the indisputable advantage of being the cheapest diving gas, but its oxygen concentration of 21% allows its use at shallow depths only. Because the O_2 partial pressure for long-term exposures must not exceed 0.5 bars, the maximum saturation depth is about 15 msw.

For operations at greater depths (e.g., for scientific expeditions), an economic solution might be nitrox. In this case, as opposed to those dealt with in section 9.6, a nitrox mixture with a lower oxygen concentration than air is chosen. To be breathable at the surface, the O_2 concentration must be at least 16%. Using a nitrox mix 16/84 and taking into account the limit of $ppO_2 = 0.5$ bars, a saturation depth of approximately 21 msw can be achieved.

For greater depths, the oxygen portion of the nitrox must be further reduced and the N_2 increased. Due to the narcotic potential of nitrogen, its partial pressure must not exceed 4 bars, resulting in a saturation depth between 30 and 35 msw. Decompression will be lengthy due to the high percentage of nitrogen ($> 90\%$ N_2). It takes much longer to remove nitrogen from the tissues than to remove the lighter helium.

For commercial saturation dives, the breathing gas is generally heliox, an oxygen/helium composition. At depths of more than 200 msw combined with high pressurization rates, disturbances of the central nervous system (CNS), known as High Pressure Nervous Syndrome (HPNS), have been noticed (see section 5.6). The phenomena and effects of HPNS have been investigated, among others, by Bennett in reference [13]. He showed that adding 5 to 10% nitrogen effectively suppresses HPNS. This mixture of oxygen, helium, and nitrogen is known as trimix and has been used successfully for a number of deep-dive operations, including the U.S. record dive to 686 m found in references [13 and 135]. All GUSI dives, with a depth range between 150 and 600 m, also used a trimix with 5% nitrogen, according to [55].

The density of diving gases is an essential factor; it influences breathing at increased depths. Despite the high helium portion in the trimix, its density rises to 15 g/l at a depth of 600 m (see Fig. 9.22). This problem can be overcome by using lighter gases such as hydrogen. Mixes of oxygen and hydrogen, known as hydrox, or a trimix of oxygen, helium, and hydrogen known as hydreliox, are used. The latter has been used very

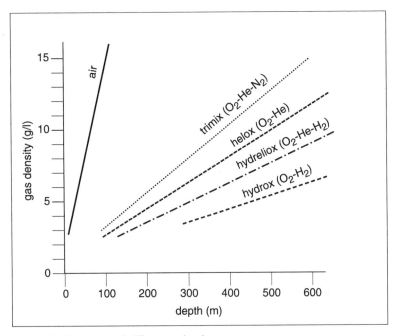

Fig. 9.22 Densities of different mixed gases

successfully by the French for their record dive. The use of hydrox (O_2/H_2), for example, reduces the gas density to 6 g/l, at 600 m (Fig. 9.22). This mixture is only 4.5 times denser than atmospheric air.

Hydrogen is a very active gas, but it acts physiologically as an inert gas. The narcotic potential of hydrogen is between that of nitrogen and helium (see table 5.3). Therefore HPNS effects do not occur, and additional nitrogen can be omitted.

The French diving company Comex, now Stolt Comex Seaway, has used mixes of oxygen/hydrogen and oxygen/helium/hydrogen successfully in their HYDRA experiments, according to references [14, 45, 129]. Using hydreliox ($O_2/H_2/He$), Comex achieved a depth of 534 msw in open water during their HYDRA VIII experiments, as noted in reference [45, 46]. The trimix consisted of 47% to 49% of helium and hydrogen, while the remaining 1% was oxygen. During the HYDRA X experiment at the end of 1992, the world depth record was broken with a 701 m chamber dive in Marseille, France, as seen in reference [129]. Here, too, a trimix of oxygen, helium, and hydrogen was used as the breathing gas.

Handling hydrogen requires stringent safety precautions due to its explosive potential. Therefore, Comex has conducted numerous investigations on safety, published, among others, in reference [136]. The results show that in the pressure range between 15 and 75 bars for different helium/hydrogen mixtures, the flammability threshold is roughly the same as that of 4% oxygen (see Fig. 5.8). Therefore, the safety boundary is fixed at an O_2 content of 2.5% to be on the safe side.

Because in deep diving the oxygen portion must be limited to avoid O_2 poisoning, hydrogen mixes can be used from 200 msw, keeping an oxygen partial pressure level of 0.5 bars. If the O_2 partial pressure is limited to 0.2 bars, hydrogen mixes can be used from 70 msw without exceeding the safety threshold (see Fig. 5.8). During decompression, the hydrogen must be eliminated to keep the oxygen content below the threshold of 2.5% O_2. A very elegant method is to oxidize the hydrogen to water. With this method, the total pressure is reduced without relieving gas. In the end, only an oxygen/helium mix is left. This method of hydrogen oxidation is also used to eliminate hydrogen leaking from the chamber system. A special cover is arranged above the chambers to catch the escaping hydrogen. Hydrogen mixtures offer the potential for dives to much greater depths.

NOTES

CHAPTER 10

Diving in Contaminated Waters

10.1 INTRODUCTION

Our industrial society produces, transports, and consumes many products which may lead directly or indirectly to environmental contamination. Here, only water pollution, which may endanger the diver during underwater operations, is discussed. In adddition to the pollution load to which the public in general is exposed, the individual diver may be exposed to additional environmental loads, as noted in reference [137]. In some cases, higher risks must be accepted by the diver in order to avert greater damage to the public. More than once, divers have subjected themselves to personal risk to salvage dangerous products from the waters or to remove dangerous contaminents to avert further environmental damage. Industrialization, increasing traffic, and growing urbanization have led to contamination of rivers, coastal areas, and the seas by different harmful substances and increased pollution. The natural potential for regeneration is limited and is sometimes greatly exceeded by the presence of substances that decompose very slowly.

Diving in highly-contaminated waters requires protection for the diver. Moreover, divers are often involved in special diving operations for the chemical and nuclear industries, to mention only some dangerous situations. There is a wide spectrum of contaminents with which the diver may come into contact during his underwater work. These contaminents include: thermal contaminents; biological contaminents; chemical contaminents; and radiological contaminents. Contamination by noise is also possible in diving from sound emissions generated by sonar or underwater explosions. The possible severe damage caused by high energy sound waves has been dealt with in section 3.2.

10.2 THERMAL CONTAMINENTS

Thermal contaminents are simply temperature loads of waters. Thermal contaminents often occur in combination with other kinds of pollutants, multiplying the undesired effects. Heated waters, e.g., are ideal for the explosive multiplying of pathological organisms when biological contamination is also present.

Heating water causes an increase of the molecules' kinetic energy. No change of matter takes place in thermal contamination. The high specific heat of the water compared to the air results in much faster cooling of an unprotected body. But from the diver's point of view, the thermal problem is not cold waters, but warm waters. Protecting against cold waters is relatively easy compared to protecting against hot water. Because the diver needs a tight suit to protect against the polluted environment, the removal of the heat generated during work is impeded, leading to dangerous heat stresses. Heat removal measures or strict limitation of the diver's operational time are the only remedies. Thermal contamination usually occurs at sites where the water is used for cooling power stations or similar plants. Each steam process uses a condenser by which the heat of condensation of the exhaust steam is removed to convert it into condensate. The heat produced by condensation is roughly 2/3 of the total process heat which is removed by the cooling water. In the case of a 1000 MWs power plant, approximately 2000 MWs of heat must be removed by the cooling water. Even for great rivers, this thermal load may be too high. Therefore, the legislature has limited water temperatures to 28°C, independent of whether the heat source is natural or artificial.

10.3 BIOLOGICAL CONTAMINENTS

Waste and sewage, including faeces, introduced into waters without sufficient treatment, are the sources of the biological contamination that endanger the diver, as noted in references [47, 48, 137]. There are many places in the world, especially large harbors, where biological contamination rates are extremely high. There are many kinds of bacteria that may be dangerous for divers and swimmers. Protozoans and viruses are also sources of infection and disease. These enter the body via the mouth or nose and may cause cholera, infections of the gastrointestinal tract, or liver disease, to name only some effects. External skin or ear infections may also occur.

Some of these organisms need water for life, and their rate of reproduction depends, among other things, on water temperature, salinity, etc. Unfortunately, thermal and biological contaminents often occur together and offer an ideal breeding ground for pathogenic microorganisms. When the water is further contaminated by chemicals, the harmful effects of bacteria are increased. Chemical pollutants may weaken the natural protective function of the skin and give bacteria a better chance of penetrating the body. An especially unpleasant bacteria is *Pseudomonas aeroginosa,* which causes infections of the external ear if the head is not protected by a helmet. The best protection against biological contaminents is protective clothing such as a tight diving suit which prevents the diver coming into direct contact with the polluted waters. It is recommended that the suit be cleaned after the dive, and, especially, that the diving mask or hood be rinsed with a suitable disinfectant.

10.4 CHEMICAL CONTAMINENTS

As with biological contaminents, there is a very broad field of contaminents of chemical origin ranging from substances which are not dangerous for human beings or animals even in the highest concentrations to highly toxic substances that endanger the environment even in the smallest concentrations, according to references [47, 137]. Modern industry produces a host of chemical compounds that have varying effects on man and his environment. It is helpful to classify the chemical compounds according to their main characteristics. One possibility is to use the UN classification system which differentiates among nine categories of hazardous materials. Class 5, for example, includes oxidizing substances, class 6 poisonous and infectious substances, class 7 radioactive materials, and class 8 corrosives.

Chemical contamination of water is caused by a number of industries besides the chemical industry—agriculture and private households also play a part in the chemical pollution of rivers, coastal areas, and oceans. Thousands of tons of chlorides, sulphates, nitrates, phosphates, and heavy metals such as lead, cadmium, mercury, etc. are transported every year via rivers into the sea. The shipping industry pollutes the waters by jettisoning dangerous goods, wastes, or the residues of tank cleaning. The shipping industry also contaminates water with oil and oil derivatives. Hydrocarbons are released into the waters by the oil/offshore industry, by households, and simply by rain. In some parts of rivers and coastal zones, concentrations of chemical contaminents have been noticed; these concentrations are caused by still water zones, tidal effects, or currents. Thus unexpectedly high contamination rates may occur in very limited diving areas. Spectacular tanker accidents and industrial disasters have drawn the public's attention to the severe consequences of pollution to our waters, but diving operations to moderate these effects go largely unnoticed.

Chemical contamination may begin at a concentrated source or at a distributed source, depending on the local circumstances. Unprotected divers are harmed by these contaminents externally, sustaining damage to the eyes, ears, and skin. These chemical substances may also attack the diver's equipment. But more alarming are the consequences when contaminated water gets into the body via the mouth or nose. Possible effects on man are diverse—almost every organ is affected. It is important to know that repeated dives in only slightly contaminated waters may cause problems. Continuous doses of even harmless chemical contaminents accumulate in the body and eventually cause problems. Again, the best protection against chemical contaminents and their consequences is sufficient protective clothing. An appropriate suit prevents the diver's contact with polluted waters. Special attention must be paid to the supply equipment for the breathing gas. Appropriate technical measures can prevent the ingestion of contaminated water via the regulator and mouth. It is obvious that the material of the diver's suit must be resistent to aggressive chemical substances. After the dive, cleaning diving equipment is essential. When diving in heated waters and doing heavy underwater work, the diver must again pay special attention to the danger of heat exhaustion.

10.5 RADIOLOGICAL CONTAMINENTS
10.5.1 Radioactivity
One consequence of the technical utilization of nuclear energy is the handling of radioactive material on an industrial scale. Compared to radioactivity from natural sources, radioactivity levels generated by nuclear fission are much higher. In spite of careful handling of radioactive materials, leakage of these substances into the environment and into waters cannot be completely prevented. Consequently, it must be assumed that divers come into contact with radioactive materials underwater, as seen in references [49, 50, 137]. On the other hand, diving operations have been successfully carried out to maintain and repair nuclear plants for years.

The nature of radioactive contaminants and the handling of radioactive materials differs markedly from most people's practical experience, so some introductory remarks will be given to help the reader better understand the nature of, and effective protection against, radioactive radiation. Radioactivity is, like other physical or chemical characteristics, a typical property of special kinds of atoms or nuclei. These atoms naturally change via intermediate stages into other, stable, atoms. During this decay process radiation is emitted. There are different kinds of radiation, and they have different effects on human tissues.

The decay process occurs for every kind of atom (nucleus) over a certain length of time, which is characteristic for each nucleus and which cannot be influenced in any way. The temporal pattern of this decay process is described as the radiological half-life $T_{1/2}$. The half-life is the time it takes for the activity of a specific type of nucleus to be reduced by one half. After a second half-life period, the activity is reduced to a quarter of the initial activity, and so forth (see Fig. 10.1).

After ten half-life periods, the activity is only about one thousandth of the initial activity. The decay process is described mathematically by a simple exponential function, using the half-life $T_{1/2}$.

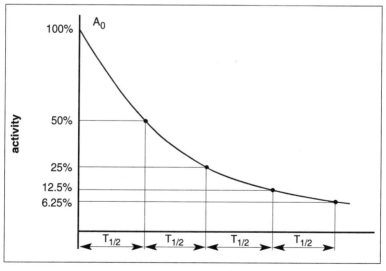

Fig. 10.1 Radioactive decay described by radiological half-life

$$A(t) = A_0 \exp(t / T_{1/2})$$ (10.1)

with $A(t)$ = activity at time t

      A_0 = initial activity of the nuclei

      $T_{1/2}$ = half-life of the nuclei.

The half-lifes of different nuclei vary widely from fractions of a second up to millions of years. Therefore scientists speak of long-term and short-term radiation sources. It must be understood that radioactivity cannot be seen or tasted and that it cannot be destroyed by external physical or chemical processes such as burning. Only the half-life of a nucleus determines its actual activity level and allows an estimation of the time when the activity is below a harmful level. The manifestations of radioactive radiation can differ. Different kinds of radiation lead, depending on their energy, to a multitude of interactions with radiated matter. The biological effects of the radiation are based on ionizing processes within human and animal tissues. Although the radiation energy is small, it is sufficient to trigger biochemical processes in the cells that change or kill the cells. Enzymes, necessary for control of the cell's metabolism, may be inactivated, and cells can be damaged by changes in their chromosomes. Such mutations are transmitted to the next generation of cells, leading to genetic damage years later. Metabolic enzymes and chromosomes are the most sensitive parts of a cell; muscle and bone tissues are less sensitive to radiation. The origin of radioactive radiation, natural or artificial, has no influence on the effects of the radiation. Only the kind and energy of the radiation are important in this regard.

For millions of years, man has lived with natural radioactive radiation and has adapted to it in his evolutionary process. The body has learned to handle radiation effects and repairs damaged cells and eliminates dead cells.

10.5.2 Radiological Units and Limits

To evaluate the effects of radiation quantitatively, suitable units of measurement must be available to judge its dangers. Radioactive radiation is physically described as the transport of energy from a source to a given spot, such as radiation of heat or light (see Fig. 10.2). The strength or activity of a source is the number of disintegrations or emitted particles per unit of time. The activity unit is Becquerel (Bq), after the French physicist A. H. Becquerel. One Bq = 1 disintegration per second. But the activity does not describe the kind of particles and their energy, and therefore is not indicative of the danger to human tissues.

The effect of radiation on matter is characterized by the absorbed dose. The energy dose is the absorbed energy of radiation per unit mass of matter, caused by interactions of ionizing radiation with that matter. The unit of energy dose is Gray (Gy), after the British scientist S. Gray. One Gray is the absorbed energy of radiation of 1 Joule per kg matter. The dose per unit of time is the dose rate. The dose rate multiplied by the exposure time results in the absorbed dose.

To evaluate the harmfulness of radiation to tissues, the different kinds of radiation must be judged with respect to their biological effects; this is done using a Quality Factor QF. This factor evaluates the kind of radiation; it is 1 for x-rays, beta, and gamma radiation, is 10 for fast neutrons, and is 20 for alpha rays. This means that alpha radiation is 20 times more harmful to human tissues than, e.g., x-rays or gamma radiation. The equivalent dose allows evaluation of the effects of different types of radiation. The equivalent dose is the product of the energy dose times the Quality Factor. The unit of equivalent dose is Sievert (Sv), after the Swedish physicist R.M. Sievert. The equivalent dose naturally has the same dimension as the energy dose, 1 Sv = 1 Joule/kg matter. In health

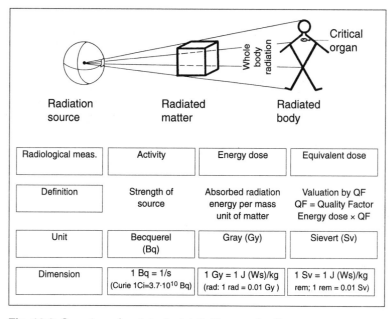

Radiological meas.	Activity	Energy dose	Equivalent dose
Definition	Strength of source	Absorbed radiation energy per mass unit of matter	Valuation by QF QF = Quality Factor Energy dose × QF
Unit	Becquerel (Bq)	Gray (Gy)	Sievert (Sv)
Dimension	1 Bq = 1/s (Curie 1Ci=$3.7 \cdot 10^{10}$ Bq)	1 Gy = 1 J (Ws)/kg (rad: 1 rad = 0.01 Gy)	1 Sv = 1 J (Ws)/kg rem; 1 rem = 0.01 Sv)

Fig. 10.2 Overview of radiological definitions and units

physics, the former unit rem, which stands for roentgen equivalent man, is sometimes used. Sievert and rem differ by the factor 100:

$$1 \text{ Sv} = 100 \text{ rem}; \qquad 1 \text{ rem} = 0.01 \text{ Sv}.$$

The definition of the equivalent dose rate is similar to the energy dose rate; it is simply dose per unit of time. If the unit of time is 1 hour, the dose rate is 1 Sv/h, or for smaller dose rates, 1 mSv/h.

The utilization of radioactive sources in medicine and engineering and nuclear power generation creates new potential dangers. The fact is that the release of radioactivity cannot be completely prevented and even small dose rates result in considerable doses when they are accumulated in the body over a whole lifetime. These doses may cause damage later, like cancer or damage to the genes. Therefore, most countries have issued stringent safety rules for the handling and supervision of radioactive material, in Germany, e.g., in reference [51], The regulations, based on the Atomic Law, restrict the permissible radiation exposure for the public to a level which is of the same order of magnitude as that of natural radiation. According to reference [51], the permissible, external whole body dose rate for nonnuclear workers is 1.5 µSv per year (150 mrem/a) or 0.17 µSv/h.

Radioactivity can also enter the body via the air (inhalation) or via water and food (ingestion). Radioactive nuclei are often accumulated in specific organs of the body, the socalled critical organs. Over long periods of time, such critical organs are enriched with specific radioactive nuclei. If this nucleus has a relatively long half-life as, e.g., in the case of strontium (Sr 90) which emits beta rays with a half-life of about 28 years, the activity is practically constant for a whole lifetime. Because strontium is chemically similar to calcium, the main component of our bones, it will be deposited in the bones near the bone marrow. That means a radioactive source is in direct contact with the sensitive bone marrow; this radioactivity may have long-term effects such as bone cancer or blood cancer (leukemia).

10.5.3 Radioactive Sources and Shielding Aspects

Radiological con-tamination of water may occur at a concentrated source or may be distributed over a greater area. Distributed contaminations result, for example, from leaks from components of nuclear plants or from nuclear waste drums. Transportation accidents may also result in radiological contamination of rivers, lakes, and the seas. A further source of radioactivity is wash-out of radioactive materials from the atmosphere as a consequence of earlier atomic bomb tests or as the result of reactor accidents like that at Chernobyl. We still know little about accidents and environmental contamination caused by the Russian nuclear industry in Siberia. Nuclear dangers there may also endanger our area. Unfortunately, acts of sabotage, such as the intentional contamination of water reservoirs, may also occur. Examples of concentrated radioactive sources are burnt fuel elements and nuclear fuels, both handled in special transport containers. Engineering and medicine also use highly radioactive materials. In the past, even atomic bombs have been lost, and divers have been involved in searching for them.

Divers come in contact with radioactive materials not only as a consequence of mistakes or accidents, but also when performing repairs in nuclear power plants. Divers have done repair work very successfully in U.S. and German power plants, according to reference [86]. The probability of nuclear accidents will increase with the increasing age of nuclear plants and with respect to developments in the Russian nuclear industry. Therefore, the diving industry should be adequately prepared for diving actions in radiologically contaminated waters. In the following, some basics on shielding will be introduced briefly to give the diver some ideas about how to protect himself.

The spread of radioactive radiation follows the same physical laws as the radiation of light, decreasing with the squared distance from the source.

$$A (D) = A_0 \ 1/D^2 \tag{10.2}$$

with $A (D)$ = activity at distance D from source
        A_0 = activity of source
        D = distance from source in units of length

In the case of an idealized point source, the activity at any given distance D, without shielding material, results in

$$A (D) = A_0 \ 1/4\pi D^2 \tag{10.3}$$

The first possible protection measure is simply to stay a sufficient distance away from the radioactive source. But often actions must be taken near the source, in which case this measure cannot be used. Fortunately, water has effective shielding properties against radioactive radiation including high-energy gamma radiation. The energy-dependent absorption coefficient μ for gamma rays enters the equation exponentially and gives the formula for total attenuation of a gamma source at distance D

$$A (\mu,D) = A_0 \, 1/4\pi D^2 \times \exp (-\mu D) \qquad\qquad (10.4)$$

At a distance of 1 m (3.3 ft) from the source, corresponding roughly to an arm's length, the radiation is attenuated by 10^{-8}. At a distance of 2 m (6.6 ft) the attenuation increases to 10^{-10}, and so forth.

It must be added that the tolerable equivalent dose for hands is many times the dose tolerated by the body as a whole. Therefore, underwater operations are possible, even near relatively strong radioactive sources, without endangering the divers. By following some basic rules when diving in radiologically contaminated waters, the diver can protect himself effectively. The first rule is to avoid any direct contact with the contaminated environment. As in other cases of contamination, a tight diving suit offers sufficient protection. It also protects against distributed radiological contaminants—the effects on man in terms of whole body radiation exposure are negligible due to the high absorption qualities of water. The diving equipment must guarantee that no contaminated water can get into the diver's mouth. The fact is that low concentrations which would not endanger the diver externally may cause long-term problems due to accumulation in critical organs. Therefore, a tight dry suit is essential. The number of penetrations should be as low as possible; for example, valves should be constructed as double valves for safety reasons. Also two pairs of gloves should be used with additional cuff rings to ensure that the hands stay dry, as noted in reference [137].

Often radiological contamination and thermal contamination occur together. In that case, because the suit must be tight, generated body heat cannot be removed to the warmed up environment. There is a high risk of heat stroke, especially when the diver is doing heavy work. The remedy may be the use of closed-circuit hot water suits where instead of hot water cold water circulates to remove the generated heat, according to reference [47].

The material of the suit and equipment must be resistant to the contaminants. It is advantageous to have suits with smooth surfaces for easier cleaning and decontamination. For diving operations in nuclear plants, decontamination procedures of all the equipment may be very costly. In such cases, the diving equipment is left in the control area of the plant and is used again for the next operation.

CHAPTER 11

Compression and Decompression

11.1 INTRODUCTION

Diving always means being at a higher pressure than atmospheric pressure. The environment can be wet as in the case of divers or dry as in the case of compressed air workers. Descent and stay at depth normally cause no problems if the depth is no more than 200 msw. The return to surface or to shallower depths causes physiological problems. If the ascent does not follow given decompression procedures, especially after long and deep dives, the diver may experience severe health problems which may finally cause his death. The physical goal of decompression is to eliminate surplus gas which was dissolved in the tissues under hyperbaric conditions. Questions about decompression occur in diving medicine as well as in space and aeromedicine, both of which deal with similar phenomena.

Improper decompression of divers first occurred when technical advances made longer dives possible. But within the last century, compressed air workers were the first group to be confronted with the phenomenon and consequences of decompression sickness (DCS). These people had worked for eight hours and more under increased pressure conditions in caissons. Box-shaped caissons were lowered, for example, to a river bottom and pressurized with air to keep the surrounding water out. The caisson could be entered only via a lock. When workers were locked out after their shift, they showed symptoms at the surface which could not be explained at that time; these symptoms were called caisson sickness. Not until this century could Haldane and his coworkers in reference [52] explain the effects scientifically and develop the basics of decompression. These principles are still valid today.

11.2 COMPRESSION

The compression or descent phase generally cause no special problems, except during oxygen/helium deep dives. There are no limits for compression rates for air dives. The diver descends as fast as his personal conditions allow with respect to pressure equalization. A fast descent is economical because the descent time of a dive counts as bottom time. A fast descent extends the bottom time and vice versa.

No restrictions on compression rates exist for deep diving operations with O_2/He mixes down to approximately 180 msw. The diver determines his descent rate, which can be 25 m/min or more. In the 1960s, O_2/He deep-diving tests deeper than 200 msw, with a compression rate of 30 m/min, were performed in the UK. The divers showed symptoms, unknown before, manifested as marked tremors of hands, arms and body, dizziness, nausea, and vomiting, as noted in reference [13]. These phenomena are described as High Pressure Nervous Syndrome, or HPNS. Further symptoms of HPNS are fatigue, somnolence, decrease in intellectual and psychomotor performance, and poor sleep with nightmares, among others. Today it is known that the occurrence of HPNS in a helium atmosphere depends on hydrostatic pressure and the compression rate. Measurements of surface tensions in a lipid monolayer under increased pressures showed an increase in surface tension for helium and neon, while for nitrogen, argon, oxygen, and carbon dioxide the surface tension decreased (see Fig. 11.1). Lipids, fat-like substances, are the main structural constituents of cell membranes including those of nerve cells. A simplified model may explain HPNS effects by using a comparison with electric wire. If the wire's insulation is damaged by pressure, short circuits will occur in the system. Applied to man, pressure effects in the presence of helium also cause "short circuits," abnormal reactions of the central nervous system (CNS), manifested as HPNS symptoms. The ambient pressure of the gas and the surface tension of helium act in the same direction, compressing the lipid membranes and leading, consequently, to HPNS symptoms. But if the narcotic nitrogen is added, the pressure-induced surface tension is partly compensated for (see Fig. 11.1) and the membranes of the nerve cells resume their original volume; at the same time, HPNS symptoms disappear. The inverse effects of narcotics and increased pressures were shown in 1950/51 experiments with tadpoles found in reference [1].

Based on these findings, among others from the U.S. project ATLANTIS at the beginning of the 1980s, there are three possible ways to suppress HPNS effects: adding a narcotic gas to the breathing mixture; reducing the compression rate; and taking longer stops during compression for pressure adaptation. In practice, all three measures are used simultaneously, according to references [13, 54. 55]. Results from 20 deep dives between 150 and 600 m performed at GKSS research center (GUSI), confirmed the methods of suppressing HPNS effects. For all dives, a trimix containing 5% nitrogen, in addition to oxygen and helium, was used. A higher percentage of nitrogen may cause nitrogen narcosis at extreme depths. The compression rate was reduced with increasing depth. While the compression rate was 5 m/min to 180 m, it was reduced from stop to stop until the rate was 0.05 m/min, only one hundredth of the initial rate, at the maximum depth of 600 m.

Figure 11.2 shows the successful compression schedule for GUSI dive number 8 to 600 m. Four divers worked at 600 m for approximately 3 days performing, among other tasks, hyperbaric welding tests, without any HPNS problems. In addition to a continuous reduction of compression rates, stop times were extended at greater depths, as seen in reference [55]. The compression schedule in Fig. 11.2 shows an overproportional time

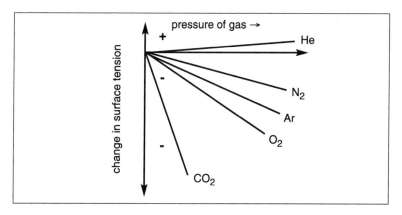

Fig. 11.1 Surface tensions in lipid monolayer for different gases exposed to increasing pressures [13]

demand with increasing depths. While compression takes roughly 10 hrs for 300 m, doubling the depth to 600 m does not require twice as much time, but instead takes more than 5 days. Even the step from 500 to 600 m, corresponding to 20% of the total depth, takes approximately 2.5 days, the same time used to descend from the surface to 500 m.

It is also remarkable that the stop times increase dramatically with depth. The compression time according to Fig. 11.2 is only 38% of the total; stop times, including night times, amount to 62% of the total decompression period.

Because the compression schedule is roughly exponential, an exponential term can be used to make a first analytical approximation.

$$t = (D/167)^{3.72} \quad \text{in hrs} \tag{11.1}$$

with   t = compression time in hrs
           D = desired depth in m

The use of hydrogen instead of helium and use of hydrogen/helium mixes has been applied very successfully by the French diving company

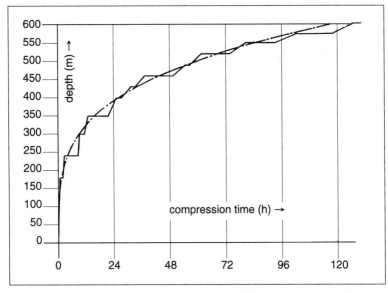

Fig. 11.2 Compression profile schedule for GUSI dive 8 to 600 m [55]

                                    Mixed Gas Diving

Comex (see sections 5.7 and 9.8.3). Hydrogen suppresses HPNS effects due to its higher narcotic potential, so there is no need to add nitrogen.

11.3 PHYSICAL-PHYSIOLOGICAL BASICS OF DECOMPRESSION

11.3.1 Mathematical Models of Gas Transport

The crucial point of all decompression procedures is the elimination of dissolved inert gases from the body as fast as possible without damaging the body's tissues. The higher solubility of gases in tissues is the consequence of higher environmental pressure and vice versa. A quantitative description of this phenomenon is given by Henry's law (see 6.2.4). The main parameter influencing the solubility of gases in liquids is the pressure; temperature and solubility coefficient have only minor effects. The solubility coefficient depends, among other factors, on the consistency of the liquid, and, in this case, the consistency of blood. Because diving causes dehydration, the blood is also dehydrated, and coagulated blood flows more slowly and eliminates dissolved inert gases at a slower rate (see, e.g., reference [57]).

The exchange of gases in blood and tissues during the decompression process is very complex and is affected by diffusion and perfusion processes, by liquid-gaseous phase separation, by the mechanics of forming and collapsing gas bubbles, and finally by the permeability of cell membranes. The complexity of body's biological system, the variety of different tissues, and the changing boundary conditions of phase transitions have until recently prevented an analytical description of decompression processes. But simplified models are available, offering usable estimates for dealing with decompression phenomena.

Simplified models include, for example, transport models, which allow mathematical estimations of gas uptake and gas elimination from body tissues, according to reference [58]. In gas transport models, tissues are subdivided into intravascular and extravascular regions. The blood, containing dissolved gases including metabolic gases, flows through the intravascular region and provides the initial and boundary conditions for subsequent gas transport through the extravascular region. In principle, three transport models can be applied: diffusion model; perfusion model; and combined diffusion-perfusion model.

The characteristic parameter for all transport models is the time-dependent gas tension $p(t)$ of the tissue. Introducing a reference tension p_r, the pressure gradient $\pi(t) = p(t) - p_r$ is the difference between the current tension p(t) of a given tissue and the reference tension p_r. The reference tension can be chosen in order to meet, for example, desired boundary conditions. Gas transport is, strictly speaking, multidimensional, but for simplification the transport equations are formulated as one dimensional equations. It is further assumed that the lungs' gas tension is in equilibrium with that of the arterial blood.

If the gas transport is determined by diffusion processes, the solution of the diffusion equation for the pressure gradient p(t) results in:

$$\frac{\delta \pi}{\delta t} = D \frac{\delta^2 \pi}{\delta x^2} \tag{11.2}$$

D = diffusion coefficient

If the gas transport to the tissues is primarily determined by the flowing processes (perfusion), the solution of the local independent exponential equation for the pressure gradient p(t) results in:

$$\frac{\delta \pi}{\delta t} = - \lambda \pi \tag{11.3}$$

λ = time constant

If diffusion as well as perfusion processes play a role in the gas transport in tissues, the solution is the Fick-Fourier equation for the pressure gradient p(t):

$$\frac{\delta \pi}{\delta t} = D \frac{\delta^2 \pi}{\delta x^2} - \chi \pi \tag{11.4}$$

D = diffusion coefficient
χ = perfusion time constant

To solve partial differential equations of the second order, suitable mathematical procedures are available, for example, separation of variables. For more details, see refrence [58], in which a multitude of mathematical references are available.

The transport models discussed do not take into account the formation of bubbles in tissues by increasing the tissues' gas solubility or the mechanism of bubble growth. The occurrence of bubbles in the circulatory system influences not only the perfusion rates in the tissues and organs, but also the pressure gradient. All transport models produce symmetrical solutions, meaning that gas uptake and elimination in a given tissue are inverse to each other, as long as the gases remain dissolved in the tissues. Otherwise, with the occurrence of bubbles, gas elimination may differ considerably from gas uptake. These transport models adequately describe gas transport in tissues under the stated boundary conditions, including the resulting gas tensions. But they are very limited for the purpose of stipulating criteria for "safe" decompressions. Although gas transport and decompression criteria are linked, the latter require special consideration and judgment.

These criteria are phenomenological statements of tolerable quantities such as the maximum permissible quantity of gas dissolved in a given tissue or the tolerable portion of bubbles in a given tissue. Due to the problem and complexity of getting reliable data, the definition of decompression criteria can only be subjective. The acquisition of reliable data is a hard and exhausting task, as data are often not only ambiguous, but sometimes controversial. When changing from deterministic to statistical models, the latter can take into account the variability of observed phenomena inherent in random events. In the 1980s, statistical models were developed in which dose-response characteristics offer the best correlations to real experimental data. Statistical models are also best for preparing decompression tables. Unfortunately, many time-consuming and costly experiments testing the most important parameters must be performed to give statistically significant results.

11.3.2 Saturation and Desaturation Processes

The classical decompression models, the basis of all of today's valid decompression tables, use the generally accepted assumption that the perfusion rate of a given tissue is the determining factor for gas uptake and elimination. Gases of special interest are the physiologically inert gases nitrogen, helium, neon, and hydrogen, which do not play a part in metabolism. Carbon dioxide (as a waste product of metabolism) and vapor also play no part in decompression. Oxygen as the basis for metabolism is not considered in decompression, although oxygen favorably influences decompression processes from the physiological point of view.

In addition to determining the perfusion rates for gas exchanges, diffusion processes may also have secondary effects which can slow down the gas exchange. The diffusion of different tissues plays an interesting role when, for example, fat tissue, which eliminates inert gas slowly, acts as gas reservoir for the next, well-perfused tissue. Diffusion processes also play a role in forming and eliminating inert gas bubbles, which are considered the most important cause of decompression sickness.

Apart from these very complex side effects, the classical perfusion model describes the transport of inert gases in the body. It is assumed that inert gas is transported in a closed circuit from the lungs to the tissues and back. The gas exchange in a given region is thus limited by the flow rate of blood and the gas solubility of tissue and blood. The transport of inert gas between areas of different concentrations or different gas tensions occurs by local gradients. The gradient p(t) is the gas tension p t) between the given tissue and the inspired inert gas pressure p_i, which corresponds to the arterial pressure (see 11.3.1):

$$\pi(t) = p(t) - p_i$$

This pressure gradient p(t) is used in equation (11.3) for the perfusion model, where the inspired inert gas pressure p_i corresponds to the constant reference pressure p_r.

$$dp/dt = \lambda(p_i - p) \qquad (11.5)$$

The coefficient λ is a characteristic time constant, describing the gas uptake and the elimination of inert gas of a given tissue.

$$\lambda \quad = \frac{\ln 2}{T_{1/2}} \quad = \frac{0.693}{T_{1/2}} \quad \text{in s}^{-1} \qquad (11.6)$$

$T_{1/2}$ in equation (11.6) is the biological half-life of the tissue under consideration. The biological half-life has the same meaning and function as the radiological half-life, dealt with in Chapter 10. It describes the temporal desaturation of a given tissue which is analogous to the temporal decay of a given radioactive nucleus. The biological half-life depends on the biophysical character of the specific tissue and the physical properties of the inert gas. Because the human body consists of very different tissues, which take up and eliminate gases very differently, the biological half-life of each individual tissue must be known. For that reason the body is divided into "compartments." Sixteen compartments are often used for modeling; each compartment is characterized by its individual half-life. These compartments cannot be assigned to specific anatomic regions; they are only used as models.

The biological half-lifes of single compartments for nitrogen are roughly between 4 minutes for well-supplied tissues like blood, the brain, or the spinal cord and 635 minutes for bone tissues and poorly-supplied fat tissues, according to reference [53, 58]. Corresponding to their half-lifes, tissues are divided into fast and slow tissues, similar to short- and long-term radioactive radiators. The half-lifes are also determined by the physical properties of inspired inert gases. If, for example, nitrogen is replaced by the lighter helium, saturation and desaturation processes are faster—helium has smaller atoms and faster diffusion rates than nitrogen.

The velocity of diffusion is determined, among other factors, by the molecular weight of the gas, which is 4g in case of helium and 28g for nitrogen. When comparing two gases, their speeds of diffusion are inversely proportional to the root of their molecular weights.

$$\frac{v_{He}}{v_{N_2}} = \sqrt{28/4} = 2.645$$

If helium is used, saturation and desaturation processes are 2.6 times faster than if nitrogen is used, and the effective biological half-lifes are

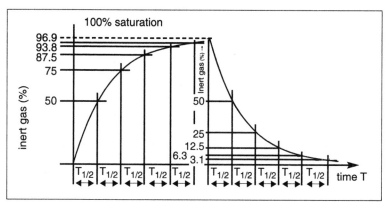

Fig. 11.3 Principle of saturation and desaturation processes

reduced by a factor of 2.6 if helium is the inert gas. The principle of saturation and desaturation processes of tissues with very different half-lifes is shown in Fig. 11.4. In this example, the fast tissue 1 is already completely saturated with inert gas after a given time period, while the degree of saturation drops for the other tissues. Tissue n, which could be, for example, a bone tissue, has just begun to be saturated. The situation is reversed for desaturation, corresponding to the decompression process. The fast tissue 1 is completely desaturated after a given time period, while the slow tissue n still holds an almost complete inert gas load. It is obvious that for saturation dives, the slow tissues like bone and cartilage determine the decompression routine.

Starting with equation (11.5) of the perfusion model and separating the variables gives the result

$$dp/(p_i - p) = \lambda \, dt$$

Integration of both sides of the equation and the introduction of boundary conditions for time $t = t_o$ results in

$$p - p_i = (p_o - p_i) \exp(-\lambda t) \qquad (11.7)$$

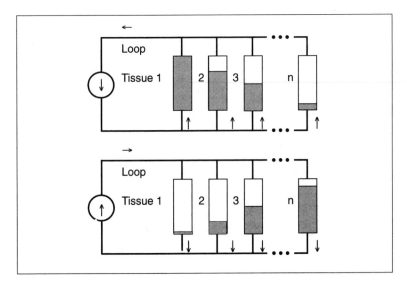

Fig. 11.4 Schematic saturation and desaturation of different tissues

with p = inert gas tension in the tissue at time t in bars

          p_o = initial gas tension in the tissue in bars

          p_i = inspirational inert gas pressure at time t in bars

          λ = biological time constant in 1/min

          t = time variable in min

The time-dependent inert gas tension p(t) in a tissue under constant ambient pressure conditions is

$$p(t) = p_i + (p_o - p_i)\exp(-\lambda t) \qquad (11.8)$$

Using a different mathematical approach results in

$$p(t) = po + (p_i - p_o)(1 - \exp(-\lambda t)) \qquad (11.8a)$$

If the ambient pressure changes during the descent or ascent phase with a constant rate c, equation (11.8a) must be extended to

$$p(t) = p_o + \qquad\qquad\qquad \text{initial gas tension} \qquad (11.9)$$
$$+ (p_i - p_o)(1 - \exp(-\lambda t)) \quad \text{isopression term}$$
$$+ c(t - 1/\lambda)(1 - \exp(-\lambda t)) \quad \text{velocity term during descent or ascent}$$

For determining the inspirational inert gas pressure p_i, a correction must be made for the vapor and carbon dioxide in the lungs:

$$p_i = (p_{amb} - 0.063)f \quad \text{in bars} \qquad (11.10)$$

with f = inert gas portion (for air f = 0.79)

          p = ambient pressure = $p_{atm} + D/10$ in bars

The ambient pressure p_{amb} is in the case of a chamber dive the chamber pressure, and in the case of a free dive $p_{amb} = p_{atm} + D/10$ with bottom depth in m.

For calculating decompression tables, in addition to the mechanism of gas transport, criteria for tolerable gas tensions in the tissues under consideration are essential. The criteria used are based on empirically determined and statistically proven data, valid for an average diver doing moderate work. But it must be remembered that the blood flow in muscle tissues and the related gas uptake (perfusion model) may change by a factor of 25 when comparing rest and heavy work. Also normal water temperatures are assumed for decompression. In cold waters of less than

10°C, some commercial U.S. companies amend the decompression procedure by increasing the actual depth by 0.55 m/°C.

11.3.3 Decompression Criteria

Although a number of questions regarding safe decompression procedures and safe decompression criteria are still open or only partly answered, there is no doubt that inert gas bubbles in tissues are the reason for decompression sicknesses. Decompression sickness (DCS) has many manifestations, which will be dealt with in Chapter 12.

Decompression is unfortunately more complex, because the appearance of bubbles in tissues, socalled " silent" bubbles, does not necessarily cause decompression problems. On the other hand, there is no decompression sickness without the occurrence of bubbles in tissues.

Safe decompression, meaning decompression without any negative side effects, depends on the prevention of inert gas bubbles in body tissues. It is assumed that every compartment can tolerate a specific gas tension, depending on the ambient pressure. The exposure time must also be taken into account. Ambient pressures that are normally tolerated by a tissue may cause decompression problems with increased exposure times. As far as we know today, an ambient pressure of 1.7 bars can be tolerated for unlimited exposure times without causing decompression problems.

The inert gas tension that can be tolerated does not depend only on the ambient pressure, but also on the perfusion rate, which is different for every compartment. Because the inert gas tension of a compartment and the specific tolerable ambient pressure are closely connected, it is easier to use as the criterion the latter or the tolerable depth at which the generation of inert gas bubbles in the compartment is just prevented. The tolerable ambient pressure depends, among other factors, on the biological half-life; the smaller the half-life of a compartment is, the higher the tolerable ambient pressure. In other words, a well-supplied or fast tissue can tolerate higher ambient pressures than can slow tissues with a correspondingly long half-life. For nitrogen, the permissible gas tension is 3 bars for fast tissues (CNS), 2 bars for skin and muscle tissues, and approximately 1.3 bars for slow tissues such as bones and cartilage, as noted in reference [53].

Slow tissues, including the poorly-supplied fat tissues, have only a small tolerance threshold to nitrogen tensions; therefore, these tissues determine decompression procedures. Animal tests have shown that roughly 80 to 90% of the nitrogen is dissolved in slow tissues with half-lifes between 150 and 250 minutes, as seen in reference [59]. The high solubility of fat tissues for nitrogen is important; it is approximately 5 times higher than that of lean tissues, and therefore, fat tissues dissolve more inert gas. This fact, combined with longer biological half-lifes, require longer decompression times for the last stops near the surface. The high fat solubility of nitrogen for fast tissues of the CNS must also be taken into account. Saturation and desaturation take little time because nerve tissues have half-lifes of only several minutes. But lipids, fat-like substances in the central and peripheral nervous system, can dissolve considerable quantities of nitrogen and thus influence deep decompression stops. Against this background it is understandable that in case of emergencies requiring a shortened decompression, the deep stops should be kept to guarantee a sufficient desaturation of at least the CNS tissues. The situation is very different when using helium. Helium diffuses much faster through cell membranes and therefore allows faster saturation and desaturation. In addition, the solubility coefficient of helium in fat is smaller, so the fast tissues mainly determine the decompression process.

The concept of tolerable ambient pressures as a decompression criterion goes back to the basic work of Haldane and his coworkers at the beginning of our century, as noted in reference [52]. In multiple test series, he developed the 2 : 1 concept, which forms the basis of decompression in stages. According to that concept, the ambient pressure at the first stop must not exceed half the initial pressure, meaning a permissible nitrogen tension of 2 : 1 for all tissues. Based on this concept, the first usable decompression tables were developed; these are applied in principle even today, in improved forms. Haldane also introduced the concept of dividing body into single compartments with their characteristic half-lifes for describing inert gas transport in tissues. Later investigations extended Haldane's compartment concept to slower tissues with considerably longer half-lifes. These investigations showed that the 2 : 1 relationship was too conservative for fast tissues, while for slow tissues the stop times were not sufficient which was made evident in reference [59].

While Haldane used the 2 : 1 concept for the relationship between inert gas tension in a given tissue and tolerable ambient pressure, newer investigations, e.g., in reference [53], use a linear relationship the tolerable ambient pressure p_{tol} with the tissue's inert gas tension p_j.

$$p_{j\,tol} = (p_j - a) b \quad \text{in bars} \tag{11.11}$$

with $p_{j\,tol}$ = tolerable ambient pressure for compartment j in bars

        p_j = inert gas tension of tissue for compartment j in bars

        a, b = empirical factors, according to reference [53]

Factors a and b depend on the inert gas used, inert gas mixes and on the half-life of each individual compartment. Both factors a and b represent the decompression criteria for a safe decompression without symptoms of DCS.

11.3.4 Calculation of Decompression Tables

Using the criterion of tolerable ambient pressure, decompression schedules can be calculated. Based on the perfusion transport model, the inert gas tension of each compartment is calculated in given time steps and compared with the tolerable ambient pressure of the same compartment. As long as the tolerable ambient pressure is not exceeded, the decompression and the diver's ascent can be continued. If the tolerable ambient pressure is exceeded, a decompression stop is necessary until the inert gas tension in the critical compartment is reduced by desaturation to the point where decompression can be continued.

Figure 11.5 shows one possible way of calculating decompression tables. The calculation starts with the inert gas tension p_o for each compartment j and the inspirational pressure p_i. These are the input data for the calculation of inert gas tension $p_j(t)$ for every given time step and for each compartment j. Using the inert gas tension p_j at a desired time step, the tolerable ambient pressure $p_{j\,tol}$ according to (11.11) is calculated for each compartment j to include the critical compartment. The critical compartment is that for which $p_{j\,tol}$ is a maximum, requiring the deepest decompression stop. This tolerable maximum pressure max $(p_{j\,tol})$ of the critical compartment will change during the ascent from fast compartments to slower ones with higher biological half-lifes. The critical compartment, which determines the decompression stops, can change from time step to time step. The decompression is finished when the maximum tolerable ambient pressure max $(p_{j\,tol})$ is less than or equal to the atmospheric pressure p_{atm}, which may be less than 1 bar in the case of altitude diving. If the tolerable ambient pressure max$(p_{j\,tol})$ is higher than the atmospheric pressure, the depth D_{deco} for the decompression stop is calculated.

$$D_{deco} = 10\ (max(p_{j\,tol}) - p_{atm}) \quad \text{in m} \tag{11.12}$$

The decompression depth D_{deco} is used for determining the new inspirational inert gas pressure according to (11.10) and the calculation is repeated for the next time steps, until the tolerable ambient pressure allows the ascent to a shallower decompression stop or to the surface (see Fig. 11.5).

MIXED GAS DIVING

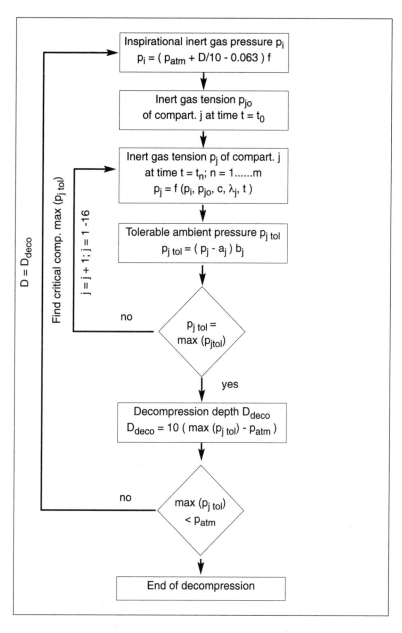

Fig. 11.5 Flow diagram for calculation of decompression tables

To simplify the arithmetic, and to estimate on the safe side, the compression time of normally a few minutes is added to the bottom time, although the arithmetical protocol can be used to calculate both the compression rate (descent) as well as the decompression rate (ascent). The compression rate is normally unlimited and depends on the diver's requirements for pressure equalization. Only the French diving rules specified in reference [133] restrict the descent rate to 30 m/min. But the decompression or ascent rate is definitely stipulated in the different decompression tables. U.S. Navy Tables published in reference [9], e.g., are based on a maximum ascent rate of 30 feet/min (1.8 bars/min) for air diving as well as for mixed gas diving with heliox. The same ascent rate is specified by German decompression rules, found in refrence [31]. The French rules, according to reference [133] are based on an average ascent rate of 12 m/min and 1.2 bars/min, while Bühlmann tables listed in reference [53], which are widely used in sports diving, require a decompression rate of 1 bar/min. The maximum ascent rate depends on the tissue's half-life. According to Bühlmann in reference [53], the decompression rate for fast tissues such as blood and the CNS must not exceed 3 bars/min, while for slow tissues the upper limit is 1 bar/min.

It must be emphasized that the calculation models for decompression tables discussed here are arithmetically correct, but they necessarily include a number of assumptions and simplifications which represent reality only very roughly. Consequently, the results contain uncertainties; they are just probability statements about the possible occurrence of decompression sickness. Also, the actual diver's condition is unknown; in one case it may contribute to a problem-free decompression, while in another case, under the same boundary conditions, decompression problems may occur.

11.3.5 Gas Exchange of Undissolved Inert Gases

These transport models for inert gas exchange and the flow diagram for calculating decompression tables assume that the inert gas is dissolved in the tissues. When inert gas bubbles occur in the course of decompression, the bubbles are isolated from the circulatory system. The bubbles must diffuse back into the tissues in order to be transported by the blood stream. The diffusion rate is the difference between the inert gas pressure in the bubble and the gas tension of the tissue. Because the inert gas of the bubble must diffuse back into the tissue for transportation, more time is needed for gas elimination than for gas uptake. The differential pressure and the diffusion coefficient both determine the diffusion rate. This coefficient depends on the physical properties of the inert gas as well as on the biological characteristics of the tissue.

Diverse models describe the mechanism of bubble generation in tissues. Different authors assume that in the course of every decompression a few bubbles are formed in limited tissue areas because the body always contains the bubble nuclei necessary for forming bubbles. The number of nuclei can be influenced by different measures. The prevention of bubble generation by reducing the number of bubble nuclei also reduces the occurrence of decompression sickness.

Mechanical movement increases the generation of bubbles in tissues (tribological effects) by the effects of adhesion. It can be assumed that generation and elimination of bubble nuclei are in thermodynamic equilibrium. Tests have shown that pressure treatments preceding the dive considerably reduce the rate of inert gas bubble generation. On the other hand, heavy work increases the perfusion rate and therefore the uptake of inert gas with the consequence that DCS risk is increased.

Bubble size is determined by pressure effects according to the gas laws; bubble volume increases when ambient pressure decreases. But bubble size is also influenced by diffusion effects under isobaric ambient conditions. Longer stays under raised pressure conditions cause a higher dissolution of inert gases in tissues. If the ambient pressure is reduced too fast (too rapid an ascent), surplus gas in the tissues cannot be eliminated in dissolved form via the circulatory system and lungs, and bubbles are also generated in tissues. Under isobaric conditions, meaning constant ambient pressure, inert gas diffuses into the bubbles and causes their expansion. In general, this causes decompression problems that must be treated appropriately (see the next chapter).

It should be mentioned here that the general procedure in case of DCS is a recompression to 18 m (60') breathing pure oxygen. One effect of this procedure is the reduction of bubble size according to Boyle's law. The other effect is that breathing pure oxygen causes a considerable diffusion difference between the inert gas bubbles and the tissue under isobaric conditions, resulting in further reduction of bubble volume. To summarize, inert gas bubbles in tissues trigger decompression sickness. But even today, we do not know every detail of the very complex mechanism of bubble generation; only further investigation will answer today's open questions.

11.4 DECOMPRESSION FOR AIR/NITROX DIVING

11.4.1 Standard Air Decompression

Decompression after air or nitrox dives follows time and depth-dependent decompression tables; their principal calculations have already been dealt with in 11.3.4. Because air diving is the most used diving method worldwide, the decompression procedures for air diving have been tested many times and are statistically correct (see Fig. 11.6). However, even strictly following proven decompression tables cannot absolutely exclude the possibility of decompression sickness. Divers and underwater tasks are too different for one table to cover all eventualities. The well-known U.S. Navy decompression table in reference [9], was scrutinized in 1985 by Weathersby *et al.,* according to reference [62]; they statistically analyzed air dives performed between 1950 and 1970. For bottom times up to 1 hour and moderate depths of less than 30 m (100'), the risk of DCS occurrences is between 1% and 3%. With increased bottom times to 2 hours and more, the risk of DCS occurrence increases to 10 to 16%. Such risk studies for other decompression tables are not known. The U.S. Navy standard air table covers depths from 12 m to 58 m (190') for normal dives, and up to 90 m (300') for exceptional dives. Canadian standard air tables cover the range from 18 to 63 m (208'). In Germany, the accident prevention rules include decompression tables found in reference [31], which cover very conservatively depths to only 50 m (165') and extensions to 60 m (198') in case of emergency. French standard air tables published in reference [133], go from 12 m to 60 m (198').

11.4.2 Decompression of Repetitive Dives

Repetitive dives are dives performed at a rate of more than one in twelve hours. Repetitive diving offers a number of advantages; but on the other hand, the inert gas loads from previous dives must be taken into account. Inert gas elimination after the dive continues at the surface. The longer the time at the surface between two dives (the surface interval), the more inert gas eliminated and the less the residual gas load of the tissues. In addition to the surface interval, the depth of the following dive must also be considered (see Fig. 11.7). The greater the depth of the repetitive dive, the less the influence of the residual inert gas load.

For air diving, the inert gas is nitrogen, which, for repetitive diving, is treated very differently by different national agencies. U.S. Navy decompression tables deal with a repetitive dive by introducing the socalled residual nitrogen time (RNT), which must be added to the actual bottom time of the following dive. On the basis of this new, fictitious bottom time and the actual depth, the decompression schedule for the repetitive dive is determined. In practice, according to reference [9], this includes determining the repetitive dive group designator for the dive just completed. The designator is an alphabetical letter which is part of the decompression table.

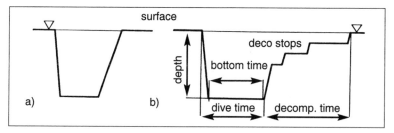

Fig. 11.6 Schematic dive course a) without decompression stop and b) with decompression stops

Depending on the surface interval, the new repetitive dive group designator is considered with the repetitive dive depth, and the RNT is determined from special tables. The same principle for dealing with repetitive dives is used by the Royal Navy in reference [63] and by Bühlmann in reference [53], whose tables are widely applied in sports diving. This repetitive dive procedure takes into account the conditions of the previous dive quite accurately, but it is not easy to use and allows the possibility of mistakes in reading the tables to determine the RNT. The French procedure for dealing with repetitive dives is simpler. In reference [133], an equivalent time is used, depending on the surface interval S/I and depth of the repetitive dive, which must be added to the actual bottom time of the following dive. This equivalent time corresponds to the RNT, but is easier to use.

The German handling of repetitive diving is simple, but very conservative; it is given in reference [31]. For determining the decompression schedule of a repetitive dive, all bottom times are added and the greatest depth is chosen, without considering surface intervals. A modified procedure is used by the German Navy. According to reference [64], the surface interval is divided very roughly into three ranges, shown in Table 11.1. For a surface interval of up to 3 hours, the procedure is the same as for commercial diving in reference [31].

Table 11.1 Repetitive Dives of the German Navy

Duration of surface interval in hrs	Bottom time to be considered
< 3	$T_2 + T_1$
3 ... 6	$T_2 + 0.5\,T_1$
6 ... 12	$T_2 + 0.25\,T_1$
> 12	T_2

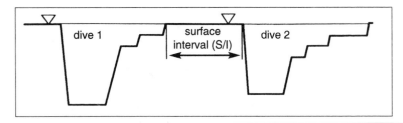

Fig. 11.7 Schematic dive course of a repetitive dive

The different procedures for dealing with repetitive diving will be demonstrated, using the following example: Dive 1: Depth 31 m (102'), bottom time 43 min, surface interval 5 hrs. Dive 2: Depth 29 m (96'), bottom time 18 min. What is the decompression schedule and decompression time for the second dive?

Table 11.2 Comparison of Decompression Times for Repetitive Dives

	U.S. Navy	Bühlmann	French Std.	German Navy	German Std.
Group Design.	C	0	N/A	N/A	N/A
Decom. schedule	100'/30	30m/20	30m/30	33m/40	33m/65
Decom. time (min)	5	3	12	25	70
Relation to U.S.N	1	0.6	2.4	5	14

U.S. Navy, Bühlmann, French, and German Standard decompression schedules and decompression times are determined and compared in Table 11.2. The relatively long surface interval requires an RNT of 10 min according to the U.S. Navy, while the RNT is zero according to Bühlmann. Therefore Bühlmann has the shortest decompression obligation, only 3 minutes, followed by 5 minutes decompression time according to the U.S. Navy standard air tables. The most conservative requirements are given in German commercial tables, which require 70

MIXED GAS DIVING

minutes for decompression without taking into account the surface interval of 5 hours. This means a decompression time 14 times longer than that required by U.S. standards for the same dive.

The French tables offer a special consideration for split level diving, where two dives at different depths and bottom times have been performed. For dive 1 a coefficient C_1, dependent on depth D_1 and bottom time T_1, is determined, according to reference [133]. The same is done for the second dive, resulting in C_2. After adding both coefficients to C_3 and taking C_3 and the time $T_3 = T_1 + T_2$, an equivalent depth D is determined and the corresponding decompression schedule is used. This method is only valid for air dives.

11.4.3 In-water Decompression Using Oxygen

One possibility for reducing decompression times is the use of oxygen instead of air. Air decompression means breathing 79% nitrogen, while when breathing oxygen the inert gas component in the breathing gas is zero. This causes a more rapid diffusion gradient between the nitrogen in the tissues and in the breathing gas and consequently a faster elimination of the inert gas.

In-water decompression with oxygen is used, for example, by the U.S. Navy for mixed gas decompression found in reference [9] and by the French for air/nitrox diving, noted in reference[133]. The French tables differentiate between the application of oxygen at the 6 m decompression stop, known as air/oxy/6m, and at the 12 m, 9 m, and 6 m decompression stops, known as air/oxy/12m (see Fig. 11.8 as example of an air/oxy/12m decompression). It should be noted that the French I/W oxygen tables omit the 3 m stop and the diver surfaces after completing the 6 m stop.

Normally, O_2 breathing is performed without interruption. But as the danger of oxygen poisoning increases with exposure time and with diver exhaustion due to heavy underwater work, 5 min air windows should be allowed after approximately every 25 mins of oxygen breathing. The air window does not count for oxygen decompression and must be added to the total decompression time. For a 1-hr dive to 30 m, decompression with air takes 55 min according to the French standard. Using air/oxy/6m, decompression time is reduced to 35 min resp. 31.5 min for air/oxy/12m. This is a reduction of 36% resp. 43% in decompression time compared with standard air decompression. Oxygen decompression saves 30 to 80% decompression time compared to air. German tables do not allow oxygen decompression.

11.4.4 Surface Decompression with Oxygen/Air

In international diving, surface decompression procedures using oxygen/air are used. A suitable pressure chamber at the surface, including chamber operators, are necessary for surface decompression (SurD). The procedure allows one or more decompression stops in water where the last stop is at 9 m. The diver surfaces, removes his diving equipment, enters the chamber, and is recompressed immediately to 12 m (40') with pure oxygen as the breathing gas (see Fig. 11.9). The diver breathes the oxygen via a BIBS mask; the chamber atmosphere is air.

The critical phase of this otherwise elegant decompression procedure is the move from the water into the chamber. Because the decompression is not nearly finished at that time, the tissues are withstanding considerable inert gas tensions which may cause early decompression sickness effects. Therefore, the surface interval, from leaving the last decompression stop in the water to being recompressed in the chamber, must be as short as possible and must not exceed 5 min, as stated in reference [9]. According to French tables in reference [133], this interval is further limited to 3 minutes. The U.S. Navy Table in reference [9] allows 2 min for surfacing from 12 m, while French standards allow 6 min from 12 m to the surface.

In order to prevent an O_2 hit in the chamber, the oxygen decompression period must be interrupted every 20 to 30 min by a 5 min air window for recovery. The diver removes his oxygen mask and breathes the air of the chamber atmosphere. The advantage of surface decompression with oxygen is again the rapid diffusion gradient and the consequent faster elimination of inert gas, described in section 11.4.3. A further advantage is that the decompression takes place in the safe and controlled environment of a chamber, independent of weather or sea conditions.

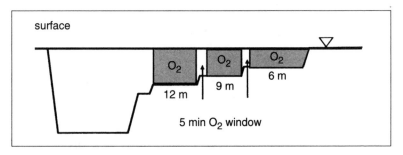

Fig. 11.8 Schematic dive course of I/W decompression with oxygen (air/oxy/12m)

The disadvantage of the inevitable surface interval for all surface decompression procedures can be avoided by use of a closed bell. Decompression with oxygen at 12 m can start in the bell, independent of the actual bell depth. At the surface, the bell is mated to the chamber and the divers move into the chamber to continue oxygen decompression, as stated in reference [65]. If no oxygen is available or if the oxygen supply is interrupted in the chamber, surface decompression can be performed with air. The last decompression stop in water is normally at 6 m. After the surface interval of less than 5 min, recompression in the chamber with air starts at 6 m, instead of at 12 m as in the case of oxygen. In the course of decompression, the depth is reduced again by half to 3 m. The total decompression time of SurD with air is roughly 25% longer than standard air decompression in water. In spite of this extended decompression time, the SurD procedure with air is used because it can be done in a safe and monitored environment in the chamber. With other decompression procedures, weather and sea conditions can prohibit the diver's safe return to the surface because it may be impossible to perform the shallow decompression stops. German decompression regulations in reference [31] allow only SurD with air and the procedure may be used only in case of emergency, not as a normal decompression routine.

11.4.5 Nitrox Decompression

A further possibility for increasing bottom times and decreasing decompression times is the use of nitrox (described in section 9.5). Nitrox is a mixture of nitrogen and oxygen that normally has a higher portion of oxygen than air. This means there is less nitrogen in the breathing gas and therefore a smaller inert gas load in the tissues (see Fig. 11.10).

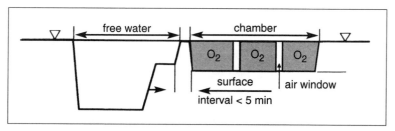

Fig. 11.9 Schematic dive course with surface decompression using oxygen

No special decompression tables are available for nitrox, which is mixed in different percentages, but tables are not necessary. By converting the actual depth into an equivalent air depth, all air tables can be used for nitrox decompression. Using the equivalent air depth (EAD), the decompression schedule is determined for a given nitrox mix.

$$\text{EAD} = \frac{N \times (D + 10)}{79} - 10 \quad \text{in m} \tag{11.12}$$

with N = nitrogen portion of nitrox in %
 D = actual depth in m

Example: For a 70 min. dive with nitrox 40/60 at 25 m depth, what is the decompression schedule?

The equivalent air depth is: EAD = 60 (25 + 10)/79 - 10 = 16.58 m → 16.6 m. Because there is less nitrogen in the nitrox mix, an equivalent air depth of 16.6 m, instead of the actual depth of 25 m, is used for determining the decompression schedule. The results are presented in Table 11.3. For a 70 min. dive, the decompression time for nitrox 40/60 is only one-sixth that of air.

Table 11.3 Comparison of Nitrox and Air

	Nitrox 40/60 EAD = 16.6m	Air, actual depth = 25m
Decompression schedule	18m/70 min	27m/70 min
Decompression time acc. to [133]	8.25 min	51.75 min
Assuming the same decompression time of	51.75 min	
Allowable bottom time	140 min	70 min

If the same decompression time of 51.75 min is assumed, the bottom time of the nitrox dive is doubled. Decompression times can be further reduced by using oxygen (see sections 11.4.3 and 11.4.4). If the nitrox supply is interrupted, it is easy to switch over to air and decompress accordingly to available air tables.

The commercial use of nitrox is economically interesting, as this example has shown, but increasing the oxygen partial pressure increases the danger of O_2 poisoning and this must be taken into account (see section 5.2). Oxygen poisoning danger may limit permissible bottom times. When nitrox is used as a breathing gas, the depths of the air decompression stops must be converted according to the corre-

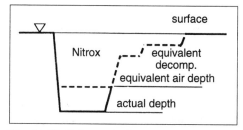

Fig. 11.10 Schematic dive course for nitrox diving

sponding nitrogen percentage of the mix. The 3 m air stop corresponds to a 7.5 m stop for nitrox 40/60 (see table 11.4). In both cases the N_2 partial pressure is 1.03 bars.

Table 11.4 Conversion of Decompression Stops for Nitrox Diving

decompression stop air	nitrox 32.5/67.5	nitrox 40/60	nitrox 50/50
3 m	5.5 m	7.5 m	10.5 m
6 m	9 m	11 m	15 m
9 m	12 m	15 m	20 m
12 m	16 m	19 m	25 m

11.4.6 Decompression for Mud Diving

Diving in media denser than water requires special consideration. Such media may be suspensions or mud in the broadest sense, as well as chemical substances. Diving operations in the chemical field, for example, in chemical tanks, is not unusual. The higher density of a liquid means a higher static pressure and consequently a higher uptake of inert gases, as compared with water. For decompression, standard air tables are applied, but an equivalent depth is used corresponding to the media's higher density. That means in every case a greater equivalent depth than the actual one. As a first approximation the equivalent depth ED is

$$ED = \rho_M/\rho_W \cdot D \quad \text{in m} \quad (11.13)$$

with ρ_M = density of diving media in kg/m^3

       ρ_W = density of water = 1000 kg/m^3

       D   = actual depth in m

The French rules listed in reference [133], give a special table for mud diving to determine the equivalent depth ED dependent on the density of the mud.

Example: A repair must be done at the bottom of a chemical tank of 15 m height filled with glycerin (ρ = 1260 kg/m^3). What is the equivalent depth for decompression?

$$ED = 1260/1000 \times 15 \text{ m} = 18.9 \text{ m}$$

Answer: For standard air decompression the table depth of 21 m must be used instead of the actual depth of 15 m.

11.5 MIXED GAS DECOMPRESSION
11.5.1 Introduction
Diving operations deeper than 50 to 60 msw require replacing the narcotic nitrogen portion by a gas with a lesser narcotic potential; usually helium. The different mixed gas diving procedures, introduced in Chapter 9, will be dealt with here as they relate to decompression. Mixed gas diving and decompression procedures can be divided into: autonomous diving (closed circuit); surface-supplied diving; and bell diving (bell bounce).

Mixed gas diving procedures using chambers at the surface offer the possibility of switching into the saturation mode, if, for example, the intended bottom time must be extended. Saturation decompression (see section 11.6) usually prevents DCS.

While other national decompression regulations include decompression procedures for mixed gas, German tables shown in reference [31] are limited to air decompression. If different breathing gases, such as nitrox or helium mixes, are used, special approval is necessary from the appropriate supervisory body.

11.5.2 Decompression for Autonomous Mixed Gas Diving
Mixed gas diving operations with open (SCUBA) or closed-circuit apparatus at depths of more than 50 msw are restricted because of the limited gas supply and other safety considerations.

The U.S. Navy offers SCUBA decompression tables for autonomous M/G diving based on a required heliox mix of 32/68, according to reference [9]. The tables cover a normal depth range up to 55 msw (180'), which can be extended to 61 msw (200') under exceptional conditions. The tables are similar to the usual standard air tables and also allow repetitive dives. In addition, the decompression can be done with oxygen. After reaching the 12 m stop, the heliox is replaced by pure oxygen within 2 minutes. Decompression is continued with oxygen until surfacing. Of course, the technical prerequisites for oxygen-supported heliox decompressions depend on the apparatus used.

French regulations in reference [133], contain decompression tables for heliox diving; these are also applicable for autonomous diving. The heliox/oxy/6m table implies the use of oxygen at the 6 m decompression stop. The heliox/oxy/12m table is not applicable for mixed gas SCUBA. The heliox/oxy/6m table can be used for different heliox mixes with oxygen portions between 18 and 30% and covers a depth range to 69 msw. After reaching the 6 m decompression stop, the breathing mix is switched to oxygen. Having finished the 6 m stop with oxygen, the diver surfaces within 1 minute.

11.5.3 Decompression for Surface-Supplied Mixed Gas Diving

Surface-supplied mixed gas diving is used widely in the industry for greater depths with restricted bottom times. International diving contractors very often have their own specific decompression tables which are not publicly available. But U.S. Navy decompression tables in reference [9] for surface-supplied mixed gas diving are available. French regulations given in reference [133] also give decompression procedures for surface-supplied diving, but only in connection with a wet bell (heliox/oxy/12m). So the following mixed gas decompression procedures are available: a) U.S. Navy in water decompression (U.S.N I/W); b) U.S. Navy surface decompression (U.S.N SurD); c) Commercial surface decompression (Com SurD); d) Company specific surface decompression (Specific SurD); and e) French in water decompression with wet bell (Heliox/oxy/12m).

All five procedures use oxygen for decompression and except for the first and last procedures, a chamber is necessary at the surface. The first three decompression methods are based on the U.S. Navy Tables included in reference [9], in which the last step has been modified for each method. A particular characteristic of the table is its structure. Instead of the normal bottom depths, the partial pressures of the inert gas portion in the breathing gas is used, given in m and in feet. Therefore, the depth as well as the breathing gas must be known in order to determine the correct decompression schedule.

Tolerable oxygen partial pressures versus exposure times are cited from three different sources (U.S. Navy tables in reference [9], NOAA proposals in reference [138] and French tables in reference [133]) in Table 11.5. It must be mentioned that the U.S.N. allows three to four times higher O_2 partial pressures for exceptional exposures.

For planning a mixed gas dive according to procedures a), b), or c), a heliox mix must be chosen or is already available. In the latter case it must be confirmed that the O_2 partial pressure of the mix corresponds to the tolerable exposure time (intended bottom time) in Table 11.5. In the first case, the intended bottom time is used to choose the maximum tolerable O_2 partial pressure and, consequently, the composition of the heliox mixture. In the following, the different mixed gas decompression procedures will be shown for one diving example: A 45-min dive will be performed at 85 m (279 ft). What is the decompression procedure? As no breathing gas is available, a suitable heliox mix must be calculated. Following Table 11.5, the tolerable O_2 partial pressure for 45 min exposure time is 1.4 bars according to the U.S. Navy and 1.6 bars according to the newer NOAA proposals and French tables. The more conservative U.S.N O_2 partial pressure is chosen—1.4 bars. The oxygen concentration, according to 6.2.3 is: conc.O_2 = 1.4/9.5 = 0.1474. The oxygen concentration, rounded down is: 14% $O_2 \rightarrow$ heliox 14/86.

Table 11.5 Tolerable O_2 Partial Pressures vs Exposure Times

tolerable O_2 pp in bars	exposure t. (9) in min	exposure t. (138) in min	esposure t. (133) in min
1.6	30	45	180
1.5	40	120	–
1.4	50	150	240
1.3	60	180	–
1.2	80	210	300
1.1	120	240	–
1.0	240	300	360
0.9	–	360	480

The 14/86 heliox mix is not breathable at the surface. Therefore, the dive starts with air to 12 msw (40'), where the gas is switched over to the desired heliox 14/86. The available mixed gas decompression tables in reference [9] cover a partial pressure range down to 89 msw (290'), which can be extended to 110 msw (360') for exceptional dives.

a) U.S. Navy in-water decompression (U.S.N I/W)

This decompression procedure does not require a chamber at the surface, but an oxygen supply must be available. The schematic dive course is shown in Fig. 11.11. The decompression schedule is determined by the partial pressure of inert gases and bottom time. If the actual figures cannot be found in the schedule, the next higher inert gas pressure or bottom time is chosen. The decompression table gives the time to the first decompression stop, so the ascent rate can be calculated; it is always less than 18 m/min (60'/min). For the further ascent, a maximum ascent rate of 18 m/min is allowed. The ascent time to the next stop is included in the stop time. After reaching the 15 m stop (50') and the 12 m stop (40') for shorter and/or shallower dives, the gas is switched from heliox to pure oxygen within 3 minutes (see example 1 in section 11.5.4). If the oxygen content of the heliox is less than 16% O_2, the descent from the surface starts with air to 12 m (40'), where the air is replaced by the chosen heliox bottom mixture.

Surface-supplied mixed gas diving with in-water decompression risks oxygen toxicity problems, especially after heavy underwater work. Dives at approximately 60 m combined with bottom times of roughly half an hour require about 1.5 hours of oxygen breathing under an ambient pressure of 2.2 bars for decompression. Therefore, this decompression procedure should be used only if no surface chamber is available.

b) U.S. Navy surface decompression (U.S.N SurD)

The decompression tables in reference [9] are valid for mixed gas diving with in-water decompression as well as for surface decompression in a chamber. The ascent follows the same steps as for in-water decompression. At the 15 m stop, the diver switches to oxygen within 3 minutes. The same amount of time spent at the 15 m stop is spent at the 12 m stop in water. The surface interval follows; it must not exceed 5 min and is followed by recompression to 12 m with pure oxygen in the chamber. Due to the risk of O_2 poisoning, 5 min air windows for recovery after every 30 min oxygen exposure are scheduled (see Fig. 11.12 and example 2 in section 11.5.4). As for method a), repetitive dives are permitted only after 12 hrs.

c) Commercial mixed gas surface decompression (Com SurD)

Commercial surface decompression is also based on the U.S. Navy mixed gas decompression tables in reference [9], but is modified for the decompression steps in water. This method does not use any oxygen in water, thus minimizing the risk of O_2 toxicity (see Fig. 11.13 and example 3 in section 11.5.4).

After reaching 36 m (120') or the first stop, if the stop depth is shallower, the mixed gas supply is switched over to air. By continuously supervising the diver's communications, the completion of the gas change can be easily identified because the helium-induced voice distortion will end. The same is true, but just the other way round, for switching from air to heliox during descent, if the oxygen content of the heliox is below 16%.

Because the breathing of oxygen at 15 m and 12 m stops in water is not applicable for this decompression procedure, the stop times must be roughly doubled. The surface interval is a critical phase and is restricted to less than 5 minutes, followed by recompression with pure oxygen to 12 m in the chamber. In order to avoid O_2 poisoning, 5 min air windows for recovery are inserted. But in contrast to U.S.N SurD (method b), an air window is scheduled every 20 min. The time interval to the next dive is extended to 18 hrs.

d) Company specific surface decompression (Specific SurD)

The world's leading diving contractors usually have developed their own decompression tables; these are not publicly available, for understandable reasons. However, the author had the opportunity to learn about mixed gas decompression routines which were used a decade ago by an internationally operating U.S. diving contractor (OI). To demonstrate

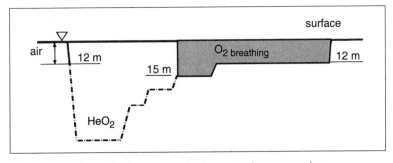

Fig. 11.11 Schematic dive course for in-water decompression

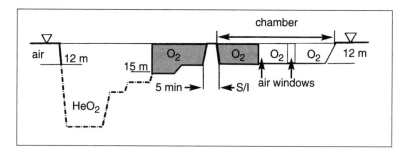

Fig. 11.12 Schematic dive course for surface decompression

company-specific decompression tables, the principles of the decompression routines used will be introduced without going into greater detail.

The decompression procedures can best be compared to method c), commercial surface decompression, but here the actual depth is used for determining the decompression schedule. The bottom mix is heliox 10/90; therefore, air is breathed during the descent to 12 m (40'). The air is replaced by bottom mix, which can easily be checked by the change of the diver's voice. When the job is finished, ascent starts to the first decompression stop, which is 52 m (170') or less. At the first stop, the bottom mix is changed to air. The change of the diver's voice serves as indicator of the completed gas switch. Decompression continues with air in 3 m (10') increments with a travel rate of 3 m/ min (10'/min); travel time is included in the stop times. There are now two possible procedures for continuing the decompression.

Using method Alpha, the breathing gas is changed from air to nitrox 50/50 after reaching the 27 m (90') stop. Decompression is continued to the 12 m (40') stop with a travel rate of 3 m/min; travel time is included in stop times. At the start of the surface interval, which is restricted to 3 minutes, the nitrox 50/50 is switched back to air. In the chamber, recompression to 12 m (40') with pure oxygen is performed. For recovery, after every 25 min of O_2 breathing a 5 min air break is added. After completion of the chamber decompression at 12 m, the diver, breathing oxygen, surfaces within 10 minutes at a travel rate of 1.2 m/min (4'/min). Using method Bravo, decompression continues with air until the 12 m (40') stop is reached. After the surface interval, which must not exceed 5 min, recompression to 15 m (50') with oxygen is performed in the chamber. Chamber decompression is carried out in 3 m (10') increments; the table

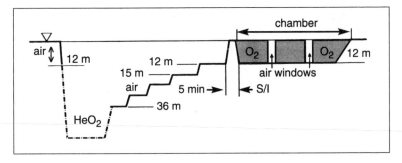

Fig. 11.13 Schematic dive course for commercial surface decompression

includes both oxygen and air times. The diver moves from the last chamber stop to the surface in 10 min, breathing pure oxygen (see Fig. 11.14 and example 4 in 11.5.4). No repetitive dives are permitted within 18 hours.

e) French in-water decompression with wet bell (Heliox/oxy/12m)

French regulatory bodies issued in 1992 a regulation on hyperbaric working conditions which also includes decompression tables. For surface-supplied mixed gas diving with a wet bell, the heliox/oxy/12m tables apply, according to reference [133]. When the 12 m (40') decompression stop is reached, decompression is continued with oxygen, interrupted by 5 min air windows. The tables are for heliox mixes with between 17% and 28% oxygen and cover a depth range to 78 m (256'). Depending on depth and bottom time, different heliox mixes can be chosen. Because the smallest oxygen portion of the possible heliox mixes is 17%, these mixes can be breathed at the surface.

The decompression procedure starts the ascent using the chosen bottom mix. The ascent occurs in 3 m (10') increments to a depth of between 20m (66') and 30m (100'), at which point heliox is replaced by air. The change of voice indicates the completion of the gas switch. The travel rate is 3 m/min (10'/min), and the travel time is included in the stop times. After reaching the 12 m (40') stop, another gas switch, from air to pure oxygen, takes place in the open bell. Oxygen exposure is restricted to maximum of 25 minutes, followed by a 5 min air window. Oxygen is breathed at the 9 m stop, if applicable, and the 6 m (20') stop. From there the diver surfaces within 1 minute. No repetitive dives are permitted within 12 hours.

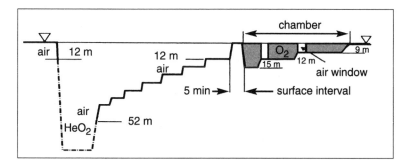

Fig. 11.14 Schematic dive course for company-specific decompression

The advantage of this in-water decompression routine is the avoidance of the critical surface interval for getting the diver into the chamber and recompressed. For the protection and safety of the divers, a wet bell is required. In addition, during decompression the bell must be manned by two divers. The principal decompression schedule is shown in Fig. 11.15 (see also example 5 in section 11.5.4).

11.5.4 Examples for Surface-supplied Mixed Gas Diving

The different surface-supplied mixed gas diving procedures will be demonstrated by an example and the results compared. The breathing gas is heliox 14/86 except for those procedures that require a different bottom mix.

General example for all decompression procedures:

A surface-supplied dive will be performed from a platform to inspect a welded connection of the northwestern platform leg at 75 m level. The job is expected to be finished in a maximum of 28 minutes. The desired

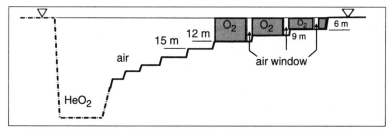

Fig. 11.15 Schematic dive course for French in-water decompression (Heliox/oxy/12m)

oxygen partial pressure is 1.2 bars. The dive will start at 9:30; a descent rate of 22.5 m/min is assumed for all procedures. For the decompression procedures a) through e), introduced in section 11.5.3, the decompression routines will be demonstrated, using the following diving report charts. Some input data are first determined:

Depth D	75 m correspond to 246'. As U.S. tables are based on feet, m must be converted.
Actual O_2 partial pressure	1.2 bars
	Company-specific tables (OI) require a specified bottom mix of heliox 10/90, resulting in an actual O_2 partial pressure of 8.5 bars × 0.10 = 0.85 bars
	French tables (heliox/oxy/12m) require a bottom mix of heliox 17/83, resulting in ppO_2 act.: 8.5 bars × 0.17 = 1.45 bars
Maximum O_2 partial pressure	According to Table 11.5 is ppO_2 (max) = 1.6 bars
	Company-specific tables (OI) allow a tolerable ppO_2 (max) = 1.5 bars
Actual oxygen concentration	Conc O_2 = 1.2/8.5 = 0.1412 → 14% O_2
Chosen heliox mixture	14% oxygen, 86% helium
Cut off depth (COD)	Maximum depth that can be tolerated given the maximum ppO_2.
	COD = ppO_2 (max)/actual O_2 conc.
Partial pressure of all other gases	pp(AOG) = (D/10 + 1)10 × (1 - O_2%)
	For decompression methods a), b), and c)
	pp(AOG) = (75/10 + 1) 0.86 = 73.1 m converting m into feet → 240'
Chosen decompression schedule for methods a), b), and c)	→ 240'/30
Chosen decompression schedule for methods d) and e)	→ 250'/30 and 75m/30

The comparison in Table 11.6 shows total decompression times between 2 hrs (128 min) and over 3 hrs (200 min) for the 28-min dive . If U.S.N I/W procedure a) is omitted, the range is between 157 and 200 minutes, meaning a difference of 43 min, or 27%, in decompression time.

Table 11.6 Comparison of Different Mixed Gas Dive Procedures

	Decom. a) example 1 U.S.N I/W	Decom. b) example 2 U.S.N SurD	Decom. c) example 3 Com SurD	Decom. d) example 4 Spec SurD	Decom. e) example 5 Heliox/oxy
Surface chamber Decom.	no	yes	yes	yes	no
Decom. schedule	240'/30	240'/30	240'/30	250'/30	75m/30
First decom. stop	30 m	30 m	30 m	39 m	39 m
Bottom mix heliox	14/86	14/86	14/86	10/90	17/83
Total dive time	156 min	186 min	226 min	228 min	185 min
Total decom. time	128 min	158 min	198 min	200 min	157 min
O_2 in water	95 min	21 min	no	no	80 min

Decompression procedures b) and e) show the same results with 2h 37 min and 2h 38 min total decompression time, although the decompression procedures are hardly comparable. For decompression procedures c) and d) the difference in decompression time is only 2 min. In these two procedures, many of the decompression routines are the same, so this result is not too surprising, even though different bottom gases are used. U.S.N I/W decompression procedure a) requires breathing oxygen for roughly 1 1/2 h at 2.2 bars in water, which means a high risk of O_2 poisoning. Introduction of air windows for recovery could reduce this risk considerably. It is also remarkable that a bottom time of 28 min, reduced by the time for descent, requires decompression times six to eight times greater than the actual working time. If longer bottom times are necessary to complete underwater jobs, the more economical solution may be saturation diving.

11.5.5 Decompression of Bell Dives (Bell Bounce)
While the use of diving bells and their technical equipment has been discussed in 9.4, the decompression aspects of bell bounce diving will be dealt with in this section and the results demonstrated by two examples.

The technical systems of a closed bell allow changing the bell atmosphere at each desired depth and guarantee, by means of a built-in-breathing-system (BIBS), a breathing gas supply independent of the bell's internal atmosphere. This provides the technical prerequisites for fast and safe gas exchanges according to decompression obligations as well as for adjustment of the pressure level in the bell, independent of the actual bell depth or the temporal course of the bell's handling. Adjusting the bell atmosphere may be done by the diver inside the bell or externally by life support personnel at the surface. Decompression started in the bell may continue in the chamber after the transfer under pressure (TUP) has been performed. Another possibility is that the diver would stay in the bell until decompression is successfully completed without using a surface chamber.

In principle, decompression schedules comparable to those introduced in section 11.5.3 for surface-supplied diving are valid for bell decompression. But the essential difference is that here the critical surface interval for transfer from the water into the chamber does not apply and, therefore, the risk of decompression problems is decreased. Another advantage is the safe transport of divers to and from their work site protected from the effects of currents and bad weather, especially when they are passing the transition zone at the surface. Bell bounce diving is widely used by international diving contractors, who have developed their own decompression tables. It is understandable that these tables are not freely available. Two decompression procedures are introduced here: f) company-specific bell decompression (Specific Bell); and g) French bell decompression (Heliox/bell).

f) Company-specific bell decompression (Specific Bell)

Procedure f) is very similar to the company-specific procedures (OI) described in section 11.5.3, where two methods are available. While method Alpha uses, in addition to air and oxygen, nitrox 50/50 as a decompression gas, method Bravo uses only air and oxygen. The latter method uses heliox 10/90 as bottom mix; it is switched to air at 54 m (180') or the first stop if that is shallower. Breathing heliox via BIBS in an air atmosphere presents no physiological problems, but breathing air via BIBS in a heliox atmosphere may cause severe problems because of isobaric counter diffusion (see section 12.4). When the diver has ascended to the 15 m (50') stop, air is replaced by oxygen. Times for oxygen breathing and for air windows are given in the table. Decompression stops are increments of 3 m (10') with an ascent rate of

3 m/min; the ascent time of 1 min is part of the stop time. The bell decompression tables cover a depth range down to 120 m (400'). Total decompression times can be as much as 8 hours for deep dives and bottom times of approximately 1 hour.

g) French bell decompression (Heliox/bell)

French government agencies in 1992 issued tables in reference [133] on bell bounce diving, covering a depth range to 120 m (400'), as for procedure f). Depending on the depth range, bottom mixtures vary from heliox 10/90 to heliox 24/76. If the mix has an oxygen content of less than 20%, then the bottom mix is changed to heliox with 20 to 22% O_2 after reaching a depth of 30 m to 45 m, depending on depth and bottom time. So the possible effects of isobaric counter diffusion are avoided. Pure oxygen breathing with 5 min air windows after each 25 min oxygen period starts at the 12 m (40') stop. The decompression tables are based on increments of 3 m (10') and an ascent rate of 3 m per minute, where the ascent time is included in the stop time. Extremely long decompression times must be used for deep dives combined with long bottom times. A 2-hr dive at 120 m (400') will require a total decompression time of more than 27 hours, according to reference [133]. For such long decompression times, a surface chamber is necessary because divers cannot tolerate 27 hours in a small bell.

Decompression procedures f) and g) will be demonstrated by examples 6 and 7, which are based on the same input data [a 28 min bottom time and a depth of 75 m (246')], used for examples 1 to 5 in section 11.5.4. The difference between the two bell decompression procedures is 39 minutes. The comparison between procedures d), e), f), and g), where surface-supplied and bell procedures of the same source can be compared, is more interesting. Based on the same company-specific tables (OI) and the same bottom mix of heliox 10/90, bell decompression f) saves 47 minutes, or 30%, compared with surface-supplied decompression routine d). One reason for this advantage is the elimination of the surface interval for diver's move from the water into the chamber.

Comparison of procedures e) and g) using the French tables gives just the opposite result. Bell decompression g) requires 35 minutes more than the surface-supplied decompression method e). Two reasons may explain this fact. While method e) uses a bottom mixture of heliox 17/83, bell decompression is based on heliox 14/86, and therefore uses more inert gas. The second reason is the in-water decompression used in procedure e) requires no surface interval, which also shortens the decompression time.

11.5.6 Emergency Procedures

The diving and decompression procedures introduced in 11.5 use prepared oxygen/helium mixtures as bottom gases as well as oxygen. Therefore, basically two emergency situations are probable—the breakdown of the mixed gas or oxygen supply and the occurrence of O_2 poisoning. Emergency procedures to overcome such events are given in the U.S. Navy diving manual found in reference [9] and in French tables found in reference [133].

a) Breakdown of mixed gas or oxygen supply

In spite of the redundant arrangements of the supply system and additional safety equipment, the possibility of a breakdown in the gas supply cannot be totally excluded. The reasons for possible failures are a special topic which is not dealt with in this book. Probabilistic analyses of diving system components have been conducted, as noted in references [139, 140]; these give an idea of the supply system's reliability.

In the case of failure of the heliox and oxygen supply, An emergency air decompression table which allows decompression with air only should be available. The table covers the depth range up to 120 m (400'). If the heliox supply fails at that depth, the diver is supplied with air and ascends to the first stop at 57 m (190'). From this stop the ascent is carried out in 19 steps of 3 m increments to the surface, taking a total decompression time of approximately 7.5 hours.

In addition to the breakdown of the heliox supply, the oxygen supply may fail after the diver has reached a depth of 15 m (50') or less. For that emergency, a helium/oxygen decompression table can be referenced in [9]; the table replaces oxygen times with heliox times. It is obvious that the heliox mix must have a minimum oxygen content of 16%. If no heliox is available, air must be used and the decompression is performed according to emergency air decompression routines, starting at 15 m (50'). If the loss of the oxygen supply occurs at the 12 m stop (40'), either surface decompression with increased decompression times or emergency heliox decompression must be performed, depending on the elapsed oxygen time (see reference [9]). French tables found in reference [133] require doubling the oxygen times for breathing heliox 20/80 or air in the case of loss of the oxygen supply.

b) Oxygen toxicity symptoms

The decompression procedures in section 11.5.3 are based on extensive use of pure oxygen, both in water after reaching the 15m and the

12m stop and always after transfer into the chamber. In the latter case, the danger of oxygen poisoning is relatively small because the diver breathes the oxygen via BIBS masks. The masks can be removed frequently in order to breathe the chamber's atmosphere, which is normally air or, in some cases, heliox 20/80. The diver stays in a dry and safe environment and is continuously monitored. Furthermore, the diver interrupts his oxygen breathing every 20 to 30 minutes for a 5 min recovery phase with air. If in spite of these precautions, symptoms of O_2 toxicity occur, the oxygen mask is removed and the diver breathes the chamber atmosphere until the symptoms disappear. After a 15 min recovery phase, the decompression procedure with oxygen is continued at the point where it had been interrupted.

The occurrence of O_2 toxicity symptoms during the decompression phase in water is more complicated. If the symptoms are severe, such as convulsions, etc., the only recourse is to bring the diver to the surface without considering decompression obligations and to start treatment procedures. If only light symptoms of oxygen toxicity occur in the water, the breathing gas is immediately switched over to heliox or air. Depending on the decompression stop (15 m or 12 m) and the elapsed stop times on O_2, emergency procedures, which include emergency surface decompression, are performed according to reference [9].

11.6 SATURATION DIVING DECOMPRESSION

Saturation diving procedures and their technical demands were discussed in detail in section 9.8. Here, the decompression aspects of saturation diving are introduced; these are very different from those of other diving procedures. In saturation diving, the elapsed time under saturation pressure plays no role in decompression; the depth alone determines the decompression schedule. But here the decompression times have another order of magnitude. While for surface-supplied dives the fast and medium fast tissues determine the decompression procedure, for saturation decompressions the slow tissues with biological half-lifes of 10 and 12 hours are decisive. This principle leads to decompression times that are roughly 100 times greater than for surface-supplied diving operations.

Standard breathing gases for saturation diving are heliox mixes and trimixes (see section 9.8.3). However, air or nitrox may be used for scientific diving at shallower depths. Decompression routines for air and nitrox saturation dives are available; they are given, for example, in references [5, 7]. For heliox saturation dives, decompression tables from the U.S. Navy, RN, French bodies, and Duke/GKSS are readily available.

But most internationally operating diving contractors have developed their own tables. Table 11.7 gives decompression rates according to the U.S. Navy and is also included in reference [9]. In addition, the U.S. Navy table recommends only 16 h for decompression within the normal 24 h cycle, with the following differentiation:

Decompression clock time: 0600 - 1400 and 1600 - 0000
Clock time of decompression stops 0000 - 0600 and 1400 - 1600

Table 11.7 Decompression Rates for Saturation Dives [9]

Depth range		Decompression rate	
in m	in ft	in m/h	in ft/h
500 ... 60	1600 ... 200	1.8	6
60 ... 30	200 ... 100	1.5	5
30 ... 15	100 ... 50	1.2	4
15 ... 0	50 ... 0	0.9	3

Table 11.8 Modified Company Specific Decompression Rates for Saturation Dives

Depth range		Decompression rate	
in m	in ft	in m/h	in ft/h
300 ... 30	1000 ...100	2.4	8
30 ... 18	100 ... 60	1.2	4
18 ... 0	60 ... 0	0.6	2

An example of company-specific decompression rates is given in Table 11.8, where the rates have been increased by 33% for the deep depth range, while for shallower ranges, the decompression rates have been decreased by 33%. The decompression is performed in a 24 h cycle without any stops.

Table 11.9 Decompression Rates for Saturation Dives [66]

Depth range in m	in ft	Stop time in hrs	Theor. dec. in m/h
305 ... 255	1000 ... 835	2	2.5
250 ... 175	825 ... 574	3	1.7
170 ... 110	557 ... 360	4	1.25
105 ... 50	344 ... 165	5	1.0
45 ... 30	147 ... 100	6	0.83
25 ... 0	82 ... 0	7	0.71

The Underwater Engineering Group (UEG) has issued the saturation decompression procedures of the Royal Navy (RN) in reference [66]; these differ considerably from other decompression routines (see Table 11.9). The ascent occurs in 5 m (16') steps, and the stop times vary from 2 to 7 hours, depending on the depth range. The ascent rate is 1 m/min and included in the stop time. In the last column of Table 11.9, the different stop times have been used for calculating a theoretical decompression rate for comparison with other decompression procedures. These theoretical rates are comparable to the decompression rates in Tables 11.7 and 11.8, but depth ranges are more differentiated.

French tables in reference [133] cover a depth range for saturation dives between 10 and 180 m (590'). They differentiate between decompressions with an O_2 partial pressure of 0.6 and 0.5 bars and use only two depth ranges (see Table 11.10).

Table 11.10 Decompression Rates for Saturation Dives [133]

Depth range in m	in ft	Decompression rates in m/h $ppO_2 = 0.6$ bars	$ppO_2 = 0.5$ bars
155 ... 15	508 ... 50	1.33	1.2
15 ... 0	50 ... 0	1.0	1.0

Decompression schedules used at GKSS research center's underwater simulation plant GUSI for saturation dives are based on results of Hall Laboratory studies at Duke University in Durham, North Carolina and published in references [54, 55]. The decompression schedules are based on a trimix with an oxygen partial pressure of 0.5 bars, 5% nitrogen as the narcotic portion to suppress HPNS effects, and a balance of helium. The trimixes were used successfully as breathing gases for all GUSI dives which covered depth ranges from 150 m (492') to 600 m (2000'). The decompression schedule goes down to 686 m (2250') in 30 m increments (see Table 11.11). From the storage depth to 14 m (46'), the ascent rate is constant, depending on the depth range. From 14 m to surface, the ascent is differentiated into four ranges, thus gradually reducing the decompression rates. Compared to other schedules, the Duke/GUSI table offers the greatest depths by far.

Table 11.11 Decompression Rates for Saturation Dives [55]

Storage depth in m	Decompression rate in m/h				
	to 14 m	14 - 9 m	9 - 6 m	6 - 3 m	3 - 0 m
0 ... 30	1.76	1.43	1.20	1.0	0.75
30 ... 60	1.66	1.30	1.11	0.91	0.70
60 ... 90	1.50	1.20	1.0	0.83	0.64
90 ... 120	1.43	1.15	0.97	0.79	0.60
120 ... 150	1.36	1.07	0.91	0.75	0.57
150 ... 180	1.25	1.03	0.86	0.70	0.54
180 ... 210	1.25	1.03	0.86	0.70	0.54
210 ... 240	1.20	0.97	0.81	0.67	0.51
240 ... 270	1.20	0.97	0.81	0.67	0.51
270 ... 300	1.11	0.91	0.77	0.63	0.48
300 ... 330	1.11	0.91	0.77	0.63	0.48
330 ... 360	1.03	0.83	0.71	0.58	0.45
360 ... 390	1.03	0.83	0.71	0.58	0.45
390 ... 420	0.97	0.79	0.67	0.54	0.41
420 ... 450	0.97	0.79	0.67	0.54	0.41
450 ... 480	0.91	0.73	0.61	0.50	0.38
480 ... 510	0.91	0.73	0.61	0.50	0.38
510 ... 540	0.83	0.67	0.56	0.45	0.35
540 ... 570	0.83	0.67	0.56	0.45	0.35
570 ... 600	0.75	0.60	0.51	0.42	0.32
600 ... 630	0.68	0.55	0.46	0.38	0.29
630 ... 686	0.60	0.48	0.41	0.33	0.25

Table 11.12 Comparison of Deco. Times for a 155m Saturation Dive

	U.S. Navy Table 11.7	Com Deco. Table 11.8	UK Navy Table 11.9	French D. Table 11.10	Duke/GUSI Table 11.11
Deco.-cycle	16/24 h	16/24 h	24 h	24 h	24 h
Deco. times (h)	153	138	159	131	132
Deco. t. (d : h)	6d : 9h	5d : 18h	6d : 15h	5d : 11h	5d : 12h

In order to compare the five decompression schedules, a saturation dive will be postulated with a storage depth of 155 m (508'), using an oxygen partial pressure of 0.5 bars. Table 11.12 shows the total decompression times, which vary from 5 1/2 to 6 1/2 days. As rule of thumb, a decompression rate of 1 m/h can be used, resulting in 155 h for the example.

International diving contractors have emergency decompression schedules available, in case a saturation dive must be stopped due to severe problems with the divers or for other reasons. In such cases, decompression times can be shortened roughly by 40%, where symptoms of decompression sickness are tolerated. If a saturation dive must be aborted prior to reaching saturation conditions, emergency abort schedules are available in reference [5], schedule 7.1, depending on depth and elapsed time.

In economical terms, a very interesting potential of saturation diving is the use of excursion dives (see also section 9.8). It is possible to descend or ascend within certain limits from the storage depth without any decompression obligations when returning to storage depth. For practical operations, the working depth, for example, can be deeper than the storage depth, but naturally it must be within the given excursion limits. When the job is finished, the decompression starts from storage depth and not from working depth, thus saving decompression time. If, for example, the difference between storage and working depth is 24 m, and assuming a decompression rate of 1 m/h, one day of decompression time can be saved. The excursion depths depend on the storage depth, and they increase with increasing storage depths (Fig. 11.16). Limits for excursion dives are given in references [9. 66, 133]. Using the example of a 155 m (508') storage depth, Table 11.13 shows excursion limits for unlimited durations.

Table 11.13 Limits for Excursion Dives from 155 m (508') Storage Depth

| | Lower limit | | Upper limit | |
	in m	in ft	in m	in ft
U.S. Navy [9, 67]	124	405	192	627
RN, UEG [66]	118	387	197	645
French Tables [133]	130	425	182	596
Company-specific	120	396	195	641

For long-term scientific investigations in shallower waters, underwater laboratories are employed, using the cheaper air or nitrox mixtures as breathing mediums instead of heliox. In addition to the decompression schedules mentioned here, references [5, 7] offer data for excursion dives with air/nitrox.

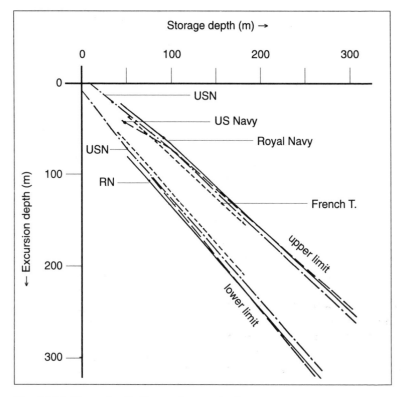

Fig. 11.16 Excursion limits vs. storage depth

CHAPTER 12

Decompression Sickness and its Treatment

12.1 DIVER SICKNESSES

Every diver is exposed to pressure changes and raised external pressures during descent, ascent, and stay at depth. Severe health problems may result if fundamental principles of interactions between pressure changes and body organs are ignored. In this chapter, the physical background of pressure related ailments will be discussed. For further discussion of the medical aspects of diving, see appropriate references, e.g., [10, 53, 54]. Single diving phases are related to typical pressure phases and correspond to the potential for specific ailments (see Fig. 12.1). The determining pressure phases are: compression phase during descent; isopression phase during the underwater stay; and decompression phase during ascent.

Compression phase:

During descent the ambient pressure increases with increasing water depth by 1 bar every 10 m (see Chapter 2). The greatest pressure difference occurs during the first 10 m of water depth (see Chapter 6). While the body's tissues are comparable to incompressible water, pressure related mechanical ailments (barotrauma) may occur in the air-filled cavities of the body. This happens when pressure equalization is not achieved between the increasing ambient pressure and the body cavity, such as the inner ear or sinus. Normally, the cavities are ventilated from the pharyngeal space via the Eustachian tube. But, when one has a cold for example, the tube swells so that pressure equalization is impossible. Further increasing the external pressure leads to an increasing underpressure in the cavity, possibly resulting in rupture of the ear drum or edema in the rigid sinus of the skull.

The largest air-filled organ of the body is the lungs. During descent, the regulator supplies the diver with breathing gas that is appropriate for his ambient pressure. But if the regulator's breathing resistance is too high, traumatic lung damage may occur. Other problems caused by relative underpressure may occur when using snorkels that are too long (> 35 cm) or by skin diving deeper than approximately 30 m. Also, if a diver falls, the sudden unintentional descent will cause barotrauma to the lungs and the upper body due to the sudden underpressure inside the diver's rigid helmet and the rigid parts of his diving dress. Damage to the eyes and skin caused by relative underpressure due to poor ventilation of the half-face mask or suit during the descent phase may also occur.

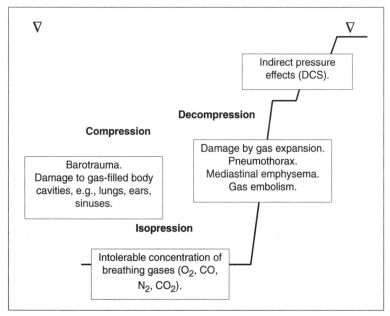

Fig. 12.1 Overview of diving-related ailments

Isopression phase:

When the desired water depth has been reached, the ambient pressure is constant and mechanically-related ailments due to pressure differences cannot occur. But during this phase indirect damage caused by incorrectly mixed breathing gases is possible. Oxygen concentrations that are too high or too low, for example, result in oxygen poisoning or lead to an oxygen deficiency (hypoxia). Carbon dioxide concentrations that are too high result in CO_2 poisoning (hypercapnia). Also contaminants in the breathing gas which can be tolerated under atmospheric conditions are toxic under raised pressure conditions.

Decompression phase:

During the ascent to the surface, the pressure relations are the inverse of those relations during descent. The ambient pressure is continuously reduced until atmospheric conditions are reached at the surface. Direct damage to gas-filled cavities caused by insufficient pressure equalization may occur as in case of compression, but they are reversed: a relative overpressure builds up in the cavities in relation to the decreasing ambient pressure. While the gas normally escapes from cavities like the middle ear or sinus when internal overpressure occurs, the situation is more critical and dangerous with regard to the lungs if the breathing gas is not exhaled during ascent. Even a slight overpressure of approximately 0.3 bars or 3 m is sufficient to rupture the delicate alveoli (air sacks). A blockage of the bronchial tubes has the same effect. Breathing gas gets into the body via the ruptured air sacks and leads to many symptoms. If the gas enters the pleural cavity, the space between lungs and chest wall, a pneumothorax occurs. Gas entering the mediastinum, the space in the vicinity of the heart, leads to mediastinal emphysema. A subcutaneous emphysema occurs if the gas is present just under the skin, very often in the area of the neck. The most critical case is a cerebral gas embolism, where gas bubbles directly enter the brain via the circulatory system and block the oxygen supply to parts of the brain. Besides direct pressure-related ailments during the decompression phase there exists the group of ailments caused by indirect pressure exposures known as decompression sickness. The following sections will deal with the reasons, symptoms, and treatments of decompression sickness; this topic is important for divers and tunnel workers, but it is also of interest in aero and space medicine.

12.2 DECOMPRESSION SICKNESS (DCS)

If the inert gas dissolved in the different tissues of the body is not removed sufficiently, decompression sickness will occur, manifested by many different symptoms. The cause of these symptoms is without any doubt the presence of inert gas bubbles in the body's tissues. Although the exact mechanism of bubble generation and the site of this generation is still unknown in detail due to the complexity of biological processes, the effects on specific tissues are relatively well known. But it should be mentioned that the first occurrence of bubbles does not automatically cause decompression problems (these are the socalled silent bubbles). On the other hand, decompression sickness symptoms are always associated with gas bubbles in the relevant tissues, as illustrated in references [9, 53, 70], etc.

In 1670, Boyles described the generation of gas bubbles in animals when they were exposed to a sudden drop in ambient pressure. He also noticed disturbances of blood circulation due to the gas bubbles. In the middle of nineteenth century the French mining engineer Triger reported on symptoms of decompression sickness in mining workers; he named these symptoms caisson disease. In 1878, Paul Bert published the results of his extensive decompression investigations. He already knew that the gas bubbles generated by fast pressure drops consisted mainly of nitrogen, meaning that undissolved inert gases in the tissues cause decompression sickness. He also knew of the negative role of high nitrogen solubility in fat tissues. Bert described successful recompression treatment for decompression sickness and the advantageous use of oxygen. Important names in the framework of decompression research work are those of J. S. Haldane and his coworkers. In 1905, Haldane began his development of decompression procedures for the British Navy. He suggested, for example, the step-wise decompression which is used in a modified form even today, according to reference [52].

The most important parameters for the release of inert gas taken up by the tissues is the amount of gas in the body, which depends on the biological half-life of the tissues and the ambient pressure drop. The distribution of inert gas bubbles inside the body is not uniform. Instead, there are preferred regions, which may change with changing boundary conditions. Among these preferred regions are the joints, especially those of the knee, elbow, and upper arm. Tribological effects form bubble nuclei which will grow with decreasing ambient pressure and will cause decompression sickness (DCS) symptoms (see Table 12.1). But the generation of gas bubbles is seen in all other parts of the body as well (Table 12.1), especially in the spinal cord. The venous nerve structure of the spinal cord is poorly supplied with blood, and that blood changes directions. Gas bubbles in the spinal cord will disturb the sensory and motor nervous systems, especially in the lower extremities. Gas bubbles in the venous blood are normally filtered out very effectively by the lungs. But if the amount of bubbles increases, lung irritation and choking can occur. If there are so many venous bubbles that the filtering capacity of the lungs is exceeded, bubbles may get into the arterial system and cause ailments such as gas embolisms.

Table 12.1 Symptoms and Frequency of DCS [9]

Symptoms of DCS	Frequency of DCS in%
Local pain in arms	62
Local pain in legs	27
Dizziness	5.3
Paralysis	2.3
Shortness of breath (chokes)	1.6
Extreme fatigue and pain	1.3
Collapse with unconsciousness	0.5

There are two causes of bubble growth. First, inert gas diffuses to the bubbles from oversaturated tissues; second, a pressure reduction causes the bubbles to grow according to the gas laws. The beginning of decompression sickness after the generation of inert gas bubbles depends on the perfusion of the corresponding tissue and on the biological half-life of the tissue. According to reference [9], the onset of DCS symptoms after surfacing shows the following distribution: 50% of all cases occurred within 30 minutes; 85% of all cases occurred within 1 hr; and 95% of all cases occurred within 3 hrs. Only 1% of all known DCS cases began after more than 6 hrs. It must be added that these results are based on standard air dives where slow tissues play only a secondary role due to limited bottom times. The fast and medium tissues are the determinants, as the above results show. These statistics are naturally not valid for bounce or saturation dives where the slow tissues determine the decompression procedure, which uses much slower decompression rates. For that reason DCS symptoms can be expected mostly in slow tissues like joints and bones and the time of onset of DCS symptoms after surfacing will be correspondingly extended. It is therefore common practice to observe divers for 24 hours after a saturation dive.

Because decompression sickness manifests in a variety of different symptoms and signs, it is difficult for non-medical personnel to classify its symptoms for adequate treatment. To simplify DCS treatments in the field, only two types of symptoms are differentiated, DCS Type I and Type II.

I symptoms are pain symptoms; in the lightest forms these include skin bends with a prickling, itching, or burning sensation of the diver's skin. Other symptoms are pain in the arms or legs, as mentioned above, usually in the joints of the knees, hips, shoulders, and elbows. Usually the pain is only slight when it is first noticed by the diver. But it may grow progressively to become unbearable. Slight pain may be easily misinterpreted, but if in doubt the diver should be always be treated for DCS to avoid later damage to joints and bones. Approximately 90% of all DCS cases are Type I; only 10% are neurologically related Type II cases. Unfortunately the latter type is increasing noticeably as sport diving increases as stated in reference [71].

Type II are all cases with symptoms other than only pain. Because in Type II DCS the central nervous system (CNS) is almost certainly involved, immediate recompression is necessary. Type II symptoms include, in addition to visual, hearing, and speech difficulties, numbness of the extremities, disturbances of balance, nausea, vertigo, and unconsciousness, among others. For saturation dives, which require slow decompression rates with respect to the slow tissues, the occurrence of Type II symptoms is very unlikely and can be almost excluded as a possibility.

There are some conditions which increase the generation of inert gas bubbles in tissues and consequently the risk of DCS. One is physical exercise before and during decompression, which causes an increased gas uptake. Because the decompression tables are calculated only for medium work, heavy work requires that the next longer time step be used for decompression to be on the safe side. Thermal effects also influence the occurrence of DCS. Warm tissues can take up inert gas more easily than cold ones. A hot-water suit increases the risk of DCS symptoms, as stated in reference [89], as does taking a hot shower after the dive. The opposite is true for cold tissues which take up inert gas much more slowly, but also release it more slowly. A further factor is the individual's susceptibly for DCS and the adaptation to raised pressure conditions. In that case the generation of bubbles by free inert gas in the body is suppressed.

Hyperbaric oxygen effectively supports the elimination of bubble nuclei. Susceptibility to DCS increases with age and obesity. The high solubility of nitrogen in fat tissues has already been mentioned; obesity creates a larger storage capacity for nitrogen, causing a higher risk of DCS.

Special consideration must be given to flying after dive operations. On long distance flights the cabin pressure in airplanes is reduced, for economic reasons, by approximately 30% to 0.7 bars. For diving personnel who have just finished a dive, decompression continues in the plane and there is the risk of the onset of DCS problems. To avoid DCS, minimum time periods between surfacing and the start of the flight are recommended (see Table 12.2).

Table 12.2 Recommended Time Between Surfacing and Flight [72]

Diving Operation	Cabin Altitude	
	600m (2000')	2400m (8000')
No decompression dives(< 1 hr)	2 h	4 h
Air dives (< 4 hrs)	12 h	12 h
Air/Nitrox saturation dives (> 4 hrs)	24 h	48 h
Mixed gas dives (saturation)	12 h	12 h

This discussion of possible reasons for decompression sickness has shown that a number of environmental parameters and biological factors are responsible for the generation of gas bubbles and the exchange of inert gases in the body. Depth and bottom time, which are the parameters in decompression tables, determine the course of decompression. Other, individual factors also play a role in the decompression process. Therefore, it is understandable that the possibility of DCS symptoms cannot be excluded even when the decompression rules are followed very strictly.

The British Department of Energy (DOE) initiated an investigation of DCS incidents after commercial air dives in the UK sector of the North Sea during the period 1982-1988 according to reference [87]. Approximately 130,000 air dives offshore were performed with a total of 333 DCS episodes—209 cases of Type I DCS and 124 cases of Type II. Table 12.3 shows the percentage of diving procedures used, averaged over the 6-year period of the survey, and the total rate of DCS incidents. More than half of all offshore air dives in the British sector were surface decompression dives with oxygen. A more detailed analysis showed a decreased use of this diving procedure over the years. On the other hand, there was an increased use of bell and nitrox diving beginning in 1984/85.

Table 12.3 Distribution of Diving Procedures and DCS Rates [87]

Air diving procedure	Percentage	DCS rate in %
Surface decompression with O_2	51.4	0.42
No-decompression dives	29.9	0.02
In-water decompression dives	14.4	0.18
Bell-TUP decompression	3.1	0.48
Nitrox dives	3.2	0.05

In reference [87], an index to asses the severity of a dive is given. Severity may be caused by long bottom times or great depths. This Decompression Penalty Index (DP Index) is defined as absolute pressure times the square root of bottom time, shortened to PrT. The investigation shows that a DP Index of 25 may be considered "safe," meaning that DCS incidents can be practically excluded. In the following table, the DP Index is determined for actual decompression tables using the respective maximum bottom time.

Table 12.4 DP-Index of U.S., French, and German Air Tables

depth in m	abs. press. in bars	maximum bottom time (BT) in min U.S. Navy	DP	French table	DP	Bottom time German table	DP	f_w DP = 25
12	2.2	300	38	360	42	660	57	129
18	2.8	200	40	210	41	200	40	80
24	3.4	150	42	150	42	105	35	54
30	4.0	120	44	110	42	75	35	39
36	4.6	100	46	90	44	55	34	30
42	5.2	80	47	70	44	45	35	23
50	6.0	60	46	50	42	35	35	18

It is interesting to note that the allowed maximum bottom times for air dives in the three national decompression tables in Table 12.4 show actual DP Indexes between 35 and 45, far higher than the recommended index of 25. The solution for avoiding "stressful" dives would be to shorten the bottom time to below the allowed level. The last column in Table 12.4 gives the bottom times which correspond to a DP Index of 25.

As the statistics in reference [87] for practical operations have emphasized, the average diving time seldom reaches the allowed limits. So the majority of commercial air dives investigated in this study may be considered "non-stressful" dives with DP Indexes between 20 and 30.

12.3 THERAPEUTIC RECOMPRESSION AND TREATMENT
12.3.1 General

Because the generation of inert gas bubbles in the body is definitely the reason for decompression sickness, appropriate measures must be taken to decrease and eliminate these bubbles. The basis for treatment of DCS are the following measures which are used alone or in combination: recompression; oxygen treatment; additional medication; and change of breathing gases.

Recompression reduces the bubble volume according to the gas laws and supports the dissolution of free inert gases in the tissues due to the raised ambient pressure. A doubling of the ambient pressure causes a reduction of the bubble volume by half and a reduction of the bubble diameter to 80%.

Oxygen treatment under increased partial pressure causes steep concentration gradients and consequently high diffusion rates, thus washing inert gases out of the tissues. But no less important is the improved oxygen supply to body tissues in the case of blocked capillaries.

The use of drugs like aspirin to suppress blood clotting, and drinking liquids before and during recompression as countermeasures for dehydration, support the release of inert gas.

Changing the inert gas component in the breathing gas is a recommended treatment, but it cannot be used in every case. The use of heliox (helium/oxygen) supports the treatment of DCS problems after air or nitrox dives. The nitrogen in the therapy gas is replaced by helium causing a steeper diffusion gradient and increasing the washout rate of surplus nitrogen from the body tissues. This method is known in the chemical industry as "gas stripping." But the inverse procedure is not allowed when the diver has breathed heliox and now is breathing air or nitrox as the therapy gas. The effects of isobaric counter diffusion (see section 12.4) make the DCS problems worse.

Decompression sickness, especially neurological Type II DCS, requires immediate recompression of the patient. For that reason, a pressure chamber must be nearby. A chamber may be a transport or a treatment chamber. The transport chamber is a one or two-man version and is used only for recompression and transport to the next treatment chamber. Treatment chambers are designed for longer stays and therefore are larger and contain additional equipment, e.g., oxygen supply via BIBS, life-support system, ECU, etc. The size and design of recompression chambers may vary to a large extent; examples may be found in references [5, 7, 33], among others. Whether a recompression chamber must be provided at the dive site or may be at a distance but reachable within a given period of time depends on the kind of diving operation and is regulated by national agencies.

12.3.2 Treatment of DCS After Air/Nitrox Dives

The majority of diving operations worldwide are air dives to depths of 50/60 m; these are the kind of dives that involve the highest risk of DCS. Each government with its own diving industry has issued decompression regulations (decompression tables) which also contain instructions on the treatment of DCS. A 1978 survey of the different treatment tables, which can be found in reference [73] was conducted; a total of 63 tables were found. But there are only slight differences in the treatment schemes, and some of them are largely identical to those of the U.S. Navy found in reference [9] and UK Navy found in reference [63].

To simplify the choice of an appropriate treatment procedure, the tables use the proven differentiation of DCS I or DCS II episodes. Flow diagrams support the decision-making process for optimal treatment. Each treatment strategy is based on recompression with the simultaneous use of oxygen. Due to the danger of O_2 poisoning, the recompression depth for oxygen treatments is limited to 18 m (60').

In cases of life-threatening symptoms recompression must immediately go to 50 m (165 feet) using air or heliox with a sufficient O_2 concentration as the breathing gas. But the disadvantage of this recompression is that the original depth may have been much shallower than 50 m. An air treatment of 6 bars causes the undesired uptake of more nitrogen from the air, which may lead to additional DCS problems. There are numerous treatment tables available, e.g., in references [5, 7, 9, 10, 31, 53, 63, 133], to name only a few. The best known treatment tables in the international diving community are without doubt the tables of the U.S. Navy, located in reference [9].

Table 12.5 gives an overview of the well-known U.S.N. and RN treatment procedures for different kinds of decompression sickness including gas embolism. All treatment procedures are based largely on the application of oxygen, with exception of Table U.S.N 4 and RN 54 in the last column, which uses air only instead of oxygen. This procedure is only used if there is no oxygen at the site because it requires more time than the comparable oxygen-supported Table U.S.N 6A and RN 63, with a total treatment time of approximately 5 hrs. The air-based U.S.N 4 table requires more than 38 hrs or roughly one and a half days.

Table 12.5 U.S. Navy/Royal Navy Treatment Tables [9, 63]

Table Use	U.S.N 5/RN 61 DCS Type I	U.S.N 6/RN 62 DCS Type II Gas embolism	U.S.N 6A/RN 63 DCS Type II Gas embolism	U.S.N 4/RN 54 DCS Type II
Depth	18 m	18 m	50 m	50 m
range	9 m	9 m	18/9 m	down to 3 m
Deco. time	2h : 15	4h : 45	5h : 19	38h : 11
O_2 time	2 h	4 h	4 h	(3 h)

The newest French regulations found in reference [133] use treatment procedures which go down to 12 m in the case of DCS Type I and 30 m in the case of DCS Type II or gas embolism. In the first case, Type I symptoms, 4 oxygen cycles are performed wherein each cycle consists of 25 minutes of oxygen breathing and a 5 minutes air window for recovery. After the last cycle, the decompression starts within 30 minutes from 12 m to the surface breathing oxygen. For Type II symptoms or gas embolism the treatment procedure is more complex. The maximum depth is only 30 m instead of 50 m, but the therapy gas is an oxygen-enriched heliox mix with 50% O_2 and a nitrox mix 50/50 if no heliox is available. After reaching the 18 m step, the therapy gas is switched to pure oxygen (see Fig. 12.2). The whole treatment takes a total of 7.5 h. Instead of differentiating between Type I and Type II DCS for the choice of an appropriate therapy, some authors suggest differentiating only between life-threatening and non life-threatening symptoms, e.g., references [74, 75].

Figure 12.3 shows the flow diagram for a treatment scheme for DCS symptoms after air/nitrox dives based on the differentiation between life-threatening and non life-threatening symptoms, following a suggestion in reference [74]. The extensive use of heliox instead of air and the use of the change of therapy gases for effective elimination of the nitrogen from the tissues is noticeable.

In Germany, the treatment procedure for DCS episodes is stipulated in regulations found in references [31], which largely follow the U.S.N scheme. In 1987, a German medical group, noted in reference [75], made a suggestion to simplify the actual DCS treatment regulations using the same differentiation as in reference [74] between life-threatening and non life-threatening cases. For non life-threatening symptoms, the patient is recompressed to 18 m using BIBS for breathing oxygen. After 3 cycles, each cycle consisting of 20 min on oxygen and 5 min on air for recovery, the decompression starts to 9 m for 30 min; after one cycle at 9 m, the diver surfaces within 30 min (Fig. 12.4). For life-threatening symptoms the patient is recompressed to 50 m on air. After 30 min, decompression starts to 18 m, following the same treatment scheme as for non life-threatening symptoms. If after 30 min at 50 m the symptoms have not been relieved, changing the therapy gas to heliox is strongly recommended (Fig. 12.4).

Whichever therapy is used, patients recover most quickly and effectively when a treatment starts immediately after the occurrence of DCS symptoms. Every delay or improper treatment reduces the chances of recovery, although help is possible even in advanced cases, according to reference [75].

In cases where an adequate therapy can start only days after symptoms appear, recompression to 50 m is no longer useful. The inert gas bubbles which have caused the neurological damage have already been dissolved in the body's tissues and removed via the lungs. The only therapy, besides proper medication, is long-term treatment with hyperbaric oxygen to support the natural healing process of the damaged tissues. The patient is recompressed to 18 m on heliox, going into saturation. Heliox is chosen to avoid renewing the nitrogen load for the tissues. Pure oxygen is breathed in cycles via BIBS, as seen in reference [75]. In general, the switch to saturation therapy, including the change of the

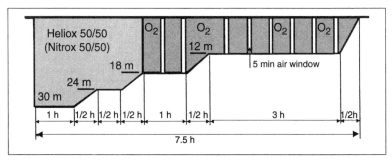

Fig. 12.2 French treatment procedure for DCS Type II occurrences [133]

MIXED GAS DIVING

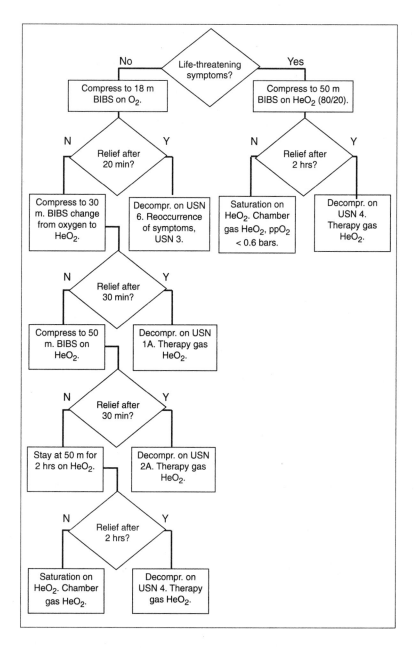

Fig. 12.3 DCS treatment scheme after air/nitrox dives [74]

therapy gas, is strongly recommended in difficult and complex cases. Decompression is performed with more conservative decompression rates, which can easily be adapted to the patient's actual condition.

Bühlmann in reference [53], offers treatment procedures for air dives exceeding the 50 m limit. The patient is recompressed to 90 m on heliox, where he stays for 3 hrs. The total treatment time is more than 32 hrs. The oxygen content is limited to 8%, corresponding to an O_2 partial pressure of 0.8 bars. Because the exposure time is only 3 hrs this raised oxygen pressure can be tolerated.

12.3.3 DCS Treatment Procedures After Mixed Gas Dives

Mixed gas is preferred for bounce and saturation diving at depths deeper than 50 m. As already discussed in section 11.6, the probability of decompression sickness symptoms is noticeably smaller for this kind of diving due to the slow decompression rates. If symptoms occur at all they will usually occur at surfacing. They will be almost exclusively DCS Type I symptoms. The general procedure at the onset of DCS symptoms is to stop the decompression and recompress to the depth at which symptoms are relieved. The recompression should not exceed 20 m in the case of DCS Type I and 30 m in the case of DCS Type II. To support the treatment, hyperbaric oxygen with a partial pressure between 1.5 and 2.5 bars is breathed in cycles of 20 minutes via BIBS. Figure 12.5 gives an overview of DCS treatment schemes after mixed gas dives following a suggestion in reference [74].

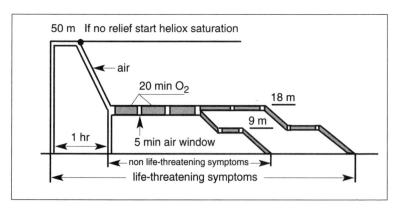

Fig. 12.4 DCS treatment scheme after air/nitrox dives [75]

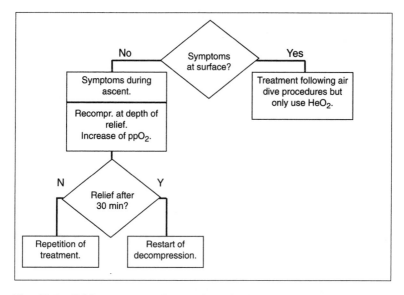

Fig. 12.5 DCS treatment scheme after mixed gas dives [74]

The treatment of decompression symptoms during and after saturation dives with heliox is also dealt with in reference [66]. The usual saturation decompression stages of 5 m are halved to 2.5 m. Because the stop times at the single stages are also halved, the total decompression time stays the same. The decompression tables in reference [7] for saturation dives using air and nitrox also offer treatment procedures for DCS. The patient is recompressed to the depth where symptoms are relieved and stays there for 2 hrs before continuing the decompression. Depending on the actual depth, the ascent rate starts at 1.5 m/h and is reduced to 0.9 m/h when surfacing.

12.4 ISOBARIC COUNTERDIFFUSION
12.4.1 Introduction and Definitions
Gas switching, the change from one breathing gas to another, is a technique widely used in diving, especially to support decompression. This technique was demonstrated in 1962 by the Swiss H. Keller, who undertook a number of spectacular deep dives to 300 m using different gases in a particular sequence.

Studies on gas switching showed that special gas combinations caused severe decompression problems with no change in ambient pressure. Because the phenomenon was apparent at a constant ambient pressure where some of the gases involved were streaming in the opposite direction of the tissues, this phenomenon was called isobaric counterdiffusion. In the 1970s, systematic investigations on isobaric counterdiffusion were conducted in the U.S. by Lambertsen *et al.* and other authors, including those in reference [68]. One major finding was that tissues may be oversaturated as well as undersaturated at constant pressure conditions, depending only on the sequence of light and heavy gases used for breathing. In this context, helium and hydrogen are considered light gases while nitrogen, neon, and argon are heavy gases.

In principle, two forms of isobaric counterdiffusion are distinguished: the steady state condition and the transient condition. In the steady state condition, the diver is surrounded by gas 1 in the chamber while he breathes gas 2 via BIBS (Fig. 12.6). After equilibrium is reached, two stable gradients will be built up. The inner parts of the body are supplied with gas 2, possibly even saturated with it, while the gradient 2 drops toward the outer part of the body. Gas 1 diffuses into the body via the skin, and gradient 1 drops towards the inner organs. The opposite gas fluxes, and the constant gradients cause supersaturation of tissues in the transient zone under steady state conditions.

This condition can be created, for example, in an underwater welding habitat where the diver is surrounded by the shielding gas while he is supplied via BIBS with a different breathing gas. This working situation, including the gases used, must be analyzed very carefully because steady state conditions are potentially dangerous.

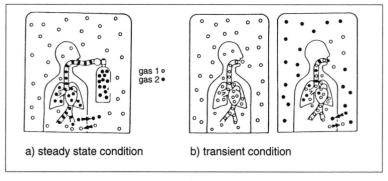

gas 1 o
gas 2 •

a) steady state condition   b) transient condition

Fig. 12.6 Principle forms of isobaric counter diffusion [68]

In the transient state, the diver is saturated with the surrounding gas 1 inside the chamber. When the gas is switched over to gas 2, the first gas is released and gas 2 starts to saturate the diver's tissues (see Fig. 12.6b). This is a dynamic process with changing supersaturations and gradients in different parts of the body and at different times. The gas change takes place mainly via the lungs. Because this is a transient state, gas 1 will be released until only a negligible amount remains, while gas 2 will now saturate the body tissues, assuming sufficient exposure time. The partial pressure of gas 2 will under no circumstances exceed the ambient pressure. These transient conditions are usually found during deep dive operations when the diver, saturated with nitrogen, breathes heliox at greater depths. As the transient condition is a dynamic process with continuously changing gradients, the risk of DCS caused by isobaric counterdiffusion is considerably smaller.

12.4.2 Mathematical and Physical Models

Different formulations for the analytical description of the phenomenon of isobaric counterdiffusion have been made in the past. To verify mathematical models in experiments is not easy because, for example, temporal oscillations in the perfusion rate cause noticeable differences in results.

To demonstrate inert gas supersaturation of tissues the physical model of a simplified bilayer tissue, composed of a lipid and an aqueous layer, may be used (see Fig. 12.7). While the heavy gas 2 continuously enters the layer from one side, the light gas 1 diffuses into the layer from the opposite side. Standing pressure gradients are built up in the two layers, corresponding to the physical properties of the two gases and the different biological properties of the layers. The result is a constant supersaturation with its maximum at the boundary of the layers (Fig. 12.7). It must be emphasized that total pressure p_T in the tissue is greater than the ambient pressure p_{amb}.

This model demonstrates the steady state situation of isobaric

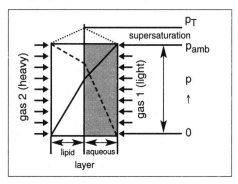

Fig. 12.7 Bilayer model for demonstration of supersaturation [68]

counterdiffusion where, due to supersaturation, DCS symptoms may occur as inert gas bubbles are generated. For the mathematical description of gases that have a lower or higher partial pressure in the tissues during desaturation of one inert gas and resaturation with another one, the perfusion model is recommended by different studies. The total tension p_T of a given tissue depends on its perfusion, or in other words on the half-life of the tissues and the properties of gases.

$$p_T = p_0 \exp(-k_1 t) + 1 - \exp(-k_2 t) \qquad (12.1)$$

with p_0 = initial tension of gas 1 in bars

       k_1 = time constant of gas 1 in s^{-1}

       k_2 = time constant of gas 2 in s^{-1}

The first term of equation 12.1 describes the desaturation of gas 1, starting with the initial tension p_O. The second term determines the saturation of gas 2. Figure 12.8 shows the temporal development of the total tension p_T after the gas switch from nitrogen to helium, according to (12.1). The heavier nitrogen desaturates more slowly than the light helium saturates, causing supersaturation in the tissues during the initial phase of the gas exchange. Because the gas exchange is a transient process, the supersaturation will stop and the temporal overpressure p_T will return to the normal ambient pressure. The perfusion rate of the blood determines the temporal distribution and relative degree of the tissue's supersaturation after the gas exchange (see reference [68]). The higher the flow rate in the capillaries, the shorter but steeper the tissue supersaturation. But this supersaturation will never exceed twice the ambient pressure.

12.4.3 Practical Application of Isobaric Counterdiffusion

As already discussed, isobaric counterdiffusion may cause over, as well as, under saturation of the tissues with inert gas, depending on the kind of gas exchange. While oversaturation increases decompression problems, undersaturation supports decompression (see Fig. 12.9). Here the light helium desaturates faster than the heavier nitrogen saturates, causing a temporary underpressure. Different authors, for example, D'Aoust *et al.,* who wrote reference [69], have investigated different inert gas combinations under transient conditions. To verify the results, tests with animals were carried out in which the generation of gas bubbles in

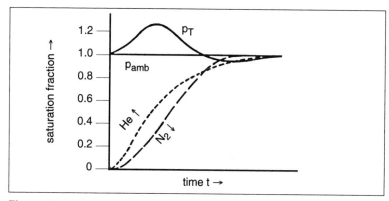

Figure 12.8 Principle of desaturation and resaturation during gas exchange from N_2 to He [68]

the animal tissues was measured. The rate of bubble generation was used as the criterion for supersaturation, allowing a prediction of the onset of DCS symptoms. All test animals had breathed the first inert gas for 17 hours, so that saturation of tissues could be assumed before the change of gas was started. The maximum gas tensions were calculated in advance using the perfusion model (12.1) and these tensions were related to the initial tension in the tissues. This tension ratio gives a good idea of whether bubbles, and consequently DCS symptoms, may be expected. If this ratio is less than 1.0, undersaturation occurs. In the opposite case, oversaturation occurs, causing bubble formations and thus decompression sickness. Some results of the inert gas combinations investigated are presented in Table 12.6.

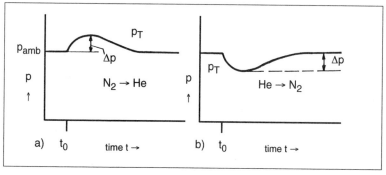

Fig. 12.9 Principle of a) oversaturation and b) undersaturation [68]

Table 12.6 Results of Gas Switches on Bubble Generation [68]

Gas change from	to	Maximum tension ratio	Generation of bubbles
helium	nitrogen	0.861	no
hydrogen	nitrogen	0.890	no
argon	nitrogen	1.015	no
neon	hydrogen	0.939	no
neon	helium	0.978	no
nitrogen	hydrogen	1.076	very few
hydrogen	helium	1.080	very few
nitrogen	helium	1.139	yes
nitrogen	neon	1.160	yes
argon	helium	1.123	yes

The analytically-determined tension ratio correlates well with predicted bubble generation, supporting the perfusion model. Table 12.6 further confirms that an oversaturation occurs when a heavy gas is replaced by a lighter one. Because the heavy inert gas desaturates more slowly than the lighter gas saturates, a supersaturation of tissues is inevitable, causing the bubbles that are the reason for DCS symptoms. In the case of transient state conditions, this may be tolerated as the oversaturation is temporally limited. In normal practice, the nitrogen-saturated diver, when switched over to heliox, breathes a helium/oxygen mix during his descent, which means that isobaric conditions are not created. On the other hand, there is the possibility of an intermediate step. Instead of a direct switch from nitrogen to helium, the first switch is from nitrogen to hydrogen. In the second step, the gas is changed from hydrogen to helium (see Table 12.6).

The situation under steady state conditions is another story. With standing gradients, the tissues are constantly oversaturated, generating inert gas bubbles and leading to the inevitable occurrence of DCS symptoms (see Table 12.6, last section). The combination of argon and helium (last row) was extremely dangerous with near-fatal results. Standing gradients are a potential danger almost entirely independent of the sequence of gases used. In that case, depending on the kind of gases available inside and outside the body, the area of maximum oversaturation is shifted toward the skin or to the deeper tissues. In neither case can generation of inert gas bubbles in the body be avoided.

Severe problems arise when both conditions, steady state and transient, occur when both the breathed gas and the gas of the chamber atmosphere are changed under isobaric conditions. This may be fatal for the diver. Gas switching in diving is an effective tool for improving decompression procedures, but it is important to understand the physical background and the potential dangers.

NOTES

CHAPTER 13

Safety and
Legal Aspects

13.1 INTRODUCTION

Every human activity presents dangers for humans and their environment. To protect themselves and the legitimate interests of their neighbors and the environment, generally accepted "rules of the game" must be available. On the one hand, these rules must guarantee the individual's freedom insofar as possible. On the other hand, sufficient protection and safety for others and the environment must be guaranteed. These "rules of the game" must balance the opposing interests of the different parties, and they are available in different forms, such as laws, regulations, guidelines, technical recommendations, codes of practice, etc.

In the interests of safety, national and international diving-related rules and regulations are formulated. These rules are subject of more or less continuous changes with the general aim of improving safety. Safety is a relative term, which can be defined as probability against failure events. It is in the nature of probabilistic considerations that absolute safety cannot be achieved. Also, even the highest possible safety standards cannot absolutely exclude failure events. But every kind of safety measure helps to reduce the probability of failure.

13.2 DIVING SAFETY

Included in diving safety are all measures taken to prevent the occurrence of diving-related accidents and to reduce the consequences of such accidents. As in every other human activity, there is the risk of accidents.

The crucial question is, "What risks is the public willing to accept?" If the benefits are great, a higher risk will be acceptable than if the benefits are small. Risk is defined in this context as the product of the probability rate of a given event times the consequences of this event. Driving, for example, is a generally-accepted risk even though thousands of fatalities and many injuries occur every year, costing huge amounts of money. But there are limitations of risk acceptance. If the risk involves a fatality rate exceeding fatalities from natural events such as disease, then the risk will not be accepted (see Fig. 13.1 and references [95, 141]).

Applied to the diving business, this means that divers' risks must not exceed other, natural, risks. First assessments of diving-related risks have been done on the basis of offshore accident statistics. In reference [96], diver fatality rates were estimated on the basis of fatal diving accidents in the Norwegian and British sector between 1971 and 1983. The estimation is based on roughly 16,500 surface-oriented dives and 25,000 bell runs. The calculated rate uses a fatality frequency that is the ratio of the number of fatalities to the total number of dives and total number of man-times (see Table 13.1). According to these statistics, an annual fatality rate for a single diver has been estimated at $3.9 \cdot 10^{-3}$. But it can be assumed that the rates in 13.1 will be noticeably reduced because safety standards have

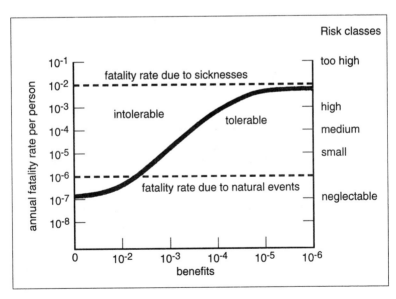

Fig. 13.1 Estimation of acceptable risks [95]

been continuously improved over the last ten years. For comparison, the natural fatality rate in Germany is $2 \cdot 10^{-4}$ fatalities per person and year or $2 \cdot 10^{-8}$ per person and hour according to reference [76].

Table 13.1 Diver Fatality Rate [96]

	Surface oriented diving	Bell diving	Chamber stay
Fatality per dive	$1.8 \cdot 10^{-4}$	$2.8 \cdot 10^{-4}$	—
Fatality per hour of diving/in chamber	$2.7 \cdot 10^{-4}$	$3.0 \cdot 10^{-5}$	$9.6 \cdot 10^{-7}$

It is interesting to analyze the reasons for fatal diving accidents. On the basis of 39 fatalities in the North Sea between 1971 and 1977, the main reason for one-third of all fatalities was human error, followed by equipment failure or lack of equipment. The third reason, accounting for 10% of the accidents, was inadequate training, as stated in refrence [96]. A closer look at the different accident events and their causes in reference [96], shows that over 50% of all fatalities have their roots in more or less human inadequacies, such as human error, inappropriate equipment, poor maintenance, inadequate training, and poor physical conditioning. The fatality rate caused by equipment failure alone is less than 20%.

During operation of the diving simulation facility GUSI at Geesthacht, Germany, a number of studies on the safety of components and equipment of a saturation system have been conducted. Probability analysis was performed for relevant subsystems using failure tree techniques. Due to the lack of failure rates for diving components, reliability data from other branches of technology had to be used, according to reference [140]. Norwegian NPD, for example, requires in its regulations a risk analysis with regard to equipment and operations and recommends Failure Mode Effect Analysis (FMEA), as stated in reference [144]. Another danger in diving systems is the possibility of fire in manned chambers, especially when using hyperbaric oxygen. In reference [139], a state-of-the-art report on aspects of fire safety in hyperbaric chambers is presented.

Considering the failures caused directly or indirectly by human error, the key role played by adequate training on a regular basis and further qualification of diving-related personnel is obvious. Good basic training, including repetition of emergency drills and periodic qualification testing, are key for providing qualified human resources. Personnel training costs money, but only one severe accident with all of its possible consequences will cost many times more. In the following, aspects of training and qualification of diving personnel will be discussed in more detail.

13.3 DIVER TRAINING

The qualified training of diving- related personnel is essential to guaranteeing high safety standards, according to references [96, 97]. This is especially true for divers because underwater work is dangerous work performed in a hostile environment. The goals of theoretical and practical diver training must be: to make perfectly clear to the trainee the risks and potential dangers of diving and to show ways to minimize those risks; to give the trainee sufficient experience in practical diving to enable him to act rationally in any situation; and to show the trainee the importance of careful diving preparations.

Theoretical training includes the basics of physics and diving medicine, including first aid, knowledge of the function and maintenance of diving systems and equipment, and last, but not least, familiarity with diving-related legislation. Practical training provides experience and safety rules in the handling of diving equipment and systems including underwater tools. Emergency drills under simulated emergency conditions are important, among other things. But gaining experience is a time-consuming process, and it takes years to become a professional.

Diver training is performed virtually everywhere in the world, but differences exist in the kinds and degree of training. The training is based on standards that are stipulated in some countries by law while in other countries recommendations for diver training are only issued by the diving industry itself. An attempt to standardize the different national training standards in Europe has been made by the European Diving Technology Committee (EDTC). In 1988, EDTC issued a European standard for training of air and mixed gas divers, offshore diving supervisors, and life support technicians, according to reference [98]. For the time being, this standard is only a recommendation. But EC countries are expected to introduce a European diver training curriculum in the future.

In the following, a selection of national training standards will be introduced. In the U.S., the USCG has issued provisions for executing diving operations, with clear responsibilities delineated for the person-in-charge and the diving supervisor, under part 197, subpart B-Commercial Diving Operations. The supervisor is responsible for the dive team and diving operation. Specific legal standards for diver qualifications are not available, but the U.S. diving industry has recommended training standards. According to the Manual of Safe Practices in Commercial Diving Operations issued by the Association of Diving Contractors (ADC), diving personnel may be designated by three levels of qualification: Systems Diver (qualified for mixed gas and air diving operations); Diver (qualified for diving operations with air down to 190' (220'); and Diver/Tender (qualified for air dives under supervision and for tending divers). Divers are usually qualified by undergoing U.S. Navy diver training or by attending commercial diving schools, followed by field experience.

Canada has, in contrast to the U.S., strict governmental training standards for diving personnel; these are published in Canada Oil and Gas Regulations—Diving, also known as reference [100]. According to these regulations three categories of diver certificates are distinguished in schedule 9: Category I (qualified for air dives to 50 m using SCUBA or surface-supplied diving equipment; Category II (qualified for air and mixed gas dives using surface-supplied diving equipment including bells—minimum one-year practice as a Category I diver); and Category III (qualified for all kinds of diving operations including saturation diving—minimum 2-year practice as a Category II diver). Adequate diver training may be completed at commercial diving schools or institutions accepted by the government body responsible.

The UK was the first country, together with Norway, to institute regulations for offshore activities, including adequate standards for diver training. The main reason for these regulations was the alarming number of 45 fatalities in the North Sea between 1971 and 1979. The legal basis for all diving operations offshore is the 1981 Diving Operations at Work Regulations (SI 399) issued by the Health and Safety Executive (HSE) and the Department of Energy (DOE), the legal bodies responsible for diving activities, as noted in reference [85]. The responsibilities of the involved parties, as well as qualification standards for divers, are among the matters stipulated by law. According to reference [85], divers must prove a satisfactory standard of competence by earning a certificate issued by HSE/DOE or bodies approved by HSE. Four standards of competence are distinguished in accordance with SI 399, regulation 10, schedule 4: HSE Part I (qualified as a commercial air diver down to 50 m using SCUBA or surface-supplied equipment; HSE Part II (qualified as mixed gas/bell/saturation diver for all kinds of operations—minimum of 1 year as a Part I diver); HSE Part III (qualified for air diving where no surface compression chamber is required on site [normally limited to 30 m/100']); and HSE Part IV (qualified for SCUBA diving, mainly for scientific divers. It must be mentioned that only divers with HSE Part I and II qualifications are qualified for offshore diving operations. For diver training, standards containing detailed training units including required in-water training times have been issued by HSE, as stated in reference [142].

Norway has qualification standards for diver training comparable to those of the UK and both countries accept the other's training certificates. The Norwegian Petroleum Directorate (NPD), the authority responsible for issuing diver certificates, stipulates two qualification levels for commercial divers. The first level covers surface oriented diving and is comparable to the HSE Part I standard, allowing air dives down to 50 m using SCUBA as well as surface-supplied equipment. The second level covers all kinds of diving operations including bell and mixed gas diving. This level corresponds to the UK's HSE Part II standard. NPD regulations require follow-up training for divers; the operator of an installation offshore has the responsibility of ensuring this requirement is met. It is also his duty to ensure that his own personnel, as well as those of his contractors and subcontractors, comply with the regulations issued for diving on the Norwegian continental shelf. Training facilities, instruction, and qualifying time for divers must be approved by the Norwegian Petroleum Directorate, but NPD has not issued its own training standards.

French training standards are part of the January 1991 revised supplement (arrete) on Hyperbaric Works, also known as reference [133]. French training certificates, abbreviated CAH, which stands for Certificat d' Aptitude à l' Hyperbarie, stipulates four different types of hyperbaric activities labelled A to D. In addition, four classes specify the pressure range for the training objectives. The types of activities are: A—Industrial divers involved in underwater operations; B—Other divers involved in underwater operations; C—Medical personnel in dry conditions; and D— Compressed air workers in dry conditions. The four classes specify the following pressure ranges: Class IA—down to 1.2 bars (< 2 m WD); Class I—down to 4.0 bars (< 30 m WD); Class II—Between 4 and 6 bars (30 - 50 m WD); and Class III—more than 6 bars (> 50 m WD).

It is obvious that commercial divers must hold a certificate (CAH) of Type A and, depending on their depth range, a Class II or III certificate. The French regulations also include medical personnel working in treatment chambers resp. tunnel workers in Types C and D. For all types of hyperbaric activities, special decompression tables are available and presented in reference [133]. The diver training can be obtained from approved diving schools or through Navy training, where the corresponding training certificates are issued, usually by the Institut National de la Plongée Professionelle (INPP).

Danish commercial diver certificates are issued by the Directorate of the Government Inspection of Ships, while the Minister of Commerce lays down rules for divers' tests including the content of the test. There are two types of dives—air down to 50 m or mixed gas with no depth limitations. In addition, the kind of diving gear used is considered, with certificates for the heavy diver, familiar with heavy diving gear, and the light diver, using light diving gear (SCUBA). A professional diver's certificate will not be issued to persons older than forty who are starting a dive career or to divers older than sixty-seven.

Germany has a very different system for training commercial divers; it is covered by the German legal training scheme which can be found in reference [99]. After successful training as a skilled worker in a diving-related trade such as mechanics, electricity, or carpentering, the trainee joins an approved diving company and goes through a two-year training period which ends with a practical and theoretical test at a chamber of industry and commerce. He is then called a commercial diver (Geprüfter Taucher) and is allowed to do any kind of underwater work with air down to 50 m. To use other breathing gases the diver needs special permission from the responsible professional trade association (Berufsgenossenschaft). In 1991, training standards for mixed gas/bell/saturation divers, following EDTC standards for mixed gas diver training, were introduced and approved by the supreme mining authority at Clausthal-Zellerfeld, which is the body responsible for all German offshore activities, according to reference [143]. Training certificates for mixed gas/bell divers are issued by the German classification society Germanischer Lloyd (German Lloyd).

13.4 DIVING-RELATED NATIONAL LEGISLATION

Each diving operation creates a potential danger for the diver, so national legislation must ensure the safety of diving personnel. The basis of safety legislation in virtually every country is that nation's constitution, which guarantees each citizen the right to life and physical integrity. This is also true in Germany where safety legislation includes, among others, regulations against risks resulting from the use of technology, according to reference [76]. While legal norms give the general framework for safety legislation, technical rules describe the exact procedures for practical application of the legislation. Technical rules represent current standards; these must adapt to continuous technical developments. In the interests of

European standardization, these national technical rules are now being changed into European standards, such as European (EN) norms or ISO (International Organization for Standardization) norms .

Virtually every country with large-scale diving activities has its own national legislation regarding diving operations. A few examples will be introduced, emphasizing the different approaches in national diving legislation. Beyond this, a North Sea standard has been extracted; it is based mainly on British and Norwegian diving regulations which represent today's highest safety standard, as stated in reference [84] and which is often required and used in other parts of the world. In the following, some national diving standards will be briefly introduced.

United States legislation has two sources for diving-related regulations resulting from the different tasks of the two responsible government agencies. The U.S. Coast Guard (USCG) is mainly responsible for offshore activities and regulations for diving operations are stated in part 197 and, for our purposes, especially in subpart B, Commercial Diving Regulations issued in 1979, found in reference [92]. The Coast Guard is also involved in stipulating equipment requirements and construction and maintenance standards and is as well the authority responsible for investigating severe diving accidents in U.S. waters. Determining industrial health and safety standards is the responsibility of the U.S. Occupational Safety and Health Administration (OSHA) as stated in reference [93], which gives general principles for diving operations onshore as well as offshore. USCG and OSHA regulations are sometimes the same.

British legislation is based on Acts of Parliament and is enforced by means of Statuary Instruments (SI) which are indicated by the law's title and the SI serial number. The most essential British regulations dealing with diving-related operations are summarized in Table 13.2. For diving operations SI 399, the 1981 Diving Operations at Work Regulations Act, and its 1990 amendment are the most important laws regulating onshore and offshore diving in the British sector.

Table 13.2 Diving-related British Regulations

Number of Law	Title of Law	Year of Issue
SI 1232	The Health and Safety at Work Act	1974
SI 116	The Merchant Shipping Regulations (Div. Op.)	1975
SI 923	The Submarine Pipelines Regulations (Div. Op.)	1976
SI 1019	The Offshore Installations Regulations	1976
SI 399	The Diving Operations at Work Regulations	1981/1990

The government body responsible for enforcing the regulations, with exception of regulations for offshore diving, is the Health and Safety Executive (HSE). Offshore activities are delegated to another governmental body, the Department of Energy (DOE). The Diving Inspectorate, part of the DOE, is the authority responsible for supervision of all offshore diving activities. Both authorities may issue publications as guidance notes, memoranda, etc. to supplement and clarify legislation and to raise topics of general interest, especially safety-related topics. At irregular intervals, HSE and DOE issue Diving Safety Memoranda (DSM), which extend and update safety aspects, often in reference to actual events or accidents. These memos complete the legal framework of Statuary Instruments. A number of DSMs are summarized, for example, in reference [91].

This legal framework is supplemented and extended by guidelines, guidance notes, codes of practice, etc. issued by civil law institutions. AODC, the Association of Offshore Diving Contractors or as it is called now, the International Association of Underwater Engineering Contractors, must be mentioned here. Its members come from the diving and offshore industry. A considerable number of publications on safety-related topics in diving and underwater work are produced by AODC. Medical aspects are dealt with by the DMAC, the Diving Medical Advisory Committee which can be found in references [15, 24, 29, 32, 39, 88, 89, 90, 102, 107, 141]. A summary of AODC and DMAC Guidance Notes is given in reference [91]. These Guidance Notes are revised continuously to keep up with latest technical and medical developments. And last but not least, guidelines and requirements issued by insurance organizations and the classification society Lloyd's Register (LR) complete the framework of legislation. The governmental agencies place much responsibility on the oil companies (operators), which are liable for the enforcement of legislation for all activities carried out on their installations.

Norwegian legislation is based on Royal Decrees that have been passed by the Norwegian Parliament and are enforced by the Royal Norwegian Ministry of Petroleum and Energy as the responsible governmental body. The ministry has delegated the authority for all diving-related legislation related to the Norwegian continental shelf to the Norwegian Petroleum Directorate (NPD). NPD has a status comparable to that of the British DOE. In 1978, it issued Provisional Regulations for Diving on the Norwegian Continental Shelf; in 1990, the Regulations concerning manned underwater operations in the petroleum industry found in reference [144], regulating Norwegian diving activities, followed. To adapt to the latest technical developments and to secure the highest safety standards, NPD also issues Safety Notices, which are the Norwegian version of the British safety memos. A number of NPD Safety Notes are summarized in reference [91]. The Norwegian classification society, Det Norske Veritas (DNV), is also involved in legislation regarding construction, inspection, and maintenance of offshore diving equipment. Because the British and Norwegians have common interests in the continental shelf of the North Sea, the corresponding governmental bodies of both countries are working to standardize their legislation. Training certificates of British or Norwegian training centers, for example, are mutually accepted.

French legislation for diving-related activities is based on the Code du Travail issued by the responsible ministries, among others, by the ministry of work, which in 1992 stipulated the legal framework for health and safety at work. From this code of work, decrets are derived. The decret on Prevention Measures for Hyperbaric Works is of special interest for the diving industry and also for compressed air workers and for therapeutic applications under hyperbaric conditions. Decrets are supplemented by arretes, which contain detailed information for the practical implementation of the regulations. So the decret on hyperbaric works consists of arretes which deal with training and certification of personnel exposed to hyperbaric conditions and with medical fitness, for example. Very important for diving activities is the arrete on working conditions, Travaux en Milieu Hyperbare (Work under Hyperbaric Conditions), also known as reference [133]. This last contains, among other things, decompression tables worked out by Comex for diving operations with air, nitrox, and heliox.

Danish legislation is based on the Diving Act, Act No. 214, of 1979, which mainly regulates diver training and certification and log book keeping. It gives the Danish Ministry of Commerce authority to lay down corresponding rules. In 1988, the Diving Act was supplemented by orders on Safeguarding in connection with Professional Diving Operations and on Safe Performance of Professional Diving Operations in Danish Territory as well as on Diving Equipment. These orders were issued by the Danish Ministry of Industry. Inspection and classification of diving equipment is performed by the Danish Maritime Authority.

German legislation for safety at work, a part of the 1884 social security legislation, is based on the legal accident insurance act. It plays a key role in accident protection and prevention. Legal accident insurance, which cover the members of each individual trade against the risks and consequences of accidents occurring while pursuing that particular trade, is guaranteed by professional trade associations (Berufsgenossenschaften). In addition to other tasks, the professional trade associations issue regulations for prevention of trade-specific accidents (Unfallverhü-tungsvorschriften, UVV). All commercial diving in Germany is covered by the trade association of civil engineering founded in 1887. This trade association has issued regulation "UVV Taucherarbeiten" (Diving Operations at Work) in reference [31], which includes in addition to measures for safe diving, decompression and treatment tables. There are many other safety rules and regulations for diving-related activities, such as underwater welding and cutting, underwater explosives, test intervals for diving equipment, first aid measures, scientific diver operations, etc. all of which are listed in references [16, 18, 19, 20, 21, 31, 77, 79, 80, 81, 82, 83]. This diving-related legislation is valid only for onshore and coastal diving operations. For offshore activities, mining authorities are responsible in Germany—at the top is the supreme mining authority in Clausthal-Zellerfeld. The legal basis is the mining decree for the continental shelf, according to reference [78], which also contains regulations for offshore diving operations in the German sector.

13.5 DIVING COMPLETION AND RESPONSIBILITIES

Exploration and exploitation of marine resources are complex tasks that include different parties. To perform such challenging tasks efficiently, a clear organizational structure with exactly defined areas of responsibility is a fundamental prerequisite, according to reference [72, 94, 102]. Some essential aspects of the involved activities must be taken into account:

- all measures must follow the highest possible safety standards so as to reduce personnel's risks;
- optimal solutions, from technical and economical points of view, must be sought; and
- compliance with relevant legislation is necessary.

A number of parties are involved in offshore diving activities; their functions and responsibilities will be introduced briefly. The allocation of responsibilities may vary from country to country or even from project to project but some general principles apply to all operations.

First is the Concession Owner or Licensee who has the license from the government to perform work at a particular offshore location. The concession owner or licensee has the duty of ensuring compliance with relevant legislation and with diving-related legislation.

The Operator of an offshore installation carries out the practical work on behalf of the concession owner or licensee. Therefore the operator has primary responsibility for all activities on the installation including diving.

The Client is the partner of the contractor placing the contracts, for example, with a diving contractor. Clients may be concession owners or operators. The Client's Representative is nominated by the client to act on his behalf to ensure safe performance of the agreed-upon contract work. The client's representative has the authority to influence diving activities via the diving supervisor, but the supervisor may decide whether or not to agree to the representative's demands.

The Offshore Installation Manager (OIM) in the case of an installation or the Master in the case of a diving support vessel is the person responsible for the safety of the installation or vessel, including all persons on it. The OIM or Master has the authority to influence diving activities via the supervisor. But again the diving supervisor has the prime responsibility for the diving team. For onshore diving, for example, in harbors, the Harbor Master takes responsibility for the harbor and the areas under his control. He has the same functions as the OIM or the Master of a DSV.

The Diving Contractor is the partner of the client and the employer of divers performing the contract work. He is responsible for the health and safety of all persons employed by him. The diving contractor has particular responsibilities, among others, ensuring compliance with existing diving regulations, nominating the diving supervisor in writing, issuing diving rules, providing the necessary plant and equipment for dive operations, including emergency actions, ensuring documentation and communication, and other tasks. Considerable responsibility is placed on the diving contractor. Exceptions to his overall responsibility exists only in connection with activities on offshore installations or vessels where the OIM or Master is also involved. Where more than one diving team is working at the dive spot, usually on a shift basis, a Diving Superintendent appointed by the diving contractor is the person-in-charge for all diving supervisors. He is also the contractor's representative on contractual matters. The diving superintendent has the authority to instruct supervisors on operational matters and under exceptional circumstances he may even take over direct responsibility for an operation that is underway.

The Diving Supervisor is in charge of the actual dive and has immediate control of the whole operation. He must be appointed by the diving contractor in writing and has a considerable responsibility for the personnel under his control and for performing dives and chamber treatments safely. He is involved in arranging competent diving teams who have the necessary qualifications and experience for the job. He must, for example, ensure that all operations are carried out according to the contractor's diving rules, that the plant and equipment used meet legal and company requirements, that actual documentation is complete, and that divers' log books are completed correctly on a daily basis. He is responsible for adequate treatment of divers in cases of DCS. He should seek medical assistance from diving doctors, but it is up to him whether or not to follow a doctor's recommendations.

The Diver is the last link in the chain of responsibilities. He has the general duty of taking care of his own safety as well as of the safety of his team members. He is responsible for his diving equipment and must maintain and check it according to the contractor's diving rules. His main task is to carry out underwater work in accordance with the instructions of the diving supervisor. Sometimes a Lead Diver, who is the most senior diver of a team, is appointed by the diving supervisor.

In the case of saturation diving, Support Technicians are necessary to support the dive team as chamber operators, life support technicians (LSTs), winch operators, etc. They are appointed by the diving contractor and responsible to the diving supervisor. The principle of an organizational scheme for offshore operations according to reference [43], is shown in Fig. 13.2.

In Chapter 9, the technical procedures for different diving operations were introduced. In this section, some administrative measures to guarantee the highest possible diving safety standards are discussed.

The diving-related legislation of most countries requires diving rules which give detailed information on the completion of a diving job according to current legislation. The licensee, the organization that has the legal title to perform work at a particular location, is responsible for issuing proper diving rules. Very often this is a single oil company or a consortium of companies, which will normally delegate the duty of preparing diving rules to their diving contractor. With these diving rules the diving contractor gives general instructions to his personnel on company procedures for all kind of activities. The rules must be in compliance with current legislation and cover all phases of diving, such as planning, preparation, performance, and emergency routines. Diving rules give detailed descriptions of responsibility areas, including the company's chain of command, preparation steps for the different kinds of diving operations taking into account weather conditions as well as tides and currents, emergency procedures for contingencies, documentation and communication, proof of the personnel's adequate qualification and medical fitness, and last but not least, the size of the diving teams for the given diving operations. Diving operations are performed by diving teams and the number of team members depends on the kind of task and type of dive. It is the diving contractor's duty to arrange sufficient diving personnel with appropriate qualifications and certification, as well as proper equipment. But the contractor may delegate this responsibility to a competent diving supervisor of his choice.

All national legislation is based on the diving supervisor as the responsible person at the dive site; he is appointed by the diving contractor in writing and is in charge of supervising diving activities underway, keeping the operation's log book on a day-to-day basis, and choosing members for his diving team.

The number of members of a diving team is dealt with differently by different nations. While some countries, such as the UK, listed in references [72, 85, 102], and Germany, found in reference [31], have strict regulations on the size of diving teams, other countries like the U.S., France, and Norway give only general outlines about manning levels in their legislation. The size of each diving team must guarantee the safe performance of the intended dive under all circumstances. In practice, the

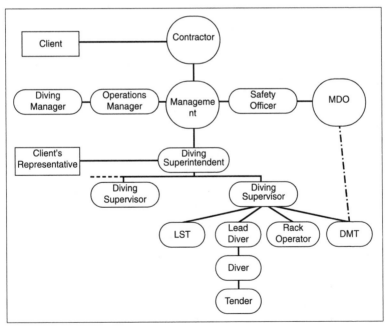

Fig. 13.2 Organizational scheme for offshore diving operations [43]

minimum size of a standard air team, for example, consists of three or four persons, including diver, standby diver, tender, and supervisor. Some national regulations allow one person as both tender and supervisor under special boundary conditions. For bell dives, at least two divers must share the bell, one diver acting as bellman while the other diver(s) is working outside the bell.

The specific problem of continuously supervising divers when they are underwater has been solved. Electronic devices, covered in reference [101], which are able to monitor the diver's bottom time and depth at any time makes supervision much easier and more reliable.

Daily working hours for diving personnel are limited by regulatory bodies. As a general rule, all diving activities should be planned on the basis of a maximum of 12 hrs work in any 24-hr period. A minimum continuous rest period of 8 hrs must be ensured within each 24-hr cycle; this time is increased by Norwegian regulations to 12 hrs. Topside personnel must have a continuous rest period of at least 8 hrs, according to references [102, 144]. French regulations specify the maximum time for underwater work, which is up to 3 hrs for commercial divers in a 12-hr period, as stated in reference [133].

In case of saturation operations, bellruns must not exceed 8 hrs, allowing a working time for the saturation diver in the water of 4 hrs, according to reference [102, 144]. Norwegian regulations limit the working time in the case of deep diving, meaning dives deeper than 180 m, to 3 hrs in the water, as stated in reference [144].

NPD restricts the number of the days at working depth for saturation dives to 10-14 days, which does not include decompression time, according to reference [144]. Danish regulations limit the duration of a saturation dive to 20 days, with the possibility of extension up to 28 days. French regulations allow 30 days as the maximum for saturation diving operations, as stated in reference[133]. The UK has an indirect restriction of saturation times. A 1987 agreement between the Offshore Diving Industry and the National Union of Seamen (NUS) restricts the tour of offshore duty for all employees to 28 days with the option of extending this duty time. This means that under normal circumstances saturation dives are limited to approximately 26 days, leaving 2 days for medical checks after the dive. It is common practice, underscored by different national regulations, that the time between saturation periods must be at least equal to the duration of the preceding dive.

NOTES

CHAPTER 14

Diving Activities Offshore

14.1 INTRODUCTION

The exploration and economic utilization of marine resources are closely connected to diving operations. Without an efficient diving industry, today's offshore oil and gas production would be impossible. Offshore, in this context, means the areas of the continental shelf which can be exploited with modern technology. Commercial diving down to 300 msw, and in special cases even down to 450 msw, is the depth range possible given present diving technology. But we know of huge oil resources off the coast of Brazil (Campus Basin) at depths between 400 and approximately 1500 msw. To exploit these resources, new and more effective technologies, which replace the diver by manned and unmanned remotely operated systems, are being developed. But even these technologies need human support.

Divers' present day offshore diving tasks include: support of exploration drilling; support during the installation and construction phase of offshore installations and pipelines, maintenance, inspection, and repair of offshore installations and pipelines; and salvage/removal of underwater installations. Figure 14.1 shows the diver's main offshore activities, but it is only a rough and incomplete overview.

Worldwide there are thousands of platforms. In the Gulf of Mexico alone there are more than 4000 with a maximum depth of more than 400 msw. In addition, more than 50,000 km of underwater pipelines have

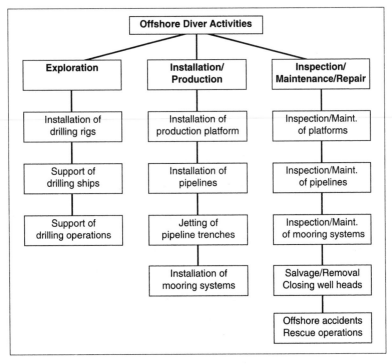

Fig. 14.1 Overview of divers' offshore activities

been laid, and these must be inspected and repaired, and new ones installed. The best way of introducing divers' tasks is to follow the sequence of activities for the exploration and exploitation of marine oil and gas resources. There are basically three phases: exploration phase; installation/production phase; and inspection/maintenance/repair (IMR) phase.

While exploration and installation/production activities are sequential, inspection, maintenance, and repair (IMR) work goes on continuously during both phases to keep the installations in good order and to ensure the highest possible safety standards. Diver activities in the oil and gas business are dealt with, for example, in references [39, 97, 105].

14.2 OVERVIEW OF DIVER ACTIVITIES OFFSHORE
14.2.1 Exploration Phase

The exploration of marine resources requires extensive and costly preparations. Despite geological studies and seismic measurements only test drills can prove the existence of a marine deposit with certainty.

Marine test drills make considerable technical and financial demands which depend, among other things, on weather and sea conditions and especially on water depths at the proposed location. Drilling installations used offshore are, according to reference [123]: jack-ups with extendable legs (maximum operational depth rd. 120 msw); semi-submersibles (maximum operational depth rd. 1500 msw); and drillships (maximum operational depth rd. 1500 msw).

Water depths for jack-up operations are limited by the length of the legs, while semi-submersibles and drillships are theoretically independent of the operational depth. But anchoring is critical, as surface movements of the vessel must be limited lest the drill string be endangered. Positioning is done by anchors with automatic winches, or, in deep water, by dynamic positioning (DP) systems. Figure 14.2 shows the scheme of a marine drilling unit. An important detail of each drilling unit is the blow-out preventer (BOP), which seals the drill hole.

Divers do multiple tasks during the exploration phase. While some of the tasks are very specific, depending on the kind of drilling unit in use, other tasks are common to the drilling business. In the case of jack-ups the location for the jack-up must be inspected in advance and the position for the legs cleared of debris. The penetration of the legs and the formation of scours around the legs must be checked. If necessary, scour holes must be filled. In the case of semi-submersibles or drillships, divers must inspect all underwater parts of the structure, especially the thrusters. If the drilling unit is positioned by means of anchors, divers assist in the rigging of

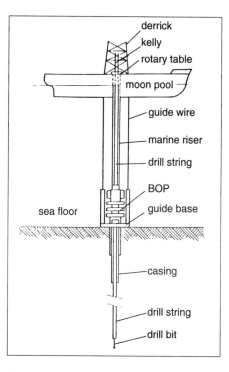

Fig. 14.2 Scheme of a marine drilling system

anchor pendant wires. The blow-out preventer, necessary for each drilling activity, is a kind of safety valve, but it acts just the other way round. It seals the drill hole and prevents an uncontrolled blow-out of oil or gas. Hydraulic-operated rams take over the sealing functions if the pressure of the oil/gas deposit exceeds the external hydraulic pressure head. Because the BOP is a complex system with mechanical, hydraulic, and electrical subsystems, troubleshooting is one of the diver's main tasks. He assists in the preparation work and the installation of the BOP and carries out all kinds of maintenance and repair work, especially changing the gasket between the BOP and the connector housing. A continuous task for the diver during drilling, but not only then, is assisting in the recovery of lost equipment. Recovery of lost or damaged equipment is among his duties during any offshore activity.

14.2.2 Installation/Production Phase

If the exploration of the field was successful, reliable data on the extent and productivity of the oil or gas deposit are available. Depending on the drilling results, production starts with economic exploitation of the new deposit. This phase includes, in addition to production, transportation of oil and gas to the shore for further distribution.

Depending on the field's size, one or more production platforms is installed. Each platform is usually connected to a number of satellite wells via pipelines on the sea floor. What kind of production platform is best suited for the particular location depends on water depth, sea conditions, production concept, and, last but not least, on the financial resources available. There are different technical options available for production platforms, e.g., fixed platforms, gravity platforms, tension leg platforms, etc. The dimensions and masses of platforms are enormous, from 60,000 t for steel platforms up to 800,000 t for concrete ones. Platforms are now used in waters down to 400 msw, according to reference [123]. A production platform contains not only the technical installations for production and separation of crude oil and gas, but also diving equipment, workshops, and accommodations for the 200 or more persons on board. The person-in-charge is the Offshore Installation Manager (OIM).

Insofar as possible, the platform is constructed onshore to reduce offshore assembly work, which is dependent on the weather. Floating cranes or crane barges with lifting capacities up to 7000 t support the platform assembly. Shipment of oil from the platform to the shore may be done by tanker or pipeline; each option has its advantages and disadvantages.

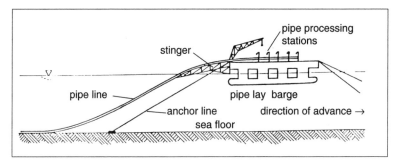

Fig. 14.3 Laying marine pipelines using a pipelay barge

Although the installation of a pipeline is considerably more expensive, in the long run it is the cheaper and more reliable solution compared with transport by tanker, assuming the deposit is sufficiently productive. Transport by tanker requires a mooring system for the ship, generally a Single Point Mooring (SPM), available in different designs, as shown in references [39, 123].

A number of diver tasks are related to the installation of platforms and mooring systems. The first task is to survey the sea floor, and eventually, to remove debris at the planned location. Further, a foundation must be prepared for erection of the platform and mooring system. During installation divers assist in the underwater civil engineering work and help with the assembly of the mooring system including its anchoring and hose connections. Installation of risers and pipeline tie-ins are other diver tasks, as is the building of antiscour systems on the sea bed. The diver's second main task during this phase is to assist in the installation of pipelines from the production platform to the shore. The diameter of the pipes depends on the properties of the medium to be transported and the required flow rate. In practice, pipeline diameters are between 6" (15 cm) and 48" (120 cm). Laying marine pipelines at depths of 200 to 300 msw in the North Sea is done by special pipelay barges (see Fig. 14.3). Standard pipes are 40' (12 m) long and are encased in concrete to protect the pipe from external damage. The concrete coating also helps to compensate for the pipe's buoyancy in water. To assemble the pipeline, standard pipes pass through different stations on board the barge. First, pipes are lined up, then they are welded together and the welded joint is checked by x-ray resp. U.S. measurements. At the dope station the field joint is protected with an additional coating. The "endless" pipeline is lowered via the stinger to the sea floor (Fig. 14.3). To further protect the pipeline, trenches are excavated where the pipeline is buried. This is done by special trenching barges using sledges with high pressure water jets. The excavated material from the trench, which may have a depth between 1 and 5 m (3' - 15'), is used to bury the pipeline.

Many diver activities are involved during pipeline laying and burying. A major task is to check the operation of the stinger. This includes, among other things, adjusting the desired profile of the stinger and checking that the pipeline is riding smoothly in the stinger's rollers. In heavy weather pipeline laying must be interrupted. Then the pipeline's head is closed and laid down on the sea floor. When weather conditions have improved the head is picked up by the barge's crane, and work continues. These actions must be supported by divers too, as is the handling of valves to flood or dewater the pipe. When the pipeline is laid, one of the last tasks is the connection of the pipeline to the production platform's riser, the socalled tie-in. There are different types of tie-ins and methods of installation. Because the tie-in must fit accurately, great demands are made on the diver's skills. The proper working of the jetting sledge must be continuously supervised. Because HP air and water are used, trench jetting poses special hazards which must be taken into account by the diver. Safety memos and an AODC code of practice, for example, deal with these specific dangers, which can be found in references [105, 106, 107]. During pipeline laying, the barge moves according to the laying speed, using its anchoring for moving in the direction of advance. As a consequence, anchors must be removed from time to time and dropped again at a new location, an action supported by anchor handling boats. Diver assistance is necessary here for replacing anchor pendant wires.

14.2.3 Inspection

Inspection includes not only inspection, maintenance, and repair, abbreviated IMR, but also dismantling and salvage activities, including rescue operations that involve divers.

Marine installations, many of which have been in operation for many years, are exposed to winds, waves, and currents as well as to corrosion and erosion. To ensure the functioning of offshore buildings and the safety of personnel and the environment, all marine installations must be continuously supervised and maintained. Sophisticated maintenance and inspection programs have been developed and are used for that reason. Much of the normal production costs are for inspection and maintenance work carried out by divers. To save money, procedures are being developed that replace divers by automatic systems and remote control, according to reference [124]. Despite these efforts, however, there will remain many areas where divers are able to complete underwater tasks most effectively and economically.

An essential diver's task is the periodic supervision of platforms during the exploration phase; this inspection is even more important in the production phase. It includes scour and marine growth inspections, inspection of corrosion, including a check of wall thickness and imperfections, inspection of anti-corrosion measures, such as checking anodes and conducting potential readings. The inspection techniques used by divers are introduced in section 14.4.

Maintenance and repair work supplement the measures taken to keep not only large marine buildings like production platforms in working order but also to keep smaller underwater installations like satellite wells, booster stations, etc. functioning. Mooring systems, exposed to heavy sea and rough working conditions, need regular inspection and maintenance of both surface and underwater parts.

Another standard task for divers is IMR of pipelines, as stated in reference [39], where inspection tasks are supported by manned and unmanned submerged vessels, according to reference [124]. Although pipelines are buried for protection from external damage, undersea currents may free sections of the pipeline, causing them to hang free. Depending on the span of the freed pipe, additional forces build up in the pipe and exceed its design limits. Therefore, freed pipe must be reduced in length by installing suspension points if the pipeline cannot be reburied. Open laid marine pipelines are especially exposed to external damage, and in that case, the damaged part must be replaced using repair techniques described in section 14.3.

Oil and gas deposits are limited, and after some years further exploitation may be uneconomical. If a field is given up, the concession owner must restore the original conditions at the location. This means that divers must dismantle the production platform and other marine installations. Sometimes the dismantled platform can be reinstalled at a new location. But very often the construction has become technically obsolete, so complete removal is the most economical solution. The platform is cut up and the parts removed by crane or derrick barges. Piles and casings are cut below the mudline, and wells are permanently closed.

14.2.4 Accidents Offshore

Offshore accidents are a special topic. In this context divers salvage victims and remove damaged constructions. Since 1965 more than a dozen severe offshore accidents have occurred worldwide, with more than 550 fatalities. From 1980 to 1987, 54 offshore installations were lost [125, 126]. The most spectacular disasters with the greatest numbers of fatalities were the accidents involving the Norwegian accommodation platform *Alexander L. Kielland* in March 1980, the drill rig *Ocean Ranger* in February 1982, and the British production platform *Piper Alpha* in July 1988.

In the case of the *Alexander L. Kielland,* a semi-submersible with five columns serving as the accommodation rig in the Ekofisk field, a column broke during a heavy storm. The rig capsized with the loss of 123 of the 212 people on board. The drill rig *Ocean Ranger* another semi-submersible off the Canadian coast, capsized during a storm. Water that had entered the rig caused a breakdown of electrical circuits, resulting in malfunctions in the ballast system. The increasing list of the rig could not be counteracted. All 84 lives on board were lost. The production platform *Piper Alpha* was located 190 km northeast of Aberdeen; a number of explosions occurred, presumably caused by leaking gases. The platform burned out completely with the loss of 167 people.

Table 14.1 Accident Statistic for Offshore Installations [127]

Type of installation	Total number of accidents	Rig years
Jack-ups	226	3,500
Semi-submersibles	139	1,150
Drillships	40	500
Fixed platforms		46,500

There is no question that the offshore industry learned its lessons and gained experiences that are now used in new design concepts to minimize accident rates. Risk analysis is therefore an important and effective tool for estimating failure probabilities for offshore installations. Choosing the right piece of equipment for the right task results in reducing the risk of unforeseen events.

Besides the loss of lives and following financial consequences, the concession owner must also consider the economic risks connected with a breakdown in production and with the creation of oil spills. In the framework of a jack-up risk analysis, rig and offshore vessel accidents have been analyzed for the period 1979-1989, according to references [127] (see Table 14.1). The total number of accidents for fixed platforms is not

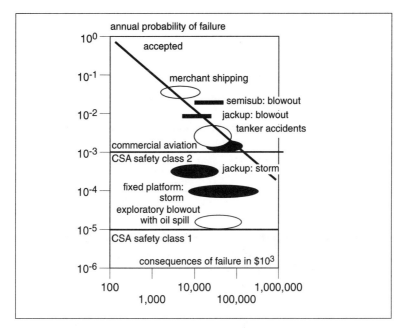

Fig. 14.4 Risk analysis for offshore installations [127]

mentioned in reference [127], but the number of rig years (number of rigs times years of operation) shows that much more information is available for this type of offshore installation than for any other. According to the available accident statistics, the most frequent causes of fixed platform mishaps are blowout and fire accidents, which together cause roughly 70% of all events. Analysis of jack-up accidents shows two typical causes. The main cause is stability problems with legs on the sea floor, followed closely by towing/transportation mishaps. These two causes account for approximately 45% of all accidents; the third cause is blowout and fire, which accounts for 18%. Twenty-five percent of semi-submersible accidents are caused by the mooring, a problem typical for that kind of rig. Towing/transportation mishaps are again the second most frequent cause of accidents. And the third most frequent cause, accounting for 14% of accidents is again blowout and fire. The main cause of accidents for drillships is blowout and fire, accounting for 18%. Mooring and transportation are only minor problems for drillships, but collision is a common risk.

The results of this risk analysis show that for fixed platforms blowout and fire are overwhelmingly the most frequent accident events. Drilling units, like jack-ups, semi-submersibles, and drillships all have more or less the same probability of blowout and fire accidents, which is in the range of 18%. To understand this figure two factors must be considered. Drilling is limited to a short time period during the exploration phase. On the other hand, the risk of a blowout accident during drilling is relatively high, independent of the kind of drilling unit. The risks of typical offshore accidents are compared to other risks listed in reference [127] in Fig. 14.4.

The role of divers in rescue operations in the case of accidental events is very limited; these activities will be organized and carried out topside. After severe accidents, divers' tasks are usually limited to salvaging victims' bodies and to clearing the scene of the accident from debris. Damaged structural parts must be removed or, if possible, repaired. As shown in the risk analysis published in reference [127], blowout accidents are a potential danger in the offshore business. Divers have been used successfully to minimize such events according to reference [128]. During the blowout process an uncontrolled flow of oil or gas escapes from the drill hole. In the immediate vicinity of the hole a calm zone builds up, depending on water depth and the hole's cross section. This calm zone can be used by divers to prepare to close the well.

14.3 UNDERWATER WORKING TECHNIQUES

The great variety of manual tasks in the processing and construction industries has resulted in a wide range of specialized trades. A similar variety of skilled tasks must be carried out underwater. Divers must deal with these tasks under adverse conditions which include a cold, hostile environment with underwater currents and very often with limited or no visibility.

The diver must be skilled and physically fit. He must also be "a jack of all trades," able to handle the different tasks safely and efficiently. Specialization has also occurred in underwater industries, meaning that divers concentrate on particular skills. With this in mind, the German diver training regulations found in reference [99], understandably require that diver trainees have successfully completed their training in a profession. It is obvious that onshore working procedures and tools must be modified for use underwater. Instead of electrically-powered tools, those with pneumatic or hydraulic drives are generally used. A partial overview of working techniques used in underwater work is given in references [39, 72, 105] (see also Fig. 14.5).

Cleaning/Conservation is a combination of tasks where cleaning is the first step, not only for conservation work, but also for inspection and/or cutting and welding. Soft and hard marine growth can be found everywhere on

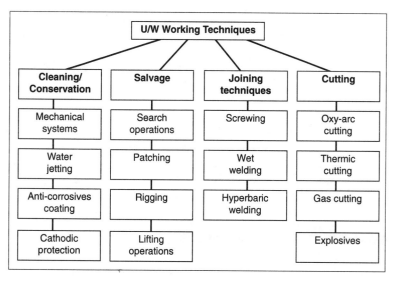

Fig. 14.5 Overview of underwater working techniques

the underwater surfaces of marine installations. These may be some centimeters thick, depending on water depth and temperature. To remove this growth, mechanical tools like brushes, grinders, needle guns, etc. or high pressure waterjets are used. Waterjetting may be done with pure water using pressures of more than 1000 bars or water plus grit or slag may be used with reduced pressures. Waterjetting is used not only for cleaning but also for cutting. Handling of HP waterjets is potentially dangerous and workers must follow stringent safety requirements, which can be found in references [106, 107].

Conservation of marine installations and corrosion protection play important roles in the diving business. To maintain the integrity of marine constructions against mechanical and chemical damage caused by aggressive sea waters and from electrochemical corrosion, installations must be sufficiently protected. Corrosion may cause considerable loss of material in a very short time under unfavorable conditions. Different metals or different parts of one metal in the presence of sea water act as electrolytes and generate a current which depends on the potential difference. A high potential difference induces a high current with correspondingly high corrosion rates. One way to protect the metal construction of offshore installations is the use of appropriate anti-corrosive coatings, such as those used successfully to protect ships' hulls. Special coatings and procedures have been developed for application underwater by divers and are listed in references [108, 109, 145]. Another possibility is to use cathodic protection either as a passive system using sacrificial anodes or as an active system using impressed currents (for example, see references [39, 146]). The diver's tasks are to conduct potential readings, to install sacrifice anodes, and to replace them or install impressed current systems.

Salvage activities include, in general, searching, patching leaks, rigging, and lifting operations. These activities are very often combined. Rigging, for example, is not limited to salvage tasks, but is necessary for any other underwater work and is among the diver's basic skills, according to reference [111]. Searching operations are standard diver tasks and use proven search procedures. Searching tasks at greater depths require technical systems such as Remote Operated Vessels (ROVs). A spectacular success was the discovery of the *Titanic* wreck in 3800 msw using an ROV. Salvage is a special field in the diving business; it requires much experience and special knowledge, as shown in reference [110]. For lifting operations, the basics of hydromechanics are applied; these are dealt with in Chapter 8.

Joining techniques include using screws to connect construction parts or pipelines, as well as welding procedures. Underwater welding procedures can be divided into wet welding and hyperbaric dry welding

Wet welding performed directly in the water was used as early as the 1920s as an underwater joining technique. Metal arc wet welding with a manually held rod is still the usual process (see Fig. 14.6). It is a flexible procedure needing only a DC generator at the surface and power cables (Fig. 14.8). A disadvantage is the poor quality of a wet-welded joint due to

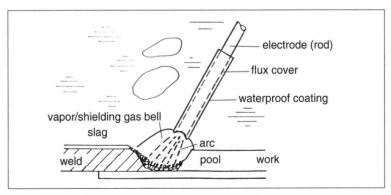

Fig. 14.6 Principle of manual metal arc wet welding

Fig. 14.7 Dry hyperbaric welding in a welding habitat

increased embrittlement caused by dissolved hydrogen in the molten metal and a high cooling rate caused by the surrounding water—the rate is approximately 15 times higher than in air. An appropriate flux cover on the rods may improve wet-welded joints, as investigations with different rods types have shown, according to reference [114]. The flux cover must have a waterproof coating to avoid getting water into the cover. Using electricity underwater creates a potential danger for the diver. During the welding process, a current of several hundreds amps is needed, while the voltage is only in the range of 15 to 25 volts. Safety measures and safety procedures, for example those dealt with in reference [88], guarantee the highest possible protection for the diver and are also found in references [112, 113, 148]. If high quality joints are required, e.g., for pipelines, then dry hyperbaric welding methods are necessary. Containers keep the work environment dry, thus avoiding the disadvantages in quality that occur with wet welding. Containers may be simply a dry box, or, in the most advanced technologies, a welding habitat (see Fig. 14.7). In principle, underwater dry welding has the same conditions and possibilities as at the surface, with one exception—the hyperbaric environment. Dry welding has been carried out successfully down to depths of 600 m. The hyperbaric environment clearly influences the welding process, according to references [147, 148]. The static pressure, for example, constricts the arc, causing unstable conditions, but higher voltages remedy this problem.

In addition to classic manual metal arc welding in a dry atmosphere, metal inert gas and metal active gas (MIG/MAG) procedures are used widely, as is tungsten inert gas (TIG) welding as illustrated in references [115, 116, 117, 148]. Instead of manual procedures, semiautomatic processes are used, for example, the orbital head developed for pipeline welding and inspection which can be found in references [117, 149].

There is no question that hyperbaric dry welding is more costly, especially when advanced welding habitats are used. But a habitat offers the divers comfort and much better working conditions. So the required high standards for welded joints are guaranteed. One-bar welding, a specialty in underwater welding, will only be mentioned. Here a pressure-tight container ensures atmospheric conditions independent of the actual depth. As this procedure is extremely costly, it is not used today according to reference [150].

Cutting is one of the working techniques most often used underwater. Different procedures are in use, depending on the task: oxy-arc cutting with a tabular metal electrode; thermic procedures with an ultra electrode (with thermic lance or with Kerie cable); gas cutting with a cutting torch; water jetting; and explosives.

The standard method is oxy-arc cutting where an electric arc melts the ferrous base material and an oxygen jet oxidizes the molten material and blows it away. The equipment necessary is the same as for metal arc welding, but here an oxygen supply and a supply hose must also be available at the surface. Instead of the electrode holder, a cutting torch is necessary to supply the tabular electrode with oxygen (see Fig. 14.8 courtesy of references [112, 116]). Safety considerations for handling electricity underwater are similar to those for wet welding, according to references [82, 88], but additional safety concerns, such as gas pockets and the danger of explosions, as illustrated in references [151, 152], must be taken into account. To increase cutting temperatures, tabular metal or carbon electrodes are replaced by ultrathermic electrodes. These electrodes consist of a thin steel tube containing small mild steel rods and one aluminum/magnesium rod. Due to thermochemical reactions, cutting temperatures of 5000°C and more are achieved. Ferrous metals, non-ferrous metals, rock, concrete, etc. can be cut. Thermic lance and Kerie cable use the same principle as ultrathermic electrodes. The thermic lance, a thin steel tube approximately 3 m length, contains small mild steel rods and is supplied with oxygen. After being electrically ignited, it continues to burn, consuming oxygen at a fast rate. Due to its very high temperature, it burns through almost anything. When cutting rock or concrete, explosive mixtures may be generated in cavities, causing deflagrations. In these situations, the diver is endangered by induced pressure waves. The Kerie cable, 30 m long, is a modification of the thermic lance; it consists of flexible steel wires covered by a plastic cable. After being ignited electrically, it burns like the thermic lance and is supplied from an oxygen bank. The cutting temperatures are lower, with a maximum of only approximately 2700°C.

Underwater gas cutting, based on oxygen and a fuel like petrol, acetylene, hydrogen, etc., uses a cutting torch very similar to those used for cutting tasks at the surface. Precautions to allow for the undisturbed escape of gases during each cutting procedure are essential. Otherwise, burning gases enriched with oxygen may be caught in confined spaces and cause explosions.

Waterjetting, already discussed as a cleaning method, may also be used for cutting, as shown in references [117, 148]. Water pressures up to 2500 bars are used with dry and wet abrasives. Efficiency is dependent on the hyperbaric environment. Down to 100 msw, good results can be achieved, but with increasing depths problems in focusing the waterjet must be considered.

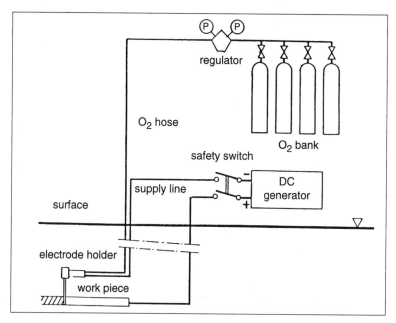

Fig. 14.8 Oxy-arc cutting equipment

Explosives are often used for cutting underwater. The cutting effect is based on the enormous shock wave caused by chemical reactions of the explosive; the shock wave destroys the material in its way. For underwater uses, only high order explosives with high velocities of detonation (> 7500 m/s) are used, such plastic explosives as TNT, PETN, etc. Explosives are used for preparing trenches, removing underwater obstacles like rock or shipwrecks, dismantling marine installations, preparing repair tasks, and cutting heavy wires or shafts. For cutting pipes, piles, wires, shafts, or blowing exactly dimensioned holes into structures, shaped charges are successfully used (see Fig. 14.9). The charge is not directly mounted on the material to be cut but is held in a container sealed with an inner liner. The explosive force is directed to the work piece, where it is most powerful. Due to the high risks in dealing with explosives, stringent requirements must be followed for transport, handling, preparing, and any possible ignition of the charges. National rules and regulations, e.g. reference [83], have strict requirements for the use of explosives and for the training of personnel who use explosives.

14.4 UNDERWATER INSPECTION

Inspection of marine installations is one of the main tasks in underwater work. Regular inspections provide exact data about the actual condition of an underwater building. Because the lifetime of such buildings may be 25 years or more, and because they are often exposed to very rough weather and sea conditions, maintaining the integrity and effectiveness of marine installations has the highest priority, both for safety and also for economic reasons. Figure 14.10 gives a rough overview of inspection methods used in the underwater field constructed with information found in references [39, 118, 119, 148]. In the following some methods will be discussed briefly.

Visual inspections are conducted to get preliminary information about the general condition of an underwater installation or of a specific structural

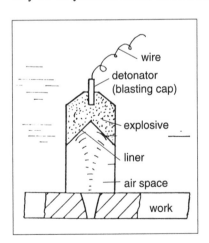

Fig. 14.9 Scheme of a shaped charge for underwater cutting

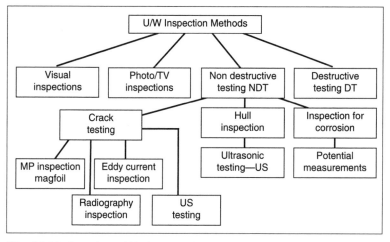

Fig. 14.10 Overview of Underwater Inspection Methods

part. Visual inspection is also used for general checks of interesting areas of the sea floor or for first inspections of the scene of an accident. The main and only tool for visual inspections is the diver's eye, a very effective tool. But some skills and experience are necessary for this kind of job—among other things, the different optical relations must be taken into account.

Photo/TV Inspections using technical tools very often support visual inspections. Very effective TV cameras are on the market today, offering, for example, optical possibilities like high photosensitivity and the ability to enlarge details. These capabilities far exceed those of the human eye. Furthermore, inspection results can be continually observed at surface monitors, offering an exact evaluation of the documented data at a later date. Unmanned systems, such as ROVs equipped with TV cameras, are widely used, especially for internal inspections of pipelines or of spaces dangerous for human beings.

14.4.1 Non-Destructive Testing (NDT)

Non-destructive testing is widely applied in technical fields and forms the basic technology for almost every inspection procedure. It is the aim of all inspection methods to learn about the actual status of a building without endangering its integrity by testing. Visual and photo/TV inspections are ultimately NDT methods too. But very often defects are small and are undetected by visual inspections, so more sophisticated methods must be applied. While the two above-mentioned methods give a general overview of the status of an installation or a part of it, the following testing procedures concentrate on local areas where defects are suspected.

In this overview, only the following procedures are dealt with as non-destructive testing methods according to Fig. 14.10: crack testing; hull inspection; and corrosion inspection. Failure of a structural element usually starts from flaws or cracks in the material. In time cracks progress until they reach a critical size where the structure cannot bear the design loads any longer and it fails. Not every flaw will cause a complete failure—there are materials that tolerate undercritical flaws. Since defects like flaws are responsible for the beginning of complete structural failures, careful crack detection is essential.

Crack testing is therefore the most important proof of the integrity of the structure's members. A number of different testing methods are available; these are also applied, with some modifications, in the underwater field. Some of these methods will be briefly introduced here: magnetic particle inspection (MPI)/Magfoil; eddy current inspection; radiographical inspection; and ultrasonic (US) inspection.

Magnetic particle inspection (MPI) is a method used for detection of surface or near-surface defects in ferrous materials. A magnetic field is induced with strong magnets while fine ferrous particles mixed with a special luminous dye are distributed equally on the surface to be checked. The particles follow the magnetic flux, and imperfections in the material will disturb the equal flux and cause a concentration of particles at the location of a defect. Using ultraviolet light in dark environment, the fluorescent particles are visible, marking the location and size of the defect. Taking photos is one way to document the defect.

A similar procedure called Magfoil, according to reference [117] is a modification of MPI. Here the ferrous particles are placed in a plastic bag 160 × 80 mm (6.3" × 3.15") together with a special liquid. Before use, the particles and liquid are mixed in the bag and applied the same way as for standard MPI. Defects will be shown by the disturbed orientation of the ferrous particles; the liquid hardens and fixes the position of the particles in the bag. The bag can then be used for documentation and further evaluation at surface.

Eddy current inspection is another method for detecting surface defects. The procedure uses the changes of permeability and polarity caused by material defects. Results are monitored and evaluated only at the surface. The diver checks the material's surface with an electromagnetic spool following orders from the surface.

Radiographical inspection uses a strong radioactive source which radiates the sample and exposes a film like a photo. Imperfections are more or less visible on the film. This procedure allows detection of flaws even in thick-walled structures, but evaluation of the exposed films is difficult. In addition, handling strong radioactive sources may endanger the diver.

Ultrasonic (US) Inspection is widely applied for the detection of flaws at the sample's surface as well as inside. A transmitter inside of a handy watertight probe transmits ultrasonic waves within the frequency range of some megacycles (MHz). The reflected echoes are monitored and evaluated at the surface; the echoes indicate flaws at the sample's surface and also flaws inside the sample. Angular probes of 30, 45, 60 and 75 degrees are applied to detect flaws even inside welding roots. Good contact between the probe and sample is important. The diver carries out his checks according surface orders, as in the case of eddy current inspection. In the meantime, an intensity meter has been designed for the diver that shows him the intensity of the fault signal, thus enabling him to look for the maximum fault signal, according to references [121, 122].

Hull inspections are carried out to determine the geometrical dimensions of an offshore structure which may be weakened by abrasion and corrosion. The main goal is to check wall thicknesses of platform structures, pipelines, and other underwater constructions using non-destructive testing procedures.

The standard procedure for thickness measurements is ultrasonic (US) testing using the ultrasonic inspection method. Again, good contact between the US probe and the sample's surface is essential and requires prior cleaning of the surface. The transmitted waves pass through the wall and are reflected at the back, generating an echo on the screen which corresponds exactly to the wall's thickness.

Corrosion inspection is also an NDT procedure, but it is a very different kind of inspection than the preceding ones. The diver's main task here is to conduct potential readings to check the efficiency of the impressed current system. To ensure correct readings, good contact between the probe and the metal surface is necessary.

Destructive Testing is mentioned here for reasons of completeness, although it is not used in the field under normal circumstances. Destructive testing is used mainly for laboratory tests, for example, in the course of developing new materials or in the field of accident research where the reasons for material failures are being sought.

14.5 OFFSHORE WORKING CONDITIONS

Working conditions for offshore personnel may vary from country to country and even from platform to platform according to a particular company's policy; however, a working standard has been established based on a 12-hour shift. For offshore personnel, this means 12 hrs on duty, 12 hrs off, 7 days a week. This routine also must be adopted by the diving teams on board, who work on a 2-shift basis in 24 hrs. In the North Sea, crew changes are arranged every 2 or 4 weeks, depending again on the company's policy and kind of work being done. The time off, 2 to 4 weeks for recreation, is the same as the time worked.

Accommodations on board depend on the size of the platform or vessel. On a spacious platform double cabins are standard; on board smaller vessels cabins must be shared by 4 or even 8 crew members. A station bill instructs everybody on board regarding their duties in case of emergency. The person-in-charge is the offshore installation manager (OIM), the master of a vessel. Excellent food is normally free, including soft drinks, but alcohol and drugs are strictly prohibited. Violations lead to immediate dismissal. The North Sea safety standard, mentioned in Chapter 13, states that everybody must undergo a one-week survival training course before being allowed to enter an offshore installation. This training is mandatory for technical as well as non-technical personnel and must be repeated every 3 years.

Payment schemes only will be discussed because actual payments are naturally subject to continuous changes, following the laws of market economies, and depending, among other things, on economic developments in the home country. Actual figures for diver's payments are available from relevant unions. In Europe, for example, payments for diving personnel are regulated by agreements between the diving industry and the responsible unions.

In the UK, the National Union of Seamen (NUS) represents the interests of diving and offshore personnel. Payments are based on a daily rate for days spent offshore—the number of dives and depths of dives during that time play no role. Only in the case of saturation dives is a bonus per hour (from seal to seal) paid, independent of bottom depth reached. Additional allowances are paid for travel, medical and survival training, and protective clothing.

The daily rates are graded according to the diver's qualifications and experience. There are two classification standards, divers and professional divers, according to reference [103], for air and mixed gas divers. Classification as a professional diver requires proof of at least 300 days offshore and a minimum of 150 dives. Similar payment schemes are used in the Norwegian sector and also in other countries in Europe and overseas.

Germany has a very different payment scheme for divers, according to reference [104]. It is based on weekly or monthly wages, the wages depending on the diver's experience and seniority. In addition, a dive bonus (Tauchzulage) is paid for each dive on an hourly basis, taking into account working depth and degree of difficulty, such as chamber dives or dives in open waters.

NOTES

References

1   Smith, E. B.: On the science of deep-sea diving; observations on the respiration of different kinds of air. Undersea Biom. Research 14, 1978

2   Gesetz über die Einheiten im Meßwesen. Bonn: Bundesgesetz-blatt I, 1973 S. 720 ff

3   DIN 1301, Teil 1: Einheiten, Einheitsnamen, Einheitszeichen.

    Teil 2: Einheiten, allgemein angewendete Teile u. Vielfache Berlin: Beuth 1978

4   Myers, J.J. (Ed.); Holm, C.H.; McAllister, R.F.: Handbook of ocean and underwater engineering. New York: McGraw-Hill 1969

5   Shilling, Ch.W.; Werts, M.F.; Schandelmeier, N.R.: The underwater handbook. New York, London: Plenum Press 1976

6   The British sub-aqua club: Safety and rescue for divers. London: Stanley Paul 1987

7   Miller, J.W. (Ed.): NOAA diving manual, diving for science and technology, 2. ed. Flagstaff, AZ: Best Publishing Co 1979

8   Tammeling, G.J.; Quanjer, Ph.H.: Physiologie der Atmung I und II. Frankfurt/M: pharm- und medical information 1984

9   Navy Department: US Navy diving manual, 2. ed. Flagstaff, AZ: Best Publishing Co 1980

10 Bennett, P.B.; Elliott, H.D. (Ed.): The physiology and medicine of diving, 3. ed. London: Bailliere Tindall 1982

11 Webb, P.: Thermal Problems. Chapt. 12 in 10, p. 297 ff

12 Luther, G.; Fock, H.: Klimatisierung von Tauchern. Geesthacht: GKSS-Forschungszzentrum, Bericht 88/E/68 1988

13 Bennett, P.B.; McLeod, M.: Probing the limits of human deep diving. Phil. Trans. Royal Society B 304 1984

14 Gortan, C.; Fructus, X.; Gardette, B.; Delauze, H.G.: Deep diving hydrogenated breathing mixture. Luxemburg: EC-Symposium 1988

15 AODC 014 Guidance note on the minimum quantities of gas required offshore. London: Ass. of Offshore Diving Contractors 1983

16 Verordnung über Druckbehälter, Druckgasbehälter und Füllanlagen. Bonn: Bundesgesetzblatt I 1980, S. 173 ff

17 TRG 102 Technische Gasgemische. Berlin: Beuth 1985

18 TRG 402 Betreiben von Füllanlagen. Berlin: Beuth 1972

19 Unfallverhütungsvorschrift Gase (VBG 61). München: Tiefbau-Berufsgenossenschaft 1977

20 Unfallverhütungsvorschrift Verdichter - Kompressoren (VBG 16). München: Tiefbau-Berufsgenossenschaft 1979

21 Unfallverhütungsvorschrift Sauerstoff (VBG 62). München: Tiefbau-Berufsgenossenschaft 1969

22 DIN 3171 Nahtlose Stahlflaschen für Druckluft und verdichteten Sauerstoff. Berlin: Beuth 1977

23 DIN 58 640 Autonome Leichttauchgeräte mit Druckluft, Teil 1 und 2. Berlin: Beuth 1985

24 AODC 016 Guidance note on colour coding and marking of diving gas cylinders and banks. London: Ass. of Offshore Diving Contractors 1983

25 Vorschriften für Unterwassertechnik, Kapitel 1: Tauchanlagen und Tauchsimulatoren. Hamburg: Germanischer Lloyd 1986

26 DIN 3188 Druckluft für Atemgeräte. Berlin: Beuth 1984

27 Diving Safety Memo 7/1984: Diving gases - suppliers standard. London: Diving Inspectorate, Dept. of Energy 1984

28 Bartmann, H.: Taucher-Handbuch. Landsberg/Leck: ecomed Verlagsgesellschaft 1989

29 AODC 029 Guidance note on oxygen cleaning. London: Ass. of Offshore Diving Contractors

30 SUT: Developments in diving technology, vol. 1. London: Graham & Trotman 1985

31 Unfallverhütungsvorschrift Taucherarbeiten (VBG 39). München: Tiefbau-Berufsgenossenschaft 1985

32 AODC 038 Guidance note on the use of inert gases. London: Ass. of Offshore Diving Contractors 1986

33 Haux, G.: Subsea manned engineering. Flagstaff, AZ: Best Publishing Co 1982

34 Technical specification and information. Vanvouver: International Hard Suits Inc. 1988

35 Friesbie, F.R.: Inspecting and repairing offshore platforms today. Ocean Industry 22 1987

36 DIN 3179 Einteilung von Atemgeräten. Berlin: Beuth 1977

37 Hauptverband gewerblicher Berufsgenossenschaften: Sicherheits-regeln für Druckluft-Leichttauchgeräte (ZH1/237). Köln: C. Heymanns 1986

38 Haux, G.: Tauchtechnik. Berlin, Heidelberg, New York: Springer 1969

39 Sisman, D. (Ed.): The professional diver's handbook. London: Submex 1982

40 Schütt, W.: Dräger Mischgas-Tauchsystem. Lübeck: Drägerwerk AG 1976

41 Boe, J.; Hartung, K.H.: Einsatz des Taucher-Gasmischers Polycom 101 bei einem Großprojekt in Norwegen. Lübeck: Dräger-werk AG H. 326 1983

42 Altner. A.: Taucher-Fachtagung der Tiefbau-Berufsgenossenschaft in Regensburg. München: Tiefbau-Berufsgenossenschaft 99 1987

43 Commercial diver training manual, 2. ed. Los Angeles: College of Oceaneering 1983

44 Lettnin, H.: Sättigungstauchtechnik erleichtert marine Rohstoff-gewinnung, Teil 1 und 2. technik heute 37 1984

45 Comex completes record dive. London: Lloyd's List 28. 3. 1986

46 Rekordtiefe 531 Meter. tauchen 6 1988

47 Lotz, W.E. (Ed.): Protection of divers in water containing hazardous chemicals, pathogenic organisms and radioactive material. Bethesda: Undersea Medical Society 1982

48 Lettnin, H.K.J.: Arbeiten unter Überdruck in kontaminierter Umgebung. München: Tiefbau-Berufsgenossenschaft 101 1989

49 Lettnin, H.K.J.: Über den Umgang mit radioaktiven Material beim Tauchen. Geesthacht: GKSS-Forschungszentrum GKSS 81/I/20 1981

50   Lettnin, H. Polluted water diving. Diving equipment for diving in contaminated atmospheres, especially in radioactive cont. waters. in 47 p. 259

51   Rosenbaum, O.: Die neue Strahlenschutzverordnung, 2. Auflage. Kissing: Weka-Verlag 1978

52   Boycott, A.E.; Damant, G.C.C.; Haldane, J.S.: Prevention of compressed air illness. London: Journal Hyg. 8 1908

53   Bühlmann, A.A.: Dekompression - Dekompressionskrankheit. Berlin, Heidelberg, New York: Springer 1983

54   Yu-Chong, L.; Niu, A.K.C.: Hyperbaric physiology and medicine. Flagstaff, AZ: Best Publishing Co 1988

55   Bennett, P.B.; Schafstall, H.G.; Schnegelsberg, W.; Holthaus, J.; Vann, R.D.: An analysis of 14 successful Trimix 5 deep saturation dives between 150-600 m. Kobe: 9. Int. Symp. on U/W and Hyperbaric Physiology 1986

56   Lettnin, H.: GUSI-Taucher als Forscher und Erforschte. technik heute 40

57   Holthaus, J.: Tauchrisiken Stand 1989. tauchen 9 1989

58   Wienke, B.R.: Tissue gas exchange models and decompression computations: a review. Und. Bio. Research 16 1989

59   Workman, R.D.; Bornman, R.C.: Decompression theory: American practice. Chapt. 17 in 10 p. 307

60   Hempleman, H.V.: Decompression theory: British practice. Chapt. 18 in 10

61   Gase-Handbuch, 3. Auflage. Frankfurt: Messer-Griesheim

62   Weathersby, P.K.; Homer, L.D.; Flynn, L.T.: On the likelihood of decompression sickness. Journal Appl. Physiology 57 1984

63   Royal Navy diving manual, B.R. 2806. London: H.M.S.O. 1976

64   Betriebsschutzweisung 17, Taucherdienst im Geschäftsbereich des BWB Koblenz: Bund. f. Wehrtechnik und Beschaffung 1988

65   Holthaus, J.: Längere Tauchzeiten in Tiefen bis 50 m. Geesthacht: GKSS-Forschungszentrum GKSS 86/E/42 1986

66   Oxy-helium saturation diving tables. London: Underwater Engineering Group, report UR 11 1978

67   Thalman, E.D.: Testing of revised unlimited duration upward excursions during helium-oxygen saturation dives. Und. Bio. Research 16 1989

68   D'Aoust, B.G.; Lambertsen, C.J.: Isobaric gas exchange and supersaturation by counterdiffusion. Chapt. 15 in 10 p. 383

69   D'Aoust, B.G.: Investigations of transient and steady-state isobaric supersaturation by Doppler bubble detection. Virginia Mason Research Center ONR N 00014-78-C-0749 1980

70   Vann, R.D.: Decompression theory and applications. Chapt. 14 in 10

71   The DMAC & EUBS Workshop, Newsletter 10. Aberdeen: European Und. Bio Society 1988

72   The principles of safe diving practice. London: Underwater Engineering Group, report UR 23 1984

73   Berghage, T.E.; Vorosmarti, J.; Barnard, E.E.P.: Recompression treatment tables used throughout the world by government and industry. Bethesda: Naval Med. Research Inst., report 78-16 1978

74   James, P.B.: The choice of a therapeutic compression table in relation to the causative dive. Dundee: AOCD-Symposium 1983

75   Holthaus, J.: Stand der therapeutischen Kompression, 20/80 Helox-saturation - Mittel der Wahl bei Spätfällen. Zentralblatt für Arbeitsmedizin, Arbeitsschutz, Prophylaxe u. Ergonometrie 39 1989

76   Kuhlmann, A.: Einführung in die Sicherheitswissenschaft. Wiesbaden: Friedr. Vieweg & Sohn 1981

77   Hauptverband gewerblicher Berufsgenossenschaften: Richtlinien für den Einsatz von Forschungstauchern (ZH1/540) Köln: C. Heymanns 1988

78   Bergverordnung für den Festlandssockel (Fls Berg V). Bonn: Bundesgesetzblatt I 1989 S. 554 ff

79   Unfallverhütungsvorschrift Allgemeine Vorschriften (VBG 1). München: Tiefbau-Berufsgenossenschaft 1985

80   Unfallverhütungsvorschrift Arbeitsmedizinische Vorsorge (VBG 100). München: Tiefbau-Berufsgenossenschaft 1985

81   Unfallverhütungsvorschrift Erste Hilfe (VBG 109). München: Tiefbau-Berufsgenossenschaft 1980

82   Unfallverhütungsvorschrift Schweißen, Schneiden und verwandte Arbeitsverfahren (VBG 15). München: Tiefbau-Berufs-genossenschaft 1978

83   Unfallverhütungsvorschrift Sprengarbeiten (VBG 46). München: Tiefbau-Berufsgenossenschaft 1985

84   Arnoux, G.A.: Safety in diving operations. Operational acquaintance course for engineers, Plymouth 1988

85   SI 399 Diving operations at work regulations London: Dept of Energy, H.M.S.O. 1981

86   Götz, A.: Die erste Revision im Kernkraftwerk Stade. Atomwirtschaft 19 1974 s. 302 ff

87   Shields, T.G.; Duff, P.M.; Wilcock, S.E.; Giles, R.: Decompression sickness from commercial offshore air-diving operations on the UK continental shelf during 1982 to 1988. SUT vol. 23 Subtech 89 Dordrecht, Boston, London: Kluwer Academic Publ. 1990 p. 259

88 AODC 035 Code of practice for the safe use of electricity under water. London: Ass. of Offshore Diving Contractors 1985

89 AODC 032 Remotely operated vehicle/diver involvement. London: Ass. of Offshore Diving Contractors

90 AODC 022 Code of practice for the operation of manned submersible craft. London: Ass. of Offshore Diving Contractors

91 The diving supervisors manual. London: The Underwater Centre and Ass. of Offshore Diving Contractors 1986

92 US Coast Guard: Commercial diving regulations, part 197. Washington: Department of Transportation 1979

93 Commercial diving operations. Washington: Occupational Safety and Health Standards, part 1910, title 29 1977

94 Betriebssicherheit und Gesundheitsschutz beim Tauchen. Luxemburg: Kommission der Europ. Gemeinschaft 1985

95 Borsch, P.; Münch, E.: Nutzen und Risiko der Kernenergie, 3. Auflage Jülich: KFA Jülich, Jül-Conf-17 1977

96 Jacobsen, E.; Tönjum, S.; Omarheim, J.; Pedersen, O.: Safety in manned diving. Stavanger, Oslo, Bergen, Tromsö: Universitetsforlaget 1984

97 Barrett, B.; Hindley, B.; Howells, R.: Safety in the offshore petroleum industry. London: Kogan Page Ltd 1987

98 Training standards. Luxemburg: Europ. Div. Tech. Com. (EDTC) 1988

99 Verordnung über die Prüfung zum anerkannten Abschluß Geprüfter Taucher. Bonn: Bundesgesetzblatt I 1980 S. 1936 ff

100 Canada oil and gas regulations - diving. Ottawa: Oil and Gas Production and Conservation Act 1982

101 Lafferty, C.F.; Graves, D.F.; Jones, B.A.: Automatic dive data monitoring/recording. SUT Vol. 23 Subtech 89 Kluwer Academic Publ. 1990

102 AODC 048 Offshore diving team manning levels. London: Ass. of Offshore Diving Contractors 1988

103 Diver grading system. London: Intern. Ass. of Underwater Engineering Contractors Newsletter 31 1989

104 Rahmentarifvertrag für das Taucherei- und Bergungsgewerbe. Stuttgart: ÖTV-Gewerkschaft 1988

105 Zinkowski, N.B.: Commercial oilfield diving, 2. Ed. Cambridge, USA: Cornell Maritime Press 1978

106 Diving Safety Memo 9/1980: Use of jetting equipment. London: Diving Inspectorate, Dept. of Energy 1980

107 AODC 049 Code of practice for the use of high pressure water jetting equipment by divers. London: Ass. of Offshore Diving Contractors 1988

108 Capeller, L.; Donker, B.; Richter, U.: Unterwasserkonservierung - Korrosionsschutz für Bauteile im Meerwasser. Geesthacht: GKSS-Forschungszentrum GKSS 80/E/41 1980

109 Donker, B.; Richter, U.; Schafstall, H.G.; Szelagowski, P.: Unterwasserreinigen und Beschichten von Stahl- und Betonstrukturen. Geesthacht: GKSS-Forschungszentrum Jahresbericht 1983

110 Brady, E.M.: Marine salvage operations. Cambridge, USA: Cornell Maritime Press 1960

111 Rossnagel, W.E.; Higgins, L.R.; McDonald, J.A.: Handbook of rigging 4. Ed. New York: McGraw-Hill 1988

112 US Navy: Diving technical manual, underwater cutting and welding. Flagstaff, AZ: Best Publishing Co 1980

113 Merkblatt DVS 1812: Arbeitsschutz beim Unterwasserschweißen und -Schneiden. Düsseldorf: Deutscher Verband für Schweißtechnik 1987

114 Loebel, P.; Schafstall, H.G.; Szelagowski, P.: Naßschweißen mit Stabelektroden. Geesthacht: GKSS-Forschungszentrum Jahresbericht 1986

115 Schäfer, R.; Schafstall, H.G.; Fortschritte beim hyperbaren Schweißen bis in große Wassertiefen infolge der Meerestechnikentwicklung. Geesthacht: GKSS-Forschungszentrum GKSS 82/E/16 1982

116 Int. Symposium Unterwasserschweißen und -schneiden. Geesthacht: GKSS-Forschungszentrum, DVS, WIM 1983

117 2. Int. GUSI-Symposium: Underwater technology. Geesthacht: GKSS-Forschungszentrum, DVS, VDMA 1987

118 Miles, P.H.: Underwater engineering surveys. Houston: Gulf Publishing Corporation 1980

119 US Navy: Diving technical manual, underwater inspection, testing, monitoring of offshore structures. Flagstaff, AZ: Best Publishing Co 1980

120 Mittleman, J.: Diving technical manual, underwater stereo photography for hull inspection. Flagstaff, AZ: Best Publishing Co 1980

121 Manthey, H.J.: Ultraschall-Prüfgerätesystem mit ORMON für den Unterwassereinsatz. Geesthacht: GKSS-Forsch.zentrum GKSS 87/I/10 1987

122 Manthey, H.J.: Entwicklungsarbeiten zur zerstörungsfreien Prüftechnik für den Unterwassereinsatz. Geesthacht: GKSS-Forschungszentrum GKSS 88/1/12 1988

123 Claus, G.; Lehmann, E.; Östergaard, C.: Meerestechnische Konstruktionen. Berlin, Heidelberg, New York: Springer 1988

124   SUT: Second generation subsea production systems, vol. 20. London: Graham & Trotman 1989

125   Smith, L.: Second incident at platform. London: Lloyd's List 8. July 1988

126   Donnerbauer, R.: Diskussion um Sicherheit der Offshore-Technik neu entbrannt. Düsseldorf: VDI-Nachrichten Nr.28 1988

127   Sharples, B.P.M.; Bennett, W.T.: Jack-up analysis reveals accurate hazard assessments. Offshore 49 1989

128   Adams, N.; Kuhlman, L.: Deepwater blowouts: can we control them? Offshore 49 1989

129   HYDRA 10. COMEX S.A. Marseille. Pressemitteilung Nov. 1992

130   Luther, G.: Bemannte Unterwasserarbeiten in kalten Gewässern. Hansa 22 1990

131   Gildhoff, J.: Atemgasversorgung in großen Tauchtiefen. Hansa 22 1990

132   Zuppke, B.: Hydromechanik im Bauwesen, 3. Auflage. Wiesbaden und Berlin: Bauverlag GmbH

133   Journal Officiel De La Republique Francaise: Travaux en Milieu Hyperbare. Paris: Direction des Journaux Officiels Juin 1992 No 1636

134   International Maritime Organisation: Code of safety for diving systems. London: 1985

135   Zheng, J.: Chen, B.: Hyperbaric diving research in CUTI (1977 - 1988). Chinese U/W Technology Inst., Shanghai. Paper presented at GUSI 1989

136   Imbert, G.: Safe deep sea diving using hydrogen. MTS Journal, vol. 23, No 4 1989

137 Barsky, S.M.: Diving in high-risk environments. Fort Collins, Colorado: Dive Rescue Inc. 1990

138 Kenyon, D.; Hamilton, R.W.: Managing oxygen exposure when preparing decompression tables. Haifa: Diving and Hyperbaric Medicine Proceedings, EUBS meeting 1989

139 Schmidt, K.: Hyperbaric fire safety. Geesthacht: GKSS-Forschungszentrum GKSS 90/E/47 1990

140 Schmidt, K.: Sicherheit und Zuverlässigkeit beim Sättigungstauchen in einer Simulationsanlage. Geesthacht: GKSS-Forschungszentrum GKSS 93/E/24 1993

141 AODC 051 Guidance note on the safe and efficient operation of remotely operated vehicles. London: Ass. of Offshore Diving Contractors 1989

142 Health and Safety Executive (HSE): Standards for assessing diver competence, part I, II, III, IV. London: HMSO

143 Ausbildungsrichtlinien für Mischgas/Sättigungstaucher. Geesthacht: GKSS-Forschungszentrum Bericht 753.1 AL B01 1991

144 Norwegian Petroleum Directorate (NPD): Regulations concerning manned underwater operations in the petroleum activity 1990

145 Offshore technology brings new anti-corrosive coatings. Marine Technology vol. 17, no 1 1986

146 Cathotic protection of offshore structures - problems and solutions. Marine Technology vol. 17, no 1 1986

147 Bäzner, R.: Experimentelle Untersuchungen zum Stoffübergang beim Unterwasserschneiden und -Schweißen. Geesthacht: GKSS-Forschungsentrum GKSS 88/E/39 1988

148 Proceedings 3. Int. Symposium on underwater technology. Geesthacht: GKSS-Forschungszentrum GKSS 91/E/3 1991

MIXED GAS DIVING

149   Mecklenburg, J.: Vollmechanisiertes Metallaktivgasschweißen der Füll-und Decklagen abnahmepflichtiger Rohrrundnähte in hyperbarer Umgebung. Geesthacht: GKSS-Forschungszentrum GKSS 91/E/80 1991

150   Schäfer, R.; Schafstall, H.G.: Fortschritte beim 1 bar-Schweißen bis in große Meerestiefen infolge der Meerestechnikentwicklung. Düsseldorf: Schweißen & Schneiden Heft 11 1981

151   AODC Safety Notice 1/92: Oxy arc cutting operations underwater. London: Int. Ass. of Underwater Engineering Contractors 1992

152   Merkblatt DVS 1816 and 1817: Elektrische Unterwasserschneidverfahren und Qualitätssicherung und Sicherheitsvorkehrungen. Düsseldorf: Deutscher Verband für Schweißtechnik DVS 1993

Index